Multivariate Statistics
A practical approach

OTHER STATISTICS TEXTS FROM
CHAPMAN AND HALL

Applied Statistics
D.R. Cox and E.J. Snell

The Analysis of Time Series
C. Chatfield

Decision Analysis: A Bayesian approach
J.Q. Smith

Statistics for Technology
C. Chatfield

Introduction to Multivariate Analysis
C. Chatfield and A.J. Collins

Introduction to Optimization Methods and their Application in Statistics
B.S. Everitt

An Introduction to Generalized Linear Modelling
A.J. Dobson

Multivariate Analysis of Variance and Repeated Measures
D.J. Hand and C.C. Taylor

Multivariate Statistical Methods: A primer
Bryan F. Manly

Statistical Methods in Agriculture and Experimental Biology
R. Mead and R.N. Curnow

Elements of Simulation
B.J.T. Morgan

Essential Statistics
D.G. Rees

Probability: Methods and measurement
A. O'Hagan

Elementary Applications of Probability Theory
H.C. Tuckwell

Problem Solving: A statistician's guide
C. Chatfield
Applied Nonparametric Statistical Methods
P. Sprent

Practical Statistics for Medical Research
D.G. Altman

Further information on the complete range of Chapman and Hall
statistics books is available from the publishers.

Multivariate Statistics
A practical approach

Bernhard Flury
and
Hans Riedwyl

CHAPMAN AND HALL

LONDON · NEW YORK · TOKYO · MELBOURNE · MADRAS

UK	Chapman and Hall, 2–6 Boundary Row, London SE7 8HN
USA	Chapman and Hall, 29 West 35th Street, New York NY10001
JAPAN	Chapman and Hall Japan, Thomson Publishing Japan, Hirakawacho Nemoto Building, 7F, 1-7-11 Hirakawa-cho, Chiyoda-ku, Tokyo 102
AUSTRALIA	Chapman and Hall Australia, Thomas Nelson Australia, 480 La Trobe Street, PO Box 4725, Melbourne 3000
INDIA	Chapman and Hall India, R. Seshadri, 32 Second Main Road, CIT East, Madras 600 035

First edition 1988
Reprinted 1990

© 1988 B. Flury and H. Riedwyl

Printed in Great Britain by the University Press, Cambridge

ISBN 0 412 30020 6 (HB)
ISBN 0 412 30030 3 (PB)

British Library Cataloguing in Publication Data

Flury, Bernhard
Multivariate statistics: a practical
approach.
1. Multivariate analysis
I. Title   II. Riedwyl, Hans
519.5'35   QA278

ISBN 0-412-30020-6
ISBN 0-412-30030-3 (pbk)

Library of Congress Cataloging in Publication Data

Flury, Bernhard, 1951-
Multivariate statistics
Rev. translation of: Angewandte multivariate Statistik.
Bibliography: p.
Includes index.
1. Multivariate analysis.   I. Riedwyl, Hans.
II. Title.
QA278.F58813   1988   519.5'35   87-18405

ISBN 0-412-30020-6
ISBN 0-412-30030-3 (pbk)

Contents

vi   Contents

Preface

During the last twenty years multivariate statistical methods have become increasingly popular among scientists in various fields. The theory had already made great progress in previous decades and routine applications of multivariate methods followed with the advent of fast computers. Nowadays statistical software packages perform in seconds what used to take weeks of tedious calculations.

Although this is certainly a welcome development, we find, on the other hand, that many users of statistical packages are not too sure of what they are doing, and this is especially true for multivariate statistical methods. Many researchers have heard about such techniques and feel intuitively that multivariate methods could be useful for their own work, but they haven't mastered the usual mathematical prerequisites. This book tries to fill the gap by explaining – in words and graphs – some basic concepts and selected methods of multivariate statistical analysis.

Why another book? Are the existing books on applied multivariate statistics all obsolete? No, some of them are up to date and, indeed, quite good. However, we think that this introduction distinguishes itself from any existing text in three ways. First, we illustrate the basic concepts mainly with graphical tools, hence the large number of figures. Second, all techniques, with just one exception, are illustrated by the same numerical data. Being familiar with the data will help the reader to understand what insights multivariate methods can offer. Third, we have avoided mathematical notation as much as possible. While we are well aware of the fact that this is a risky business, since avoiding mathematical language inevitably implies some loss of accuracy, we feel that it is possible to understand the basic ideas of multivariate analysis without mastering matrix algebra. Of course, we do not wish to discourage anybody from learning multivariate statistics the mathematical way. Indeed, many ideas and concepts can be stated in fewer words using concise mathematical language, but in order to appreciate the advantages of a more abstract approach the reader needs to be familiar with matrix theory, which most non-mathematicians tend to think of as a difficult subject.

This book has grown out of its German predecessor *Angewandte multivariate Statistik*, published in 1983 by Gustav Fischer Verlag, Stuttgart. It is not just a translation, however; many new ideas and didactic tools have been introduced, one chapter has been removed, and another one has been added. The chapter that was deleted was the one on factor analysis, which was criticized by some reviewers of the German text. Although it is probably impossible to write about factor analysis without provoking criticism, we felt that we were not sufficiently expert in this field, and that it was probably better to omit this topic altogether.

Some remarks are in order concerning Chapter 5, which deals with multiple linear regression. This chapter differs from the others in having a more compressed presentation. It was indeed conceived as a restatement of linear regression rather than a first introduction, and assumes that the reader is familiar at least with simple linear regression. We felt that it wasn't possible to omit this chapter, since a basic understanding of linear regression is extremely helpful for understanding the linear discriminant function and related concepts.

We do not claim that our book treats the various multivariate methods comprehensively – on the contrary, we purposely limited the presentation to those ideas and techniques that seemed most important to us, and tried to explain those as carefully as possible. Our selection of topics is obviously biased towards our own research areas, but this is what we feel most competent to write about.

Many chapters are followed by one or several additional examples and by a discussion. The questions stem mostly from the participants of several courses on applied multivariate analysis that we taught from 1980 to 1985. These questions gave us an opportunity to discuss additional important methods or ideas that didn't fit into the main text. The length of the discussions essentially reflects the number of times the respective chapter has been taught so far.

Some readers of the German predecessor of this book have asked us to supplement it with detailed instructions for the use of existing statistical software such as BMDP, SAS, or SPSS. We have resisted the temptation to introduce such instructions for two reasons. First, we would like the information in this book to remain correct for, say, fifteen years. Most instructions for the use of currently existing programs will probably be obsolete by that time. Second, we think that statistical software should do what textbooks propose, whereas the current situation is often just the opposite: students think of statistics as the output produced by some computer program.

Understanding this book requires relatively few prerequisites: the reader should master basic algebra and be familiar with the basic methods of univariate statistics. Knowing linear regression, at least for the case of a single regressor, will be very helpful, however. It may be a good idea to do some parallel reading in one of the books on regression given at the end of Chapter 5.

Among the many people who contributed to this book we name just a few. Rudolf Maibach wrote a preliminary version of Chapter 1. Erika Gautschi translated parts of the German text into English. George McCabe, Jean-Pierre Airoldi and three anonymous referees provided helpful comments on several chapters of the manuscript. Käthi Schütz and Emilia Bonnemain typed the manuscript with great enthusiasm, and Thomas Hänni programmed many graphics. We thank them all warmly. Finally, we would like to thank the publishers of this book, especially Elizabeth Johnston, and her colleagues at Chapman and Hall for their encouragement and cooperation.

Bernhard Flury
Hans Riedwyl
Berne, January 1987

1

The data

For the sake of simplicity we shall almost always refer to the same set of data for illustration. This comes from an inquiry that was conducted into genuine and forged thousand franc bills, henceforth called bills. How did we get hold of such unusual data?

To find the answer to this and other questions, let us listen for a while to two gentlemen sitting comfortably in their armchairs and chatting to each other. One is a statistician (S), the other an expert (E) in the fight against counterfeiting.

S: Now I'll tell you the real reason I invited you to my home this evening.

E: I thought the bottle of 1967 Gevrey-Chambertin was the reason, or am I wrong?

S: That was one reason, but not the only one. I would like to talk to you about an idea which I have been carrying around in my head for some time now.

E: Well, then – go ahead!

S: You have a lot of experience in sorting out genuine bills from forged ones, haven't you? You can tell, at first sight, whether a particular bill is genuine or not.

E: It's not quite that simple. I can certainly detect a *bad* forgery right away – say, if the water mark is missing, the paper is different, or the print contains gross errors. In sophisticated forgeries, however, one often has to look very closely to discover some small error. Forgers are becoming smarter all the time and their technical tools more and more precise and fine.

S: And so you have to rely on modern science to search for criminals.

E: Sure; but what are you driving at?

S: It occurred to me that statistics could help with this. In psychology and biology, for example, statistical methods are used for classifying items into groups and for determining which features characterize group membership.

E: That sounds very interesting, indeed. Can you be a bit more specific?

S: Alright, alright! I once examined a bill rather closely. What interests me are attributes that I can easily measure. The quality of the paper, the water mark, the colours are all attributes which do not satisfy these conditions. Linear dimensions, on the other hand, can easily be measured, even by a layman like myself. The forger, I am sure, has a lot of trouble reproducing all linear measures with perfect precision. So I could select various distances on the bill and measure them. For example, the length and height of the print image would be a good place to start.

E: Yes, sure, but how is this information going to help you?

S: I need it in order to compare genuine bills with forged ones. I could carry out the measurements on, let's say, 100 genuine and 100 forged bills. Since the forger surely does not work with absolute precision, I would find out very quickly that the measurements on the genuine bills differed from those on the forged ones – and that's precisely what I want to exploit.

E: Wait a minute! Why would you want to measure 100 bills; wouldn't a single one be enough?

S: No, because I am interested not only in the actual length of a line, but also in the variability of the measurements on a collection of bills. The variability between bills may give me information about the precision of the production process.

E: I see. One other question: is it at all possible to measure lines accurately enough in order to be able to detect a difference between genuine and forged bills?

S: That's a problem that can be solved. Either I can use sophisticated measurement equipment, or else I can try to project the bills on a screen and 'blow them up'. Naturally, there will still be some error of measurement, but it will be small compared with the variability due to the production process.

E: Alright, let's assume you have made all your measurements. Then you compare the two mean values for each given line. Correct?

S: It's not quite that simple. I can now carry out many different analyses. I consider the lengths that I have measured to be quantities subject to chance, or 'random variables'. I would like to have several of these, because the more random variables are available, the more information can be derived from them. To begin with, I would compare the genuine and the forged bills with regard to mean and standard deviation of each variable, and also with regard to correlations between the variables. Then I would represent, graphically, the various measurements of each bill. Furthermore, I'd like to know whether the group of forged bills differs markedly from the group of the genuine bills in the features under consideration. In other words, can we discriminate between the two groups? If so, I might be able to tell with high probability whether a given bill is genuine or forged, just by combining the various measurements in an optimal way. In this way I could certainly provide you with valuable help in putting the forgers out of business.

E: All these methods you describe sound very good. But I'll tell you now how we approach the problem. First of all, you have to realize that I am not the one who encounters a forgery first. Only in the rarest of cases is it the police who discover the existence of a forgery. Generally it is the bank tellers, or other people who handle a lot of paper money, who first become suspicious of a bill. If the forgery is clumsy, they will detect it right away. If, however, the bill looks just a little bit unusual, they may send it for further examination. So, when it finally comes to me, it has already been established that a forgery is at hand. My first task consists of informing all banks and other money agencies about the forgery as quickly as possible. For this purpose a leaflet with a rough description of the falsification is sent to all interested parties. After that, we give one or several samples of the forgery to the printer who produces our bills and their specialists carry out a detailed examination. They check the bill with regard to printing process, type of paper, water mark, colours and chemical composition of inks, and much more. We expect this kind of information to help us find and eliminate the forgery workshop and the distribution organization.

S: Well, it is precisely in this investigation that I want to help you. On the basis of the features that I consider, I would like to determine whether a single bill can be attributed to a group or not. I call this 'identification'. Indeed, even during the production of genuine bills, one could, with the help of 'identification analysis', discover at an early stage a change in the manufacturing process, which would cause defective bills to be produced.

E: You probably assume that the forger manufactures the false notes under exactly the same homogeneous conditions as we manufacture our genuine bills. From experience I know that most of them are produced in batches in some old cellar or in a garage. For this reason I have my doubts about comparing forged and genuine bills statistically.

S: I, too, will not necessarily assume conditions of homogeneity. I will ask whether a collection of bills, for example a set of 100 forged ones, can be divided into classes in such a way that they look homogeneous within classes, but differ from one class to another. If that is the case, then of course I would like again to describe group differences. I hope I am not confusing you too much with these ideas.

E: Let's put this to a test! In the cause of science, I can certainly get you a few genuine and forged bills.

Figure 1.1 An old Swiss 1000-franc bill

Table 1.1 Six variables measured on 100 genuine Swiss bank notes

i	LENGTH x_{1i}	LEFT x_{2i}	RIGHT x_{3i}	BOTTOM x_{4i}	TOP x_{5i}	DIAGONAL x_{6i}
1	214.8	131.0	131.1	9.0	9.7	141.0
2	214.6	129.7	129.7	8.1	9.5	141.7
3	214.8	129.7	129.7	8.7	9.6	142.2
4	214.8	129.7	129.6	7.5	10.4	142.0
5	215.0	129.6	129.7	10.4	7.7	141.8
6	215.7	130.8	130.5	9.0	10.1	141.4
7	215.5	129.5	129.7	7.9	9.6	141.6
8	214.5	129.6	129.2	7.2	10.7	141.7
9	214.9	129.4	129.7	8.2	11.0	141.9
10	215.2	130.4	130.3	9.2	10.0	140.7
11	215.3	130.4	130.3	7.9	11.7	141.8
12	215.1	129.5	129.6	7.7	10.5	142.2
13	215.2	130.8	129.6	7.9	10.8	141.4
14	214.7	129.7	129.7	7.7	10.9	141.7
15	215.1	129.9	129.7	7.7	10.8	141.8
16	214.5	129.8	129.8	9.3	8.5	141.6
17	214.6	129.9	130.1	8.2	9.8	141.7
18	215.0	129.9	129.7	9.0	9.0	141.9
19	215.2	129.6	129.6	7.4	11.5	141.5
20	214.7	130.2	129.9	8.6	10.0	141.9
21	215.0	129.9	129.3	8.4	10.0	141.4
22	215.6	130.5	130.0	8.1	10.3	141.6
23	215.3	130.6	130.0	8.4	10.8	141.5
24	215.7	130.2	130.0	8.7	10.0	141.6
25	215.1	129.7	129.9	7.4	10.8	141.1
26	215.3	130.4	130.4	8.0	11.0	142.3
27	215.5	130.2	130.1	8.9	9.8	142.4
28	215.1	130.3	130.3	9.8	9.5	141.9
29	215.1	130.0	130.0	7.4	10.5	141.8
30	214.8	129.7	129.3	8.3	9.0	142.0
31	215.2	130.1	129.8	7.9	10.7	141.8
32	214.8	129.7	129.7	8.6	9.1	142.3
33	215.0	130.0	129.6	7.7	10.5	140.7
34	215.6	130.4	130.1	8.4	10.3	141.0
35	215.9	130.4	130.0	8.9	10.6	141.4
36	214.6	130.2	130.2	9.4	9.7	141.8
37	215.5	130.3	130.0	8.4	9.7	141.8
38	215.3	129.9	129.4	7.9	10.0	142.0
39	215.3	130.3	130.1	8.5	9.3	142.1
40	213.9	130.3	129.0	8.1	9.7	141.3
41	214.4	129.8	129.2	8.9	9.4	142.3
42	214.8	130.1	129.6	8.8	9.9	140.9
43	214.9	129.6	129.4	9.3	9.0	141.7
44	214.9	130.4	129.7	9.0	9.8	140.9
45	214.8	129.4	129.1	8.2	10.2	141.0
46	214.3	129.5	129.4	8.3	10.2	141.8
47	214.8	129.9	129.7	8.3	10.2	141.5
48	214.8	129.9	129.7	7.3	10.9	142.0
49	214.6	129.7	129.8	7.9	10.3	141.1
50	214.5	129.0	129.6	7.8	9.8	142.0
51	214.6	129.8	129.4	7.2	10.0	141.3
52	215.3	130.6	130.0	9.5	9.7	141.1
53	214.5	130.1	130.0	7.8	10.9	140.9
54	215.4	130.2	130.2	7.6	10.9	141.6
55	214.5	129.4	129.5	7.9	10.0	141.4
56	215.2	129.7	129.4	9.2	9.4	142.0

Table 1.1 (Continued)

i	LENGTH x_{1i}	LEFT x_{2i}	RIGHT x_{3i}	BOTTOM x_{4i}	TOP x_{5i}	DIAGONAL x_{6i}
57	215.7	130.0	129.4	9.2	10.4	141.2
58	215.0	129.6	129.4	8.8	9.0	141.1
59	215.1	130.1	129.9	7.9	11.0	141.3
60	215.1	130.0	129.8	8.2	10.3	141.4
61	215.1	129.6	129.3	8.3	9.9	141.6
62	215.3	129.7	129.4	7.5	10.5	141.5
63	215.4	129.8	129.4	8.0	10.6	141.5
64	214.5	130.0	129.5	8.0	10.8	141.4
65	215.0	130.0	129.8	8.6	10.6	141.5
66	215.2	130.6	130.0	8.8	10.6	140.8
67	214.6	129.5	129.2	7.7	10.3	141.3
68	214.8	129.7	129.3	9.1	9.5	141.5
69	215.1	129.6	129.8	8.6	9.8	141.8
70	214.9	130.2	130.2	8.0	11.2	139.6
71	213.8	129.8	129.5	8.4	11.1	140.9
72	215.2	129.9	129.5	8.2	10.3	141.4
73	215.0	129.6	130.2	8.7	10.0	141.2
74	214.4	129.9	129.6	7.5	10.5	141.8
75	215.2	129.9	129.7	7.2	10.6	142.1
76	214.1	129.6	129.3	7.6	10.7	141.7
77	214.9	129.9	130.1	8.8	10.0	141.2
78	214.6	129.8	129.4	7.4	10.6	141.0
79	215.2	130.5	129.8	7.9	10.9	140.9
80	214.6	129.9	129.4	7.9	10.0	141.8
81	215.1	129.7	129.7	8.6	10.3	140.6
82	214.9	129.8	129.6	7.5	10.3	141.0
83	215.2	129.7	129.1	9.0	9.7	141.9
84	215.2	130.1	129.9	7.9	10.8	141.3
85	215.4	130.7	130.2	9.0	11.1	141.2
86	215.1	129.9	129.6	8.9	10.2	141.5
87	215.2	129.9	129.7	8.7	9.5	141.6
88	215.0	129.6	129.2	8.4	10.2	142.1
89	214.9	130.3	129.9	7.4	11.2	141.5
90	215.0	129.9	129.7	8.0	10.5	142.0
91	214.7	129.7	129.3	8.6	9.6	141.6
92	215.4	130.0	129.9	8.5	9.7	141.4
93	214.9	129.4	129.5	8.2	9.9	141.5
94	214.5	129.5	129.3	7.4	10.7	141.5
95	214.7	129.6	129.5	8.3	10.0	142.0
96	215.6	129.9	129.9	9.0	9.5	141.7
97	215.0	130.4	130.3	9.1	10.2	141.1
98	214.4	129.7	129.5	8.0	10.3	141.2
99	215.1	130.0	129.8	9.1	10.2	141.5
100	214.7	130.0	129.4	7.8	10.0	141.2

S: That would be wonderful! I am sure that when I have completed my analysis and can show you the results you will find it much clearer. (Besides, many readers may then, hopefully, find pleasure in multivariate statistics.)

E: I hope you won't strain my modest mathematical and statistical knowledge too much.

Table 1.2 Six variables measured on 100 forged bank notes

i	LENGTH x_{1i}	LEFT x_{2i}	RIGHT x_{3i}	BOTTOM x_{4i}	TOP x_{5i}	DIAGONAL x_{6i}
101	214.4	130.1	130.3	9.7	11.7	139.8
102	214.9	130.5	130.2	11.0	11.5	139.5
103	214.9	130.3	130.1	8.7	11.7	140.2
104	215.0	130.4	130.6	9.9	10.9	140.3
105	214.7	130.2	130.3	11.8	10.9	139.7
106	215.0	130.2	130.2	10.6	10.7	139.9
107	215.3	130.3	130.1	9.3	12.1	140.2
108	214.8	130.1	130.4	9.8	11.5	139.9
109	215.0	130.2	129.9	10.0	11.9	139.4
110	215.2	130.6	130.8	10.4	11.2	140.3
111	215.2	130.4	130.3	8.0	11.5	139.2
112	215.1	130.5	130.3	10.6	11.5	140.1
113	215.4	130.7	131.1	9.7	11.8	140.6
114	214.9	130.4	129.9	11.4	11.0	139.9
115	215.1	130.3	130.0	10.6	10.8	139.7
116	215.5	130.4	130.0	8.2	11.2	139.2
117	214.7	130.6	130.1	11.8	10.5	139.8
118	214.7	130.4	130.1	12.1	10.4	139.9
119	214.8	130.5	130.2	11.0	11.0	140.0
120	214.4	130.2	129.9	10.1	12.0	139.2
121	214.8	130.3	130.4	10.1	12.1	139.6
122	215.1	130.6	130.3	12.3	10.2	139.6
123	215.3	130.8	131.1	11.6	10.6	140.2
124	215.1	130.7	130.4	10.5	11.2	139.7
125	214.7	130.5	130.5	9.9	10.3	140.1
126	214.9	130.0	130.3	10.2	11.4	139.6
127	215.0	130.4	130.4	9.4	11.6	140.2
128	215.5	130.7	130.3	10.2	11.8	140.0
129	215.1	130.2	130.2	10.1	11.3	140.3
130	214.5	130.2	130.6	9.8	12.1	139.9
131	214.3	130.2	130.0	10.7	10.5	139.8
132	214.5	130.2	129.8	12.3	11.2	139.2
133	214.9	130.5	130.2	10.6	11.5	139.9
134	214.6	130.2	130.4	10.5	11.8	139.7
135	214.2	130.0	130.2	11.0	11.2	139.5
136	214.8	130.1	130.1	11.9	11.1	139.5
137	214.6	129.8	130.2	10.7	11.1	139.4
138	214.9	130.7	130.3	9.3	11.2	138.3
139	214.6	130.4	130.4	11.3	10.8	139.8
140	214.5	130.5	130.2	11.8	10.2	139.6
141	214.8	130.2	130.3	10.0	11.9	139.3
142	214.7	130.0	129.4	10.2	11.0	139.2
143	214.6	130.2	130.4	11.2	10.7	139.9
144	215.0	130.5	130.4	10.6	11.1	139.9
145	214.5	129.8	129.8	11.4	10.0	139.3
146	214.9	130.6	130.4	11.9	10.5	139.8
147	215.0	130.5	130.4	11.4	10.7	139.9
148	215.3	130.6	130.3	9.3	11.3	138.1
149	214.7	130.2	130.1	10.7	11.0	139.4
150	214.9	129.9	130.0	9.9	12.3	139.4
151	214.9	130.3	129.9	11.9	10.6	139.8
152	214.6	129.9	129.7	11.9	10.1	139.0
153	214.6	129.7	129.3	10.4	11.0	139.3
154	214.5	130.1	130.1	12.1	10.3	139.4
155	214.5	130.3	130.0	11.0	11.5	139.5
156	215.1	130.0	130.3	11.6	10.5	139.7

Table 1.2 (Continued)

i	LENGTH x_{1i}	LEFT x_{2i}	RIGHT x_{3i}	BOTTOM x_{4i}	TOP x_{5i}	DIAGONAL x_{6i}
157	214.2	129.7	129.6	10.3	11.4	139.5
158	214.4	130.1	130.0	11.3	10.7	139.2
159	214.8	130.4	130.6	12.5	10.0	139.3
160	214.6	130.6	130.1	8.1	12.1	137.9
161	215.6	130.1	129.7	7.4	12.2	138.4
162	214.9	130.5	130.1	9.9	10.2	138.1
163	214.6	130.1	130.0	11.5	10.6	139.5
164	214.7	130.1	130.2	11.6	10.9	139.1
165	214.3	130.3	130.0	11.4	10.5	139.8
166	215.1	130.3	130.6	10.3	12.0	139.7
167	216.3	130.7	130.4	10.0	10.1	138.8
168	215.6	130.4	130.1	9.6	11.2	138.6
169	214.8	129.9	129.8	9.6	12.0	139.6
170	214.9	130.0	129.9	11.4	10.9	139.7
171	213.9	130.7	130.5	8.7	11.5	137.8
172	214.2	130.6	130.4	12.0	10.2	139.6
173	214.8	130.5	130.3	11.8	10.5	139.4
174	214.8	129.6	130.0	10.4	11.6	139.2
175	214.8	130.1	130.0	11.4	10.5	139.6
176	214.9	130.4	130.2	11.9	10.7	139.0
177	214.3	130.1	130.1	11.6	10.5	139.7
178	214.5	130.4	130.0	9.9	12.0	139.6
179	214.8	130.5	130.3	10.2	12.1	139.1
180	214.5	130.2	130.4	8.2	11.8	137.8
181	215.0	130.4	130.1	11.4	10.7	139.1
182	214.8	130.6	130.6	8.0	11.4	138.7
183	215.0	130.5	130.1	11.0	11.4	139.3
184	214.6	130.5	130.4	10.1	11.4	139.3
185	214.7	130.2	130.1	10.7	11.1	139.5
186	214.7	130.4	130.0	11.5	10.7	139.4
187	214.5	130.4	130.0	8.0	12.2	138.5
188	214.8	130.0	129.7	11.4	10.6	139.2
189	214.8	129.9	130.2	9.6	11.9	139.4
190	214.6	130.3	130.2	12.7	9.1	139.2
191	215.1	130.2	129.8	10.2	12.0	139.4
192	215.4	130.5	130.6	8.8	11.0	138.6
193	214.7	130.3	130.2	10.8	11.1	139.2
194	215.0	130.5	130.3	9.6	11.0	138.5
195	214.9	130.3	130.5	11.6	10.6	139.8
196	215.0	130.4	130.3	9.9	12.1	139.6
197	215.1	130.3	129.9	10.3	11.5	139.7
198	214.8	130.3	130.4	10.6	11.1	140.0
199	214.7	130.7	130.8	11.2	11.2	139.4
200	214.3	129.9	129.9	10.2	11.5	139.6

S: I will try, especially through graphical presentations, to explain things very simply.

And this is how we acquired the numerical data for our book. For didactic reasons we have chosen six linear measures on one side of the bill which capture roughly the size of the print image and paper format, as well as the position of the print image on the paper (see Fig. 1).

For each attribute we introduce the following notation.

X_1: length of bill   LENGTH
X_2: width of bill, measured on the left   LEFT
X_3: width of bill, measured on the right   RIGHT
X_4: width of margin at the bottom   BOTTOM
X_5: width of margin at the top   TOP
X_6: length of the image diagonal   DIAGONAL

Tables 1.1 and 1.2 contain the data for 100 genuine and 100 forged bills, respectively. All measurements are given in millimetres.

DISCUSSION

Question:
Why did you choose exactly 100 each of genuine and forged bills?
Answer:
This was mainly because of the amount of work involved in measuring the bills. Since the variability in the six attributes was very small, the bills were projected, much enlarged, on a wall, and the measurements were taken on these projections. This is very work-intensive.

Question:
In univariate statistics there are rules for determining the sample size. Can such rules be carried over also to problems involving several variables?
Answer:
Since we had no *a priori* information about mean differences and variabilities, this was not possible in our case. As a general rule, multivariate methods do not work (for purely mathematical reasons) if the number of observations, n, is less than the number of variables, p. If n is not considerably larger than p, say at least three or four times as large, multivariate methods are often not very powerful and depend too strongly on certain assumptions. For descriptive methods like principal component analysis it is desirable, as a rule of thumb, for n to be at least ten times as large as p.

Question:
But we will certainly want to draw conclusions from the samples to the basic populations. How are the populations actually defined in this example?
Answer:
In the case of the genuine bills we could start out with all 1000-franc bills that have ever been printed, while in the case of the forged ones, the set of all bills manufactured by the specific forger would have to be considered. Because of the finiteness of these basic populations we prefer, however, to speak of *models* rather than populations, and to consider our bills as samples from manufacturing processes which theoretically are not finite. Inferential statements

thus refer to the manufacturing mechanism and not to a finite collection of objects.

Question:
Are the genuine bills really all genuine?

Answer:
We cannot answer this question by a 'yes' with absolute certainty. Neverthe-less, a few wrongly identified bills should not have a strong influence on the results. We will devote our attention to this problem again in the chapter on identification analysis.

2

Univariate plots and descriptive statistics

Inspection of Tables 1.1 and 1.2 reveals that there are some differences between genuine and forged bills. For the variable DIAGONAL, the differences are most pronounced: 99 of the genuine bills are larger than 140, while most of the forged ones are smaller than 140. It is not possible, however, to separate the groups completely on the basis of DIAGONAL alone.

The two groups can be compared graphically by drawing frequency curves, which allow differences in location, variability and shape to be distinguished. Figures 2.1 to 2.6 show frequency curves for all six variables and both groups. Apparently the forger has not quite succeeded in reproducing the distribution of the genuine bills exactly. Note the very irregular curve for the variable BOTTOM in group *Forged* (Fig. 2.4): here, some values are far away from the

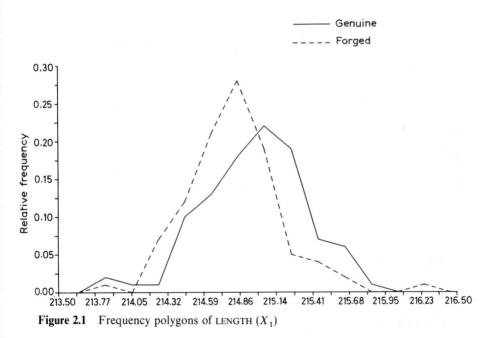

Figure 2.1 Frequency polygons of LENGTH (X_1)

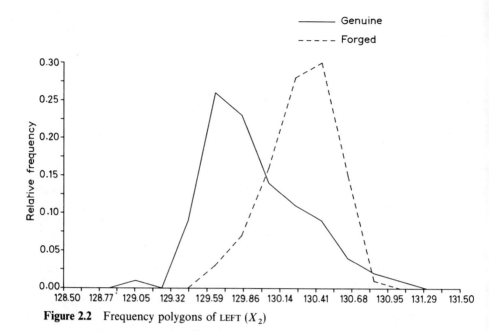

Figure 2.2 Frequency polygons of LEFT (X_2)

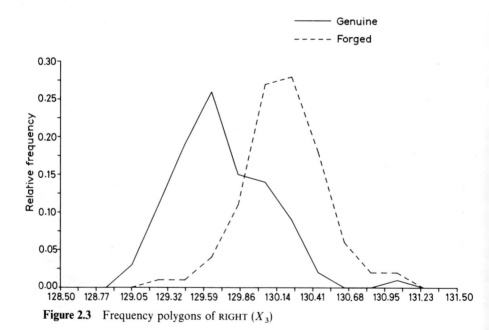

Figure 2.3 Frequency polygons of RIGHT (X_3)

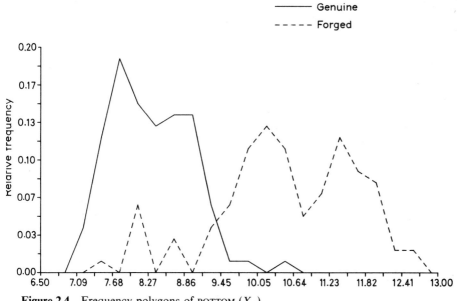

Figure 2.4 Frequency polygons of BOTTOM (X_4)

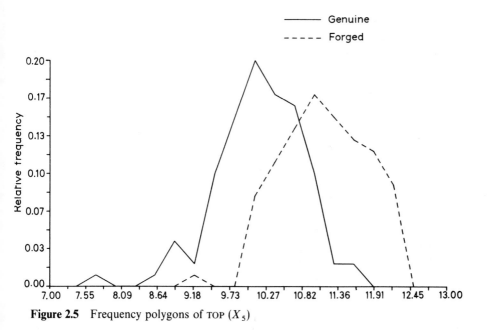

Figure 2.5 Frequency polygons of TOP (X_5)

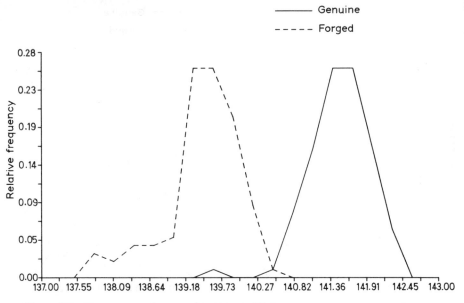

Figure 2.6   Frequency polygons of DIAGONAL (X_6)

majority of the others, and one has the impression that this group could actually be a mixture of two subgroups. We will examine this possible inhomogeneity later.

As a measure of location, we will use the sample mean of n observations

$$\bar{x} = \frac{1}{n} \sum_{i=1}^{n} x_i,$$

where x_i denotes the ith measurement of a particular variable, say LENGTH. We take the standard deviation

$$s_x = \sqrt{\left[\frac{1}{n-1} \sum_{i=1}^{n} (x_i - \bar{x})^2 \right]}$$

as a measure of variability. Accordingly, the six variables considered can each be characterized by two numbers – location and variability.

Since we are dealing with two samples, we wish to describe differences in location. For simplicity, let us denote by $\bar{x}_G$ and $\bar{x}_F$ the sample means of a particular variable (say, LENGTH) in the groups *Genuine* and *Forged*. The most obvious measure of difference in location is simply $\bar{x}_G - \bar{x}_F$, the (sample) mean difference. Although conceptually it is extremely simple, the mean difference has the disadvantage that its interpretation depends on the unit of measurement as well as on the variability within each group – we don't actually know whether a mean difference of 7.59 is 'large' unless we relate this figure to the variability in some way. Therefore, we prefer the *standard distance D*, which is defined as the absolute value of the mean difference divided by the pooled standard deviation for both groups. In symbols, if n_G and n_F denote the sample sizes and s_G, s_F the standard deviations, then D is defined as

$$D = \frac{|\bar{x}_G - \bar{x}_F|}{s},$$

where

$$s = \sqrt{\left[\frac{(n_G - 1)s_G^2 + (n_F - 1)s_F^2}{n_G + n_F - 2} \right]}$$

is the pooled standard deviation of the particular variable under consideration. Thus the standard distance D is simply the mean difference expressed in units of the standard deviation. Moreover, D is dimensionless, since it does not depend on the unit of measurement: it doesn't matter whether we measure in millimetres or in metres. It is therefore possible to compare standard distances irrespective of the scales used. We will see later (in the chapter on discriminant analysis) that the standard distance can be generalized to a measure of distance between two groups that takes several variables simultaneously into consideration. This generalization plays a central role in many multivariate methods.

It is also clear from the definition of D that the standard distance is closely related to the absolute value of the usual two-sample t-statistic:

$$|t| = D \cdot \sqrt{\left[\frac{n_G n_F}{n_G + n_F} \right]},$$

which can be used to test the hypothesis of equality of the means in the two populations (or models). We assume that the reader is familiar with this statistic. For descriptive purposes we prefer D to t, since D is not sensitive to the sample sizes in the same way as t. Table 2.1 shows sample means and standard deviations, mean differences between genuine and forged bills, and the associated standard distances.

These numbers confirm the visual impression gained from Figs 2.1 to 2.6: the largest difference between the two groups appears in variable DIAGONAL, while LENGTH shows only a moderate distance. If we compute the t-statistics associated with each of the six distances, we would conclude that (at a significance level of 5%) all six variables exhibit significant mean differences. However, since the six t-statistics cannot be regarded as independent, we delay the problem of testing for significance to a later chapter. Nevertheless, for the time being, we conclude that among the six variables, DIAGONAL separates the two groups most clearly, the two means being more than four standard deviations apart ($D = 4.09$).

Table 2.1 Univariate descriptive statistics

Variable	Mini- mum	Maxi- mum	Mean	Standard deviation	Mean difference	Standard distance
X_1 Genuine	213.8	215.9	214.969	0.3876	0.146	0.395
Forged	213.9	216.3	214.823	0.3522		
X_2 Genuine	129.0	131.0	129.943	0.3641	−0.357	1.136
Forged	129.6	130.8	130.300	0.2550		
X_3 Genuine	129.0	131.1	129.720	0.3553	−0.473	1.442
Forged	129.3	131.1	130.193	0.2982		
X_4 Genuine	7.2	10.4	8.305	0.6428	−2.225	2.417
Forged	7.4	12.7	10.530	1.1320		
X_5 Genuine	7.7	11.7	10.168	0.6490	−0.965	1.502
Forged	9.1	12.3	11.133	0.6360		
X_6 Genuine	139.6	142.4	141.517	0.4470	2.067	4.090
Forged	137.8	140.6	139.450	0.5579		

DISCUSSION

Question:
For all three variables which measure the size of the bill (X_1, X_2, X_3) the variability in group *Genuine* is larger than in group *Forged*. Does this mean that the forger cut his bills even more precisely than the official manufacturer?
Answer:
The variability of X_1, X_2, X_3 in group *Genuine* could be due to the fact that the bills are worn differently. In particular, folding of the bills could have played a role. Furthermore, the genuine bills come from productions in different time periods.

Question:
Would the genuine bill with smallest X_6 (no. 70) fit better into the group of forged ones?
Answer:
It would be dangerous to answer this question without regard to the values of this bill in all the other variables. We will return to this question in the section on classification in Chapter 7.

Question:
From the geometry of the bills it should be possible to determine X_6 from the other variables. Therefore, could one do without X_6?
Answer:
Because of random variations in the production process, different wear, and not absolutely precise measurements, this is certainly not possible.

Question:
Variable X_1 hardly seems to contribute towards a separation between *Genuine* and *Forged*. Would it be possible to ignore this variable?
Answer:
Surprisingly, even variables that show no mean difference may contribute to multivariate group separation, as we shall see later. Besides, our interest here concerns not only the separation of genuine and forged bills (discriminant analysis), but also other multidimensional questions.

Question:
From the data matrix one can see that very often the left height of the bill (X_2) is larger than the right one (X_3). Does this mean that the bills tend to be shorter on the right than on the left?
Answer:
It could also be an effect due to projection.

Question:
X_4 exhibits two peaks in the histogram of both groups. Is there an explanation for this? Is the production process responsible for this?
Answer:
Even if one assumes a normal distribution as a model, this bimodality might still be within the limits of random variability.

Question:
Would non-normality be detected better from the shape of the cumulative distribution function? Would it be better to ignore variables which are obviously not normally distributed?
Answer:
We omit testing for normal distributions for various reasons, namely:

1. Each one of the methods proposed here can also, in principle, be applied in the case of non-normal distributions; however, the method is then no longer necessarily optimal. Normality assumptions play an important role above all in testing, but not so much in descriptive methods.
2. Strictly speaking, in testing one requires even *multidimensional* normality. This makes the situation rather more complicated, since one-dimensional normality of all variables does not necessarily imply multivariate normality.
3. Very often we will consider linear combinations of variables which, thanks to the central limit theorem, correspond better to the normal distribution model than the original variables.

Question:
Could a better approximation to the normal distribution be achieved by a suitable transformation of the individual variables?

Answer:

It does not appear to be possible to transform the six variables non-linearly in a meaningful way.

Question:

Would it be possible to include measures other than distances in the same multivariate anlaysis?

Answer:

This is certainly possible; even qualitative features can be used, provided they are coded properly. However, it is then harder to interpret the linear combinations.

Question:

How should one choose the mid-points and bandwidths for the frequency polygons?

Answer:

Any introductory text on applied statistics will provide reasonable (and sometimes contradictory) rules; we omit them here for lack of space. However, in the framework of 'density estimation', such problems have found considerable attention in the recent statistical literature. See the book by Silverman (1986) for a comprehensive review.

FURTHER STUDY

Textbooks

See any introduction to applied statistics.

Software

Univariate statistics can easily be computed on a pocket calculator.

Statistics software packages like BMDP, SPSS and SAS can be used to compute univariate statistics as well as to print frequency diagrams.

3
Scatterplot, correlation and covariance

Since six measurements were taken on each object, there may exist dependencies between the six variables. Insight into the type of relationship between pairs of variables can easily be gained with *scatterplots* (Figs 3.1 to 3.15). For example, the diagram of variables LEFT and RIGHT for the group *Genuine* (Fig. 3.6) shows a positive relationship: small values of LEFT are often associated with small values of RIGHT and, *vice versa*, large values are found in both variables simultaneously.

Browsing through these diagrams, one recognizes that many pairs of variables are clearly correlated. We also find, however, that individual points are conspicuously far away from the centre of gravity of the points. For the moment, these deviations will not concern us. Rather, we shall try to characterize the visually observed strength of the relationship by a suitable number. A popular measure of association of two variables X (e.g. LENGTH) and Z (e.g. LEFT) is the *correlation coefficient*

$$r_{xz} = \frac{\sum_{i=1}^{n} (x_i - \bar{x})(z_i - \bar{z})}{\sqrt{\left[\sum_{i=1}^{n} (x_i - \bar{x})^2 \sum_{i=1}^{n} (z_i - \bar{z})^2 \right]}}.$$

For the variables LENGTH and LEFT, for example, the correlation coefficient in group *Genuine* is 0.411.

The correlation coefficients between every pair of variables are listed in Tables 3.1 and 3.2 for groups *Genuine* and *Forged*, respectively. Between LEFT and RIGHT we observe, as expected, a positive correlation in both groups. In contrast, BOTTOM and TOP show a strong negative correlation. This suggests that placing the print image onto the paper is not always a simple task. A smaller margin at the bottom obviously entails a larger margin at the top, and *vice versa*.

The Tables 3.1 and 3.2 of correlation coefficients are also called *correlation matrices*. Note that the coefficients on the diagonal are all unity, which shows the exact positive linear dependence between pairs of identical variables.

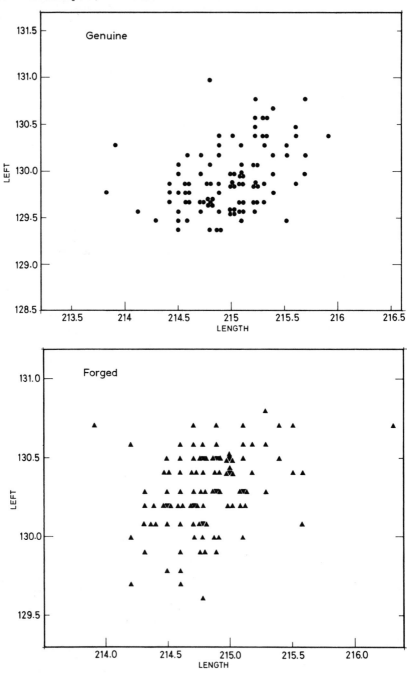

Figure 3.1   Scatterplots of LENGTH VS LEFT

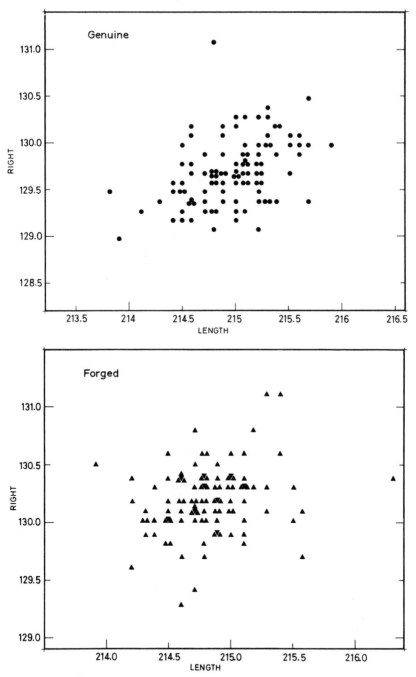

Figure 3.2   Scatterplots of LENGTH vs RIGHT

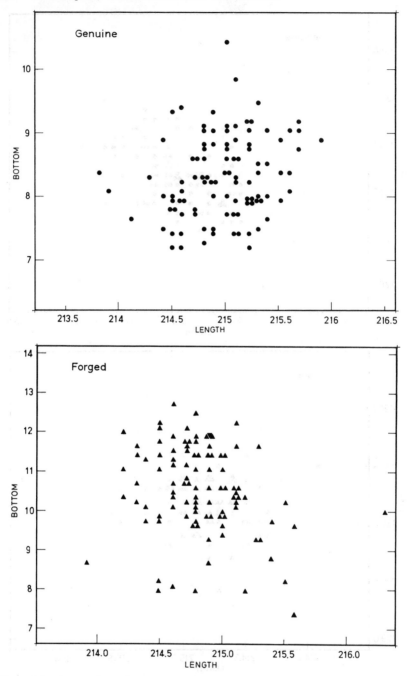

Figure 3.3   Scatterplots of LENGTH vs BOTTOM

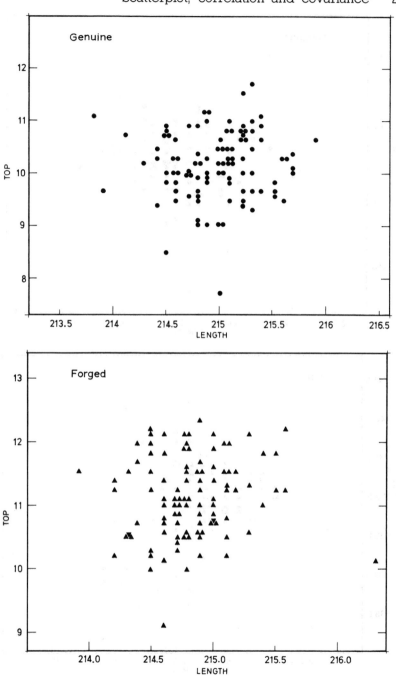

Figure 3.4 Scatterplots of LENGTH vs TOP

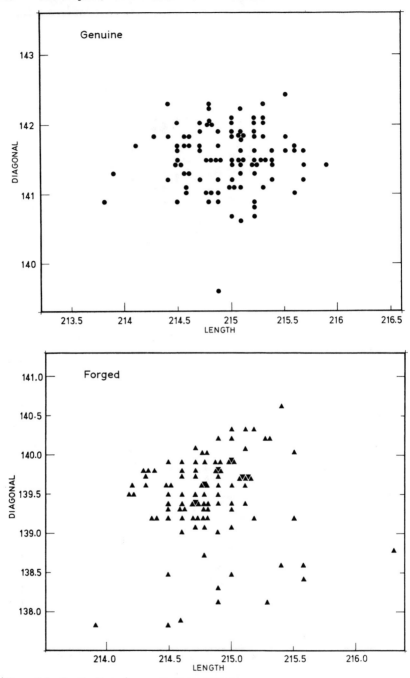

Figure 3.5   Scatterplot of LENGTH VS DIAGONAL

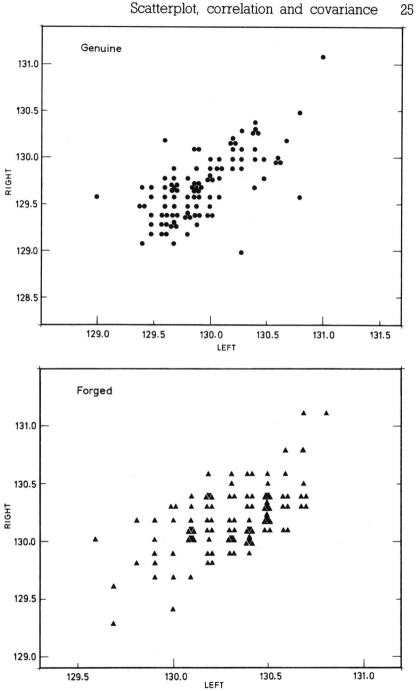

Figure 3.6   Scatterplots of LEFT VS RIGHT

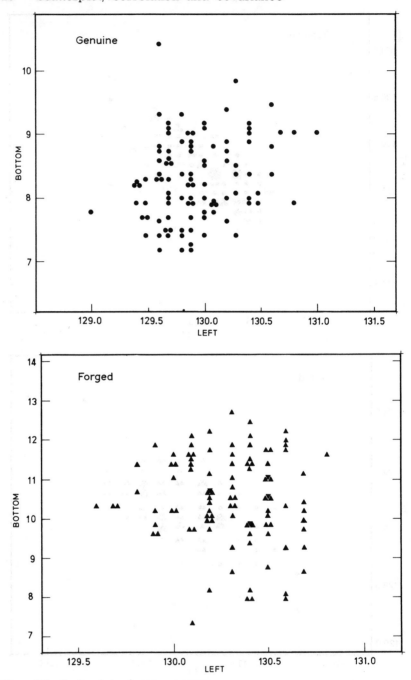

Figure 3.7   Scatterplots of LEFT VS BOTTOM

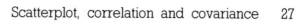
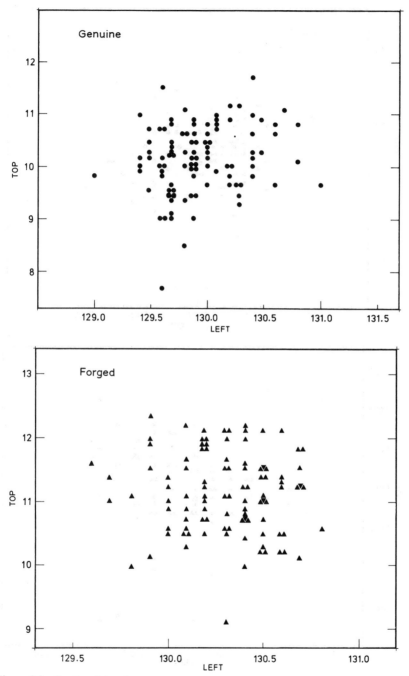

Figure 3.8 Scatterplots of LEFT vs TOP

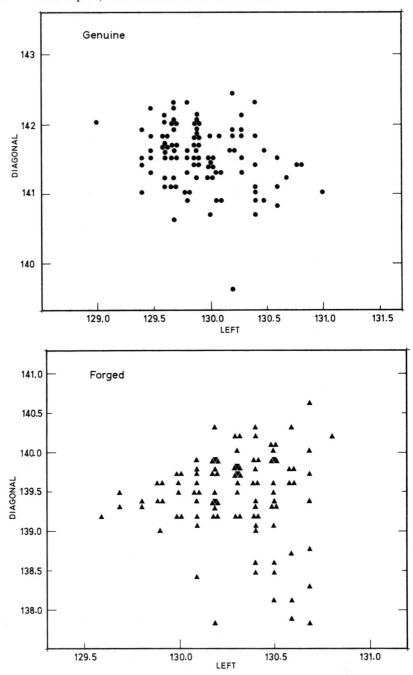

Figure 3.9 Scatterplots of LEFT vs DIAGONAL

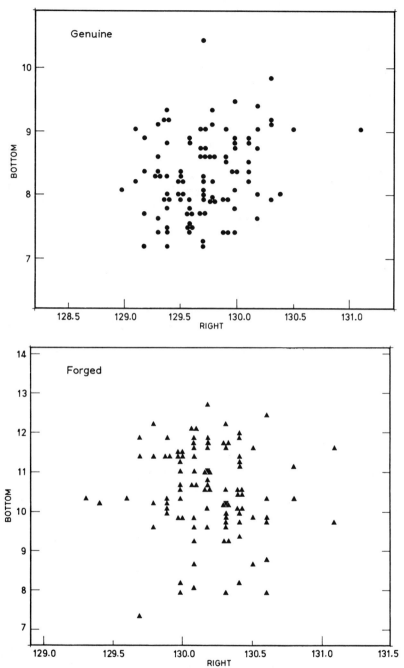

Figure 3.10 Scatterplots of RIGHT vs BOTTOM

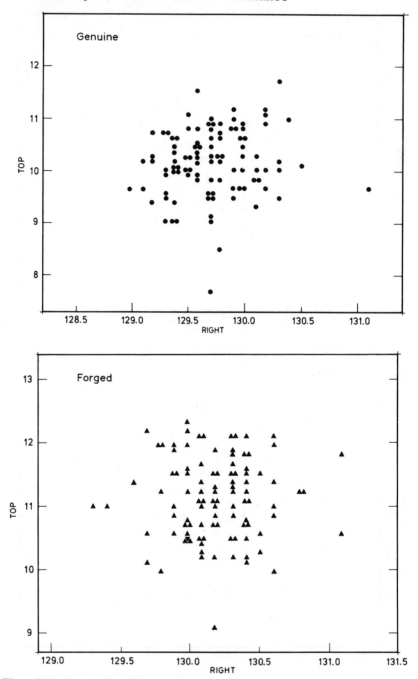

Figure 3.11   Scatterplots of RIGHT VS TOP

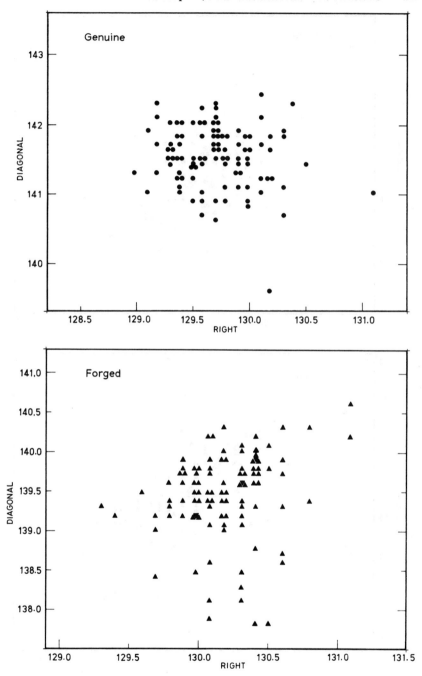

Figure 3.12   Scatterplots of RIGHT VS DIAGONAL

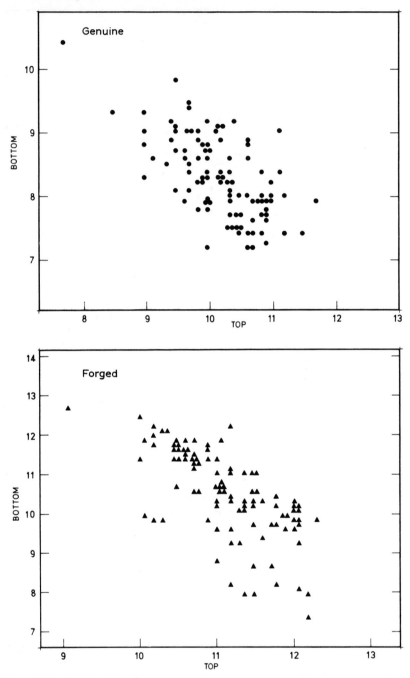

Figure 3.13   Scatterplots of BOTTOM vs TOP

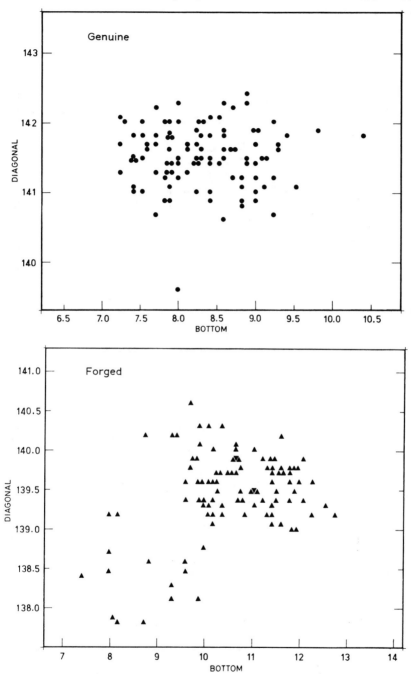

Figure 3.14   Scatterplots of BOTTOM VS DIAGONAL

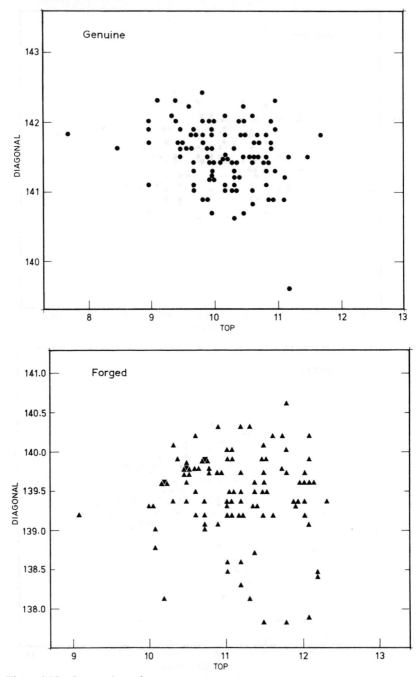

Figure 3.15   Scatterplots of TOP vs DIAGONAL

Table 3.1 Correlation matrix of the genuine bills

	LENGTH	LEFT	RIGHT	BOTTOM	TOP	DIAGONAL
LENGTH	1.0000					
LEFT	0.4111	1.0000				
RIGHT	0.4160	0.6639	1.0000			
BOTTOM	0.2293	0.2420	0.2547	1.0000		
TOP	0.0575	0.2076	0.1329	−0.6316	1.0000	
DIAGONAL	0.0316	−0.2646	−0.1497	−0.0007	−0.2596	1.0000

Table 3.2 Correlation matrix of the forged bills

	LENGTH	LEFT	RIGHT	BOTTOM	TOP	DIAGONAL
LENGTH	1.0000					
LEFT	0.3509	1.0000				
RIGHT	0.2285	0.6149	1.0000			
BOTTOM	−0.2524	−0.0833	−0.0550	1.0000		
TOP	0.0868	−0.0735	0.0007	−0.6809	1.0000	
DIAGONAL	0.0589	−0.0355	0.2055	0.3777	−0.0622	1.0000

Next to the correlation, the *covariance* also plays an important role in multivariate statistics. As the covariance between two variables X and Z we define

$$c_{xz} = \frac{1}{n-1} \sum_{i=1}^{n} (x_i - \bar{x})(z_i - \bar{z}).$$

If we denote by s_x and s_z the standard deviations of X and Z, then

$$r_{xz} = \frac{c_{xz}}{s_x s_z},$$

i.e., the correlation coefficient can be regarded as a 'standardized' covariance. Conversely, the covariance can be computed from the correlation coefficient and the standard deviations according to

$$c_{xz} = s_x s_z r_{xz}.$$

In the special case $X = Z$, the formula for the covariance simplifies to

$$c_{xx} = \frac{1}{n-1} \sum_{i=1}^{n} (x_i - \bar{x})^2 = s_x^2$$

i.e. the covariance of a variable with itself is just the square of the standard

Table 3.3 Covariance matrix of the genuine bills

	LENGTH	LEFT	RIGHT	BOTTOM	TOP	DIAGONAL
LENGTH	0.1502					
LEFT	0.0580	0.1326				
RIGHT	0.0573	0.0859	0.1263			
BOTTOM	0.0571	0.0567	0.0582	0.4132		
TOP	0.0145	0.0491	0.0306	−0.2635	0.4212	
DIAGONAL	0.0055	−0.0431	−0.0238	−0.0002	−0.0753	0.1998

Table 3.4 Covariance matrix of the forged bills

	LENGTH	LEFT	RIGHT	BOTTOM	TOP	DIAGONAL
LENGTH	0.1240					
LEFT	0.0315	0.0650				
RIGHT	0.0240	0.0468	0.0889			
BOTTOM	−0.1006	−0.0240	−0.0186	1.2813		
TOP	0.0194	−0.0119	0.0001	−0.4902	0.4045	
DIAGONAL	0.0116	−0.0050	0.0342	0.2385	−0.0221	0.3112

deviation. From this it follows immediately that the correlation of each variable with itself is 1. Note that s_x^2 is called the *variance* of X.

In the case of more than two variables the pairwise covariances are often represented – in analogy to the correlation matrix – in the form of a table, the *covariance matrix*. Note that on the diagonal of the covariance matrix we have precisely the variances.

Tables 3.3 and 3.4 show the covariance matrices for all six variables in both groups.

Since the covariance of two variables depends on the units of measurement, we usually prefer the dimensionless correlation coefficient for describing the linear dependence between two variables.

DISCUSSION

Question:
What are the criteria according to which a bill that shows up in an extreme position in a scatterplot can be regarded as an outlier?
Answer:
We shall return to this problem in the chapter on identification analysis.

Question:

Do correlation matrices permit inferences concerning the production process, perhaps even concerning differences in production between *Genuine* and *Forged*?

Answer:

If the bill image, for example, were printed on uncut paper, and subsequently a lower and an upper margin were measured off independently, there would hardly result the strong negative correlation between BOTTOM and TOP. A causal deduction, as always in statistics, cannot be made, however.

FURTHER STUDY

We would recommend the same *textbooks and software* as for Chapter 2.

4

Face plots

While the relationship between two random variables can easily be depicted by a scatterplot, a three-dimensional cloud of points is hardly a practical means for the description of three correlated variables. Four and higher dimensional representations are altogether beyond our imaginative power. The representation of all possible pairs of variables in the plane (cf. Figs 3.1 to 3.15) is also not suitable for surveying several correlated variables simultaneously. We will try, nevertheless, to represent our six-dimensional data in the plane. Following a suggestion of Chernoff, one transforms the variables into appropriate standard intervals and, on the basis of the transformed values, constructs a face for each unit. The original construction of Chernoff has been further developed; we use mainly a design in which the two halves of the face can be varied separately. This type of representation not only enlarges the number of representable variables, but also exploits the sensitivity of the human eye to asymmetries. Furthermore, our construction allows for special applications such as the representation of twin data, multivariate paired comparisons and graphical identification of outliers.

In the method proposed in this chapter, one half of the face is defined by 18 values $z_1, z_2, \ldots, z_{18}$, where we first assume that these values lie between 0 and 1. Figure 4.1 depicts the two extremal faces. The 'maximal face' corresponds to the values $z_1 = z_2 = \cdots = z_{18} = 1$ (for both sides), the 'minimal face' to $z_1 = z_2 = \cdots = z_{18} = 0$. Each parameter z_j defines a part of the face according to Table 4.1.

For z_j between 0 and 1, the corresponding part of the face is obtained by interpolation between the two extreme possibilities. For most parts of the face, the construction principle can be extended through extrapolation to z_j-values outside of $(0, 1)$. Figure 4.2 shows the extreme settings of each individual parameter, whereby all other parameters are set to be constant 0.5. For example, the first drawing on the upper left results from $z_1 = 1, z_2 = z_3 = \cdots = z_{18} = 0.5$ on one side, and from $z_1 = 0, z_2 = z_3 = \cdots = z_{18} = 0.5$ on the other side. This figure enables the user to estimate the effect of the individual face parameters upon the overall impression and therefore to assign important variables to conspicuous facial parts.

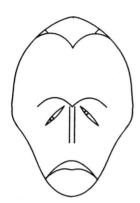
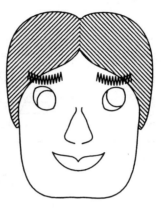

Figure 4.1   Extremal faces

Table 4.1 List of face parameters

Number of parameter	Part of face
1	size of the eyes
2	size of the pupils
3	position of the pupils
4	obliqueness of the eyes
5	horizontal position of the eyes
6	vertical position of the eyes
7	curvature of the eyebrows
8	thickness of the eyebrows
9	horizontal position of the eyebrows
10	vertical position of the eyebrows
11	upper hair line
12	lower hair line
13	face line
14	darkness of the hair (density of hatching)
15	hair shading slant
16	nose
17	opening of the mouth
18	curvature of the mouth

An important role is played not only by the assignments of variables to facial parts, but also by the type of transformation to the interval $(0, 1)$. Values of z_j outside of $(0, 1)$ may in fact result in overlaps which disturb the impression of a face. On the other hand, it is often advantageous to transform extreme values of the variables to z_j-values outside of $(0, 1)$; in this way an extreme value

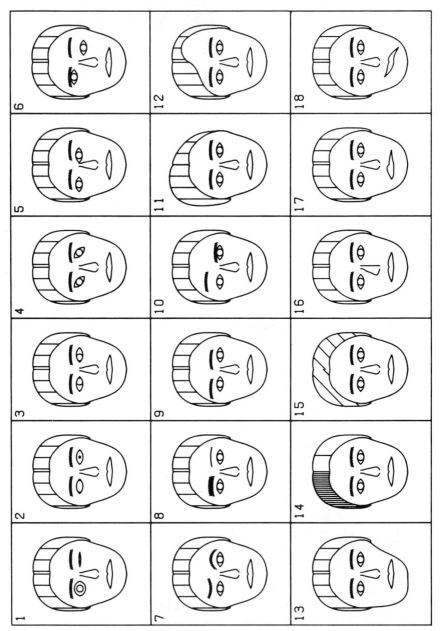

Figure 4.2 Extreme settings of the 18 face parameters

becomes immediately conspicuous in the picture. If an observation is extreme in several variables, then these are reflected simultaneously in the face.

As a rule, a variable X is transformed linearly according to

$$Z = \frac{X - a}{b - a}.$$

Choosing $a = \min X$ and $b = \max X$, the transformed measurement values fill precisely the interval $(0, 1)$.

In our example, we regard the genuine bills as standard, i.e. we choose for a

Table 4.2 Assignment of variables to face parameters

Variable	a	b	Associated face parameters	
X_1: LENGTH	213.8	215.9	(4)	obliqueness of the eyes
			(7)	curvature of the eyebrows
			(15)	hair shading slant
X_2: LEFT	129.0	131.1	(1L)	opening of the left eye
			(2L)	size of the pupil, left
			(5L)	horizontal position of the left eye
			(9L)	horizontal position of the left eyebrow
			(13L)	lower face line, left
X_3: RIGHT	129.0	131.1	same as X_2, but right side of the face	
X_4: BOTTOM	7.2	10.4	(3L)	position of pupil, left
			(8)	thickness of eyebrows
			(12)	lower hair line
$X_4^- = -X_4$	−10.4	−7.2	(6L)	vertical position of the left eye
			(10L)	vertical position of the left eyebrow
			(16L)	nose, left
X_5: TOP	7.7	11.7	(3R)	position of pupil, right
			(6R)	vertical position of the right eye
			(10R)	vertical position of the right eyebrow
			(11)	upper hair line
			(16R)	nose, right
X_6: DIAGONAL	139.6	142.4	(14)	fairness of the hair
			(17)	opening of the mouth
			(18)	curvature of the mouth

Legend: L after the number of a parameter = associated only on the *left*
R after the number of a parameter = associated only on the *right*

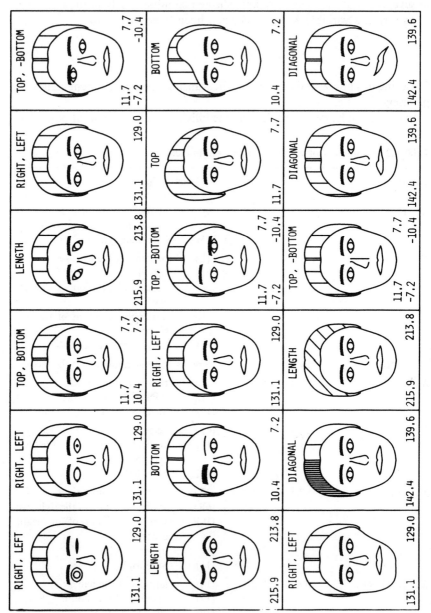

Figure 4.3 Assignment of variables to face parameters

and b the respective extremes from the group of genuine bills (cf Table 2.1). For the variables X_2 and X_3 we use the same parameters a and b, since these two variables measure the same quantity at two different locations.

Table 4.2 shows for all six variables their assignments to face parameters. Since there are substantially more face parameters at our disposal than variables, we can assign each variable to several face parameters. In addition, we introduce the variable $X_4^- = -X_4$. Since X_4 and X_5 are negatively correlated, X_4^- and X_5 have a positive correlation of the same absolute magnitude. Assigning X_4^- and X_5 to the same face parameters on the left and right side should therefore not create severe asymmetries. The assignments were based on the following considerations:

- X_2 and X_3 are positively correlated. They are thus suitable in a natural way for separate assignment to the same face parameters left and right. Asymmetries due to X_2 and X_3 indicate an oblique cut of the bill.
- In the same way, the positively correlated variables X_4^- and X_5 are transformed to the same face parameters left and right. The sum $X_4 + X_5$ (sum of the marginal widths) corresponds therefore to the width of the hair part.

In the list of assignments, 'left' always refers to the left half of the face, i.e. to the right half of the picture; and similarly for 'right'.

In addition to Table 4.2 it is helpful to use a figure like 4.2 to show the assignments graphically. For each face part the name of the associated variable is written above the respective face, and the transformation parameters a and b are written to the right and left, respectively. This is illustrated in Fig. 4.3.

Figure 4.4 shows all 200 bills in the representation described.

Among the genuine bills, a few stand out as peculiar. The wide face and the wide-open eyes of no. 1 show that this bill was cut very wide (X_2, X_3). In face 5 one notes the thin nose, the low-placed eyes and the cross-eyed look. In addition, the hair part seems rather unusual. As can be seen from the list of assignments, this can be traced to the fact that bill 5 has a very narrow lower margin and a wide upper margin, i.e. the print image is poorly centred. Bill 40 is conspicuous because of a gross asymmetry in the eyes, traceable to an oblique cut of the bill. Notice the striking mouth of face 70, a bill with very small image diagonal.

In contrast to the genuine bills, the forged ones are notable by a severely down-turned mouth and a weak hatching of the hair (DIAGONAL). The hair

---

Note: If two different variables are assigned to the left and right sides of the same face parameter, the assignments should be interpreted as in the following example: parameter 10R (vertical position of the right eyebrow) is assigned to variable TOP with the values $a = 7.7$ and $b = 11.7$ for the transformation to the standard interval. Parameter 10L (vertical position of the left eyebrow) is assigned to variable $-$ BOTTOM $(= -X_4)$ with $a = -10.4$ and $b = -7.2$.

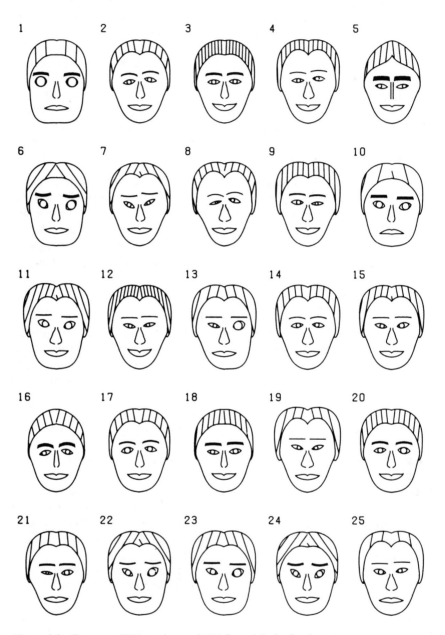

Figure 4.4   Faces on 100 genuine and 100 forged Swiss bank notes

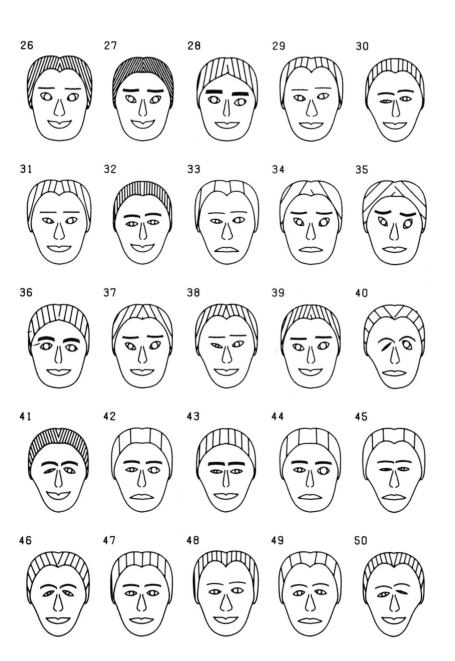

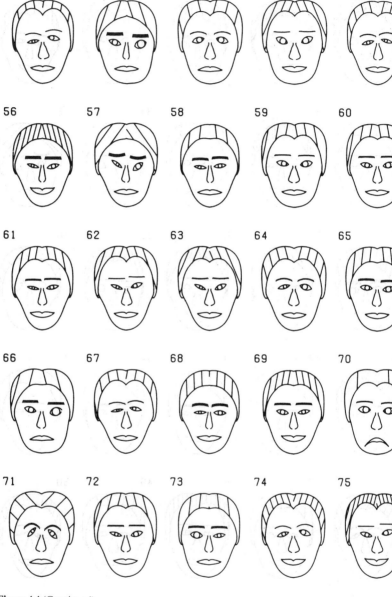

Figure 4.4 (Continued)

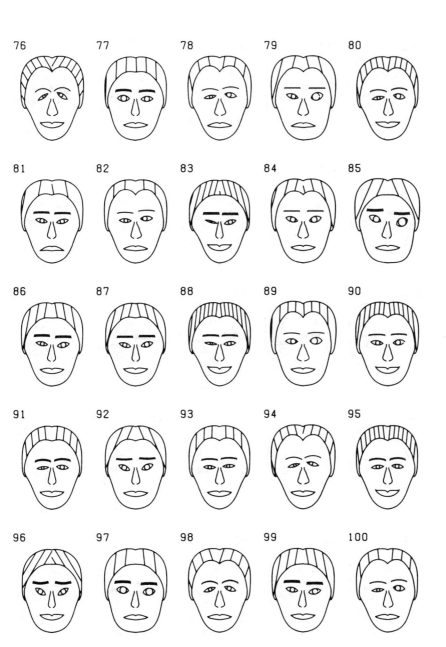

101
102
103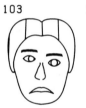
104
105

106
107
108
109
110

111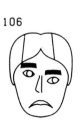
112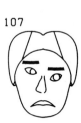
113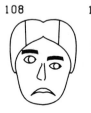
114
115

116
117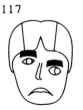
118
119
120

121
122
123
124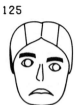
125

Figure 4.4 (Continued)

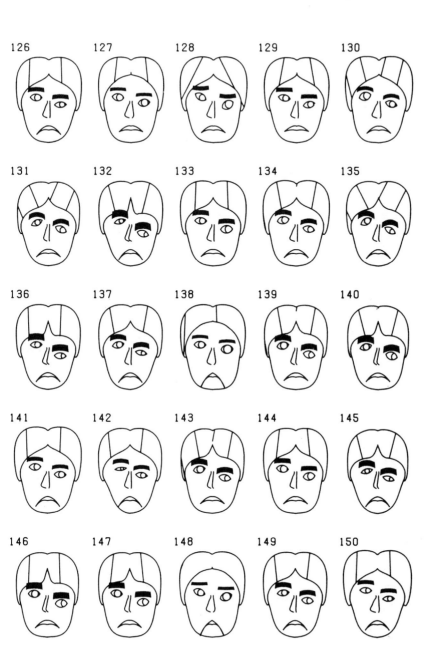

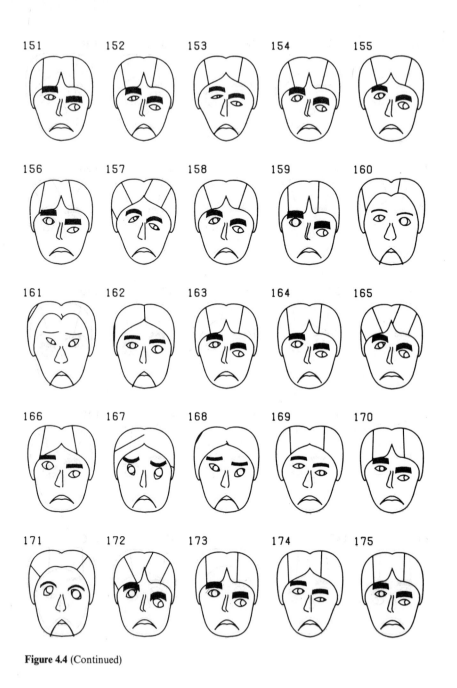

Figure 4.4 (Continued)

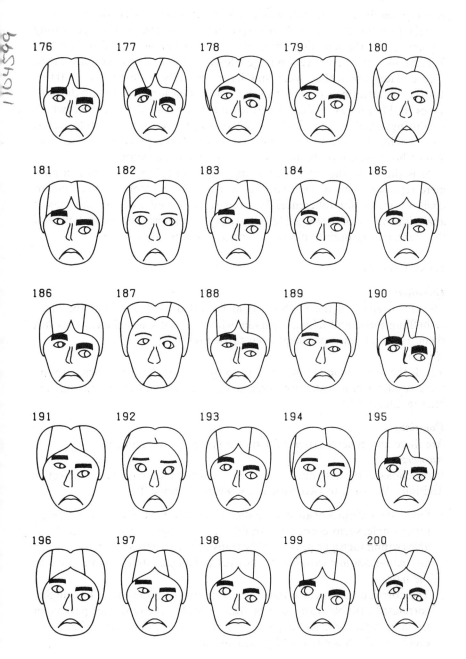

part is generally considerably wider than for genuine bills, i.e. the sum of the marginal widths $(X_4 + X_5)$ of the forged bills is too large on average. Strong asymmetries in the vertical position of the eyes and in the nose also show that forged bills very often have too large a lower margin. Moreover, most of the 'forged' faces are rather wide and have relatively wide-open eyes (LEFT, RIGHT). It is tempting to look for a subdivision of the forged faces into different 'types'. Bill 160, for example, strongly resembles bills 180, 187 and others which are distinguished by a special hair line, weak eyebrows and a severely curved mouth. Bills 110, 113 and 123 stand out through their especially wide face with almost horizontal mouth; here, too, we suspect a subgroup.

As is shown by the example, the application of face plots extends from a mere representation of multivariate data over into graphical discriminant analysis (search for differences between *Genuine* and *Forged*) and cluster analysis (division of the forged bills into *a priori* unknown subgroups). We will therefore, in appropriate places, come back to this method.

DISCUSSION

Question:
The effectiveness of the method could be tested by cutting out the faces, reshuffling them, and telling a person, who does not know the data, to sort them. Has such an experiment been carried out?
Answer:
Yes. If the test person is instructed to form two about equally large groups, there results a practically error-free separation. We will apply this method later in Chapter 12.

Question:
Are there any general criteria for the choice of the assignments?
Answer:
In the choice of the assignments there is, of course, a lot of room for subjective decisions. We stick to two basic rules, whenever possible:

1. Often, the variables of an investigation can be grouped in a meaningful way: for example, socio-economic variables, climatological variables, etc. Variables within such a group should be transformed to 'related' facial parts, e.g. all socio-economic variables to the eyes and all climatological variables to the hair.
2. The correlation structure must be taken into consideration. Two highly correlated variables can either be transformed to the same face parameter left and right, or also to parameters like vertical position of eye and eyebrow, which are related by their meaning.

It pays to think very carefully about the choice of assignments, since trying out several variants may be rather costly.

FURTHER STUDY

Textbooks

Graphical representation of multidimensional data has only recently found its way into textbooks of multivariate statistics. Chapters on face plots and other graphical methods can be found in Gnanadesikan (1977), Everitt (1978), Barnett (1981), Johnson and Wichern (1982), Seber (1984) and Hartung and Elpelt (1984). A book edited by Wang (1978) presents various applications of the original Chernoff face. A comprehensive book on visual display of data is by Tufte (1983).

Articles

The first face plots were introduced by Chernoff (1973). A documentation of the construction used here can be found in Flury (1980); applications have been given by Flury and Riedwyl (1981, 1983). A history of methods for representing multivariate data graphically has been published by Wainer (1983). Two interesting alternative methods to faces are trigonometric functions (Andrews (1972)) and stylized trees and castles (Kleiner and Hartigan (1981)).

Software

The faces of Figs 4.1 and 4.4 were plotted using a FORTRAN program called ASYM which can be obtained from the authors upon request; the hardware utilized was a CalComp plotter. Schüpbach (1984) has written a version for IBM PC. An SAS-Macro for asymmetrical faces can be obtained from Dr. M. Schüpbach, Department of Statistics, University of Berne, Sidlerstrasse 5, CH-3012 Berne, Switzerland.

5

Multiple linear regression

5.1 INTRODUCTORY REMARKS

In the following chapters we will use the multiple linear regression technique as a tool for discriminant analysis, identification analysis and specification analysis. We assume that the reader is familiar with at least simple linear regression (involving one independent variable). Those who do not know multiple regression are strongly urged to read one of the excellent books listed in the further study section following Section 5.10. This chapter is not meant as a first introduction to regression – its purpose rather is to recall the most important regression techniques and to establish some terminology and notation that will be used in subsequent chapters. Due to the special status of this chapter, we will use a different example rather than the bank note data for illustration.

5.2 THE MODEL OF MULTIPLE LINEAR REGRESSION

Quite frequently in the analysis of data we wish to study the dependence of a random variable Y on several variables $x_1, \ldots, x_p$. Regression methods are used to estimate such dependencies assuming that the *mean* μ_Y of Y is a function of $x_1, \ldots, x_p$. In *linear* regression, this function is assumed to be linear, i.e. of the form $\beta_0 + \beta_1 x_1 + \beta_2 x_2 + \cdots + \beta_p x_p$. This is an obvious extension of the simple linear regression model (involving only one x-variable), in which case the linear function $\beta_0 + \beta_1 x$ is easily interpreted as a straight line.

For illustration let us now turn to the numerical data. The example chosen has already been treated in the literature; it exhibits some typical aspects of multiple linear regression and, thanks to the small number of observations, it is very suitable for testing computer programs.

On examining the heat generated during the hardening of Portland cement, which is assumed to be a function of the chemical composition, the following variables were measured:

$$x_1 = \text{amount of tricalcium aluminate}$$
$$x_2 = \text{amount of tricalcium silicate}$$
$$x_3 = \text{amount of tetracalcium alumino ferrite}$$
$$x_4 = \text{amount of dicalcium silicate}$$
$$Y = \text{heat evolved in calories per gram of cement}$$

Table 5.1 Data of the cement hardening example

i	x_{1i}	x_{2i}	x_{3i}	x_{4i}	y_i
1	7	26	6	60	78.5
2	1	29	15	52	74.3
3	11	56	8	20	104.3
4	11	31	8	47	87.6
5	7	52	6	33	95.9
6	11	55	9	22	109.2
7	3	71	17	6	102.7
8	1	31	22	44	72.5
9	2	54	18	22	93.1
10	21	47	4	26	115.9
11	1	40	23	34	83.8
12	11	66	9	12	113.3
13	10	68	8	12	109.4

Note: These data are frequently discussed in the literature and are usually referred to as Hald's example; see the further study section at the end of this chapter.

Variables x_1 to x_4 were measured as percent of the weight of the clinkers from which the cement was made. The data, consisting of 13 observations, are displayed in Table 5.1.

Under the assumption that the heat generated during hardening is a linear function of the four variables x_1 to x_4, we postulate the model

$$\mu_Y = \mu_Y(x_1, x_2, x_3, x_4) = \beta_0 + \beta_1 x_1 + \beta_2 x_2 + \beta_3 x_3 + \beta_4 x_4.$$

This model claims that at the point $(x_{1i}, x_{2i}, x_{3i}, x_{4i})$ (ith row of the data matrix), the expected value (or mean) of the heat is $\beta_0 + \beta_1 x_{1i} + \beta_2 x_{2i} + \beta_3 x_{3i} + \beta_4 x_{4i}$. The measured value y_i is thus considered as a realization of a random variable Y_i, which consists of the above mean plus a random deviation e_i:

$$Y_i = \beta_0 + \beta_1 x_{1i} + \beta_2 x_{2i} + \beta_3 x_{3i} + \beta_4 x_{4i} + e_i$$
$$(i = 1, 2, \ldots, n).$$

The random errors e_i are usually assumed to be mutually independent and to follow a normal distribution with mean 0 and (common) variance σ^2.

In general, the coefficients β_0 to β_p are not known to the experimenter. Regression methods are used to estimate them and to test hypotheses about them.

The geometric-intuitive interpretation of the model – in analogy to the regression line in the case $p = 1$ – is a plane in the $(p + 1)$-dimensional space, which for each point $(x_{1i}, ..., x_{pi})$ determines the mean μ_Y. The intercept is β_0, i.e. the value of μ_Y at the point $(0, 0, ..., 0)$. $\beta_1, \beta_2, ..., \beta_p$ are called *partial regression coefficients*. They can be interpreted as follows: μ_Y increases by β_j if x_j increases by 1 while all other x-variables remain unchanged. Often, β_0 is referred to as the *constant*, which comes from the fact that β_0 can be considered as the partial regression coefficient for a variable x_0 that takes always the constant value $x_{0i} = 1$. We prefer to call β_0 the intercept.

Some more terminology: Y is called *dependent variable* or *response variable*; the x_j are called *regressors, carriers* or *independent variables* (although they need not be independent of each other in a statistical sense – the word 'independent' refers to their role in the function μ_Y). The x_j in this model are not considered as random variables, but rather as variables whose values have been fixed by the experimenter. If the x_j are actually random, then the statistical conclusions are conditional on the realized values.

In practice, the linear model will hardly ever be valid exactly. In many cases, however, in the domain considered, it is a good approximation to the real, more complex situation. Moreover, it will rarely be possible to know, or take into account, all the quantities influencing the mean μ_Y. The deviations e_i can thus be thought of as the sum of many such unknown or uncontrolled influences and, possibly, of a measurement error.

Summarizing, we can describe the model as follows:

1. The mean μ_Y of the random variable Y depends linearly on the regressors $x_1, x_2, ..., x_p$, i.e.

$$\mu_Y(x_1, ..., x_p) = \beta_0 + \beta_1 x_1 + \cdots + \beta_p x_p$$

2. In each point $(x_{1i}, ..., x_{pi})$ the deviations e_i from μ_Y are normally distributed with mean 0 and constant variance σ^2, in short:

$$e_i: N(0, \sigma^2)$$

3. The deviations e_i are mutually independent.

5.3   LEAST SQUARES ESTIMATION

The unknown parameters $\beta_0, \beta_1, ..., \beta_p$ are estimated as follows: for each observation y_i we form the deviation from the unknown mean μ_Y at the point $(x_{1i}, ..., x_{pi})$. The sum of the n squared differences,

$$S = \sum_{i=1}^{n} (y_i - \beta_0 - \beta_1 x_{1i} - \cdots - \beta_p x_{pi})^2$$

will be called the *sum of squares*. The latter is considered as a function of the $p + 1$ parameters $\beta_0, \beta_1, ..., \beta_p$, and, by the principle of least squares, we determine that particular p-dimensional hyperplane (i.e. the values of $\beta_0, \ldots, \beta_p$) for which S becomes minimal. The values $b_0, b_1, \ldots, b_p$ which minimize S are called *least squares estimates* for $\beta_0, \beta_1, \ldots, \beta_p$. Thus we have:

$$S_{\min} = \sum_{i=1}^{n} (y_i - b_0 - b_1 x_{1i} - \cdots - b_p x_{pi})^2 \leqslant S.$$

$S_{\min}$ is called the *minimum sum of squares* or *residual sum of squares*. The calculation of the coefficients b_j requires the solution of a system of linear equations in $p + 1$ variables. As to the precise conditions for the solvability of the equations, the interested reader is referred to Section 13.2 of the Appendix.

With the aid of the estimated parameters we can compute for each observation the estimated value (often called *predicted* value or *fitted* value)

$$\hat{y}_i = b_0 + b_1 x_{1i} + \cdots + b_p x_{pi},$$

which indicates the value of the estimated hyperplane at the point $(x_{1i}, \ldots, x_{pi})$. We will also compute the *residuals*

$$\hat{e}_i = y_i - \hat{y}_i,$$

i.e. the deviations of the measured values y_i from their predicted counterparts. If n is substantially larger than p, we can consider the list of residuals $\hat{e}_i$, $i = 1, 2, \ldots, n$, assuming the validity of the model, approximately as a random sample from a normal distribution with mean 0. The *standard deviation of the residuals* is estimated by

$$s_r = \sqrt{S_{\min}/(n - p - 1)}.$$

s_r is often called the *standard error of regression*.

In our example we obtained the equation

$$\hat{\mu}_Y = 62.418 + 1.551 x_1 + 0.510 x_2 + 0.102 x_3 - 0.144 x_4,$$

with a minimum sum of squares

$$S_{\min} = 47.945; \; s_r = 2.45.$$

Clearly, the method of least squares gives a 'best-fitting' hyperplane whether the assumptions in section 5.2 are satisfied or not. However, if the assumptions are valid, the least squares estimators have some important properties: The quantities $b_0, b_1, \ldots, b_p$ are unbiased estimates of the parameters $\beta_0, \beta_1, \ldots, \beta_p$. Among all possible unbiased estimators, which are linear functions of the y_i, the least squares estimators have the smallest variance. The quantity

$$\hat{\sigma}^2 = s_r^2 = S_{\min}/(n - p - 1)$$

is an unbiased estimator of σ^2. Moreover, from the assumption that the e_i's are independent and normally distributed, it follows that the least squares estimators $b_0, b_1, \ldots, b_p$ are also normally distributed.

5.4 RESIDUAL ANALYSIS

In order to validate the assumptions made, it is important to examine the residuals. A histogram of the residuals is a possible aid for visualizing possible violations of the normality assumptions. Also important is a scatterplot of the pairs $(\hat{y}_i, \hat{e}_i)$, i.e. of the residuals versus the predicted values, which often reveals whether or not the underlying linear model is correct. If the assumptions are satisfied, the residuals should scatter around 0 without any kind of dependency on the $\hat{y}_i$. Non-constant variance of the residuals, non-linear dependency, and other violations of the model assumptions can be uncovered by means of this plot.

Table 5.2 gives a list of the predicted values $\hat{y}_i$ and of the residuals $\hat{e}_i$ computed from the equation given at the end of Section 5.3. Figure 5.1 shows a two-dimensional representation of the table. This plot gives no reason for questioning the model assumptions. Since the number of observations is not substantially larger than the number of regressors, this plot, admittedly, could only uncover gross violations of the assumptions.

Occasionally, scatterplots of the residuals versus individual independent variables can also furnish information about non-linear dependencies. If a residual is extremely large in absolute value, we may be suspicious of an outlier, or the linear model may not be valid for that particular point. We are not going to give more details on residual analysis, which has received much attention in the recent past. Besides residual analysis, other methods have been developed to assess the validity of the regression model and the influence of

Table 5.2 Estimated values and residuals for the Hald regression example (all regressors included)

$\hat{y}_i$	$\hat{e}_i$
78.495	0.005
72.789	1.511
105.971	− 1.671
89.328	− 1.728
95.648	0.252
105.274	3.926
104.148	− 1.448
75.676	− 3.176
91.722	1.378
115.619	0.281
81.810	1.990
112.326	0.974
111.693	− 2.293

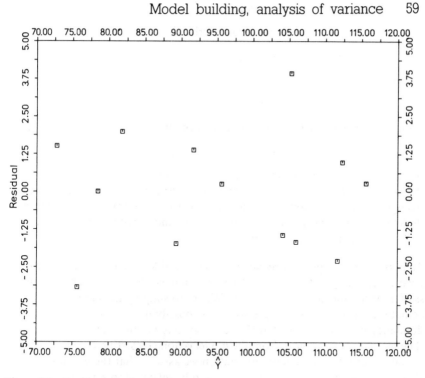

Figure 5.1   Residuals in the Hald example

particular data points on the estimation. One measure of influence, the so called *leverage*, seems particularly interesting, since it is closely related to standard distance. We will come back to this notion in Chapter 8.

5.5   MODEL BUILDING, ANALYSIS OF VARIANCE

Once the parameter estimates of the linear model are obtained, one would like to know whether it is necessary to include all independent variables in the regression equation. We can single out two cases in which a regressor can be removed from the model without any loss of information:

1. There is no relationship between x_j and Y;
2. The influence of x_j on Y is effected through other variables. This possibility can be illustrated most simply by means of a fictitious example. Assume the following model is valid:

$$\mu_Y = x_1 + 2x_2.$$

Assume, at the same time, that the variable $x_3 = x_1 + x_2$ has been measured, too. We can therefore also write the model as

$$\mu_Y = x_2 + x_3$$

or as

$$\mu_Y = 2x_3 - x_1.$$

Finally, we can describe μ_Y also as a function of all three regressors, e.g. as

$$\mu_Y = 2x_1 + 3x_2 - x_3.$$

In this model, one variable is clearly redundant – even though μ_Y is functionally dependent on x_1, x_2 and x_3. In practice it is often difficult to recognize such functional dependencies between the regressors. Often a functional relationship is additionally confounded with a measurement error, or it is not exactly linear.

In both cases we speak of *redundancy*: the variable x_j in case (1), or one of the variables x_1, x_2 and x_3 in case (2) can be removed from the model without loss of information, i.e. it is redundant. We try to simplify the model through elimination of redundant regressors. As possibility 2 shows, however, redundancy does not mean that the regressor has no influence.

The removal of variable x_j from the model is done by setting the parameter β_j equal to zero. For simplicity of notation we assume that the variables are ordered in such a way that the parameters to be set equal to zero are the last ones. The model with all p regressors

$$\mu_Y = \beta_0 + \beta_1 x_1 + \cdots + \beta_q x_q + \beta_{q+1} x_{q+1} + \cdots + \beta_p x_p$$

will be called the *full* (or *alternative*) *model*. By the so-called *linear restriction*, i.e. by setting

$$\beta_{q+1} = \beta_{q+2} = \cdots = \beta_p = 0 \qquad (0 \leqslant q < p)$$

a simplified model with q variables,

$$\mu_Y = \beta_0 + \beta_1 x_1 + \cdots + \beta_q x_q$$

is obtained. The latter model is also referred to as the *reduced model* or *null model*. Some important special reduced models are:

1. $q = 0$ or $\mu_Y = \beta_0$, i.e. all x_j variables considered have no influence on Y (*overall* hypothesis).
2. $q = p - 1$ or $\mu_Y = \beta_0 + \beta_1 x_1 + \cdots + \beta_{p-1} x_{p-1}$, i.e. only the last parameter β_p is set equal to zero. The variable x_p is redundant (*partial* hypothesis).

The full model and the reduced model can be compared as follows. For both models one estimates the parameters and computes the corresponding minimum sum of squares. The latter shall be denoted by S_{min}^p (full model) and

Table 5.3 Analysis of variance table in linear regression

Model	Minimum sum of squares	Degrees of freedom
reduced model $\beta_0 + \beta_1 x_1 + \cdots + \beta_q x_q$	S^q_{min}	$n - q - 1$
full model $\beta_0 + \beta_1 x_1 + \cdots + \beta_p x_p$	S^p_{min}	$n - p - 1$
reduction $\beta_{q+1} = \cdots = \beta_p = 0$	$S^q_{min} - S^p_{min}$	$p - q$

S^q_{min} (reduced model), respectively. Since the adjustment of the plane becomes worse by the elimination, one always has $S^p_{min} \leqslant S^q_{min}$. We now form the ratio

$$F = \frac{(S^q_{min} - S^p_{min})/(p - q)}{S^p_{min}/(n - p - 1)}$$

Under the hypothesis $\beta_{q+1} = \cdots = \beta_p = 0$ this statistic is distributed as F with $(p - q)$ degrees of freedom in the numerator and $(n - p - 1)$ degrees of freedom in the denominator. If the computed F-value is smaller than the $(1 - \alpha)$ quantile of the F-distribution with $(p - q)$ and $(n - p - 1)$ degrees of freedom, then the null hypothesis is accepted. Otherwise, we retain the full model: the annihilation of the $(p - q)$ parameters $\beta_{q+1}, \ldots, \beta_p$ was not justified for at least one parameter.

The minimum sum of squares and the F-test are usually summarized in an analysis of variance table (Table 5.3). It should be noted that the correctness of the F-test depends on the assumptions of the model. In many cases it is appropriate to view an F-value merely as a descriptive measure of the difference between the two models. This is particularly true if a series of model comparisons is carried out on one and the same set of data. We shall return to this problem in Section 5.10.

5.6   THE OVERALL TEST OF SIGNIFICANCE

The linear model with p partial regression coefficients is only meaningful if at least one coefficient is different from zero. We compare the full model

$$\mu_Y = \beta_0 + \beta_1 x_1 + \cdots + \beta_p x_p$$

with the reduced model

$$\mu_Y = \beta_0$$

Table 5.4 Test of the overall hypothesis in the Hald example

Model	Minimum sum of squares	Degrees of freedom
reduced model	2,715.762	12
full model	47.945	8
reduction	2,667.817	4

by eliminating all p variables simultaneously, i.e. by putting

$$\beta_1 = \beta_2 = \cdots = \beta_p = 0.$$

The least squares estimate of β_0 turns out to be the sample mean of Y, i.e. $b_0 = \bar{y}$; the corresponding minimum sum of squares is

$$S_{min}^0 = \sum_{i=1}^{n} (y_i - \bar{y})^2.$$

In our example, the corresponding analysis of variance table is as shown in Table 5.4. The overall F-test yields $F = 111.29$, to be compared (at $\alpha = 0.05$) with the 95% quantile of the F-distribution with 4 and 8 degrees of freedom:

$$F_{0.95}(4, 8) = 3.84.$$

Thus, there is strong evidence that at least one of the partial regression coefficients is different from zero, and we cannot dispense with all regressors.

All major computer programs for regression analysis calculate the analysis of variance table for the overall test of significance and the associated F-statistic. In contrast to our terminology, the sums of squares in the ANOVA table are usually labelled as follows in the computer printout: 'total' (for the reduced model $\mu_Y = \beta_0$), 'residual' (for the full model $\mu_Y = \beta_0 + \beta_1 x_1 + \cdots + \beta_p x_p$) and 'regression' (for the sum of squares associated with the reduction). Our terminology has the advantage of reminding the user that actually mathematical *models* are being compared and not just sums of squares.

5.7 COEFFICIENT OF DETERMINATION AND MULTIPLE CORRELATION

In addition to the overall F-value, one often computes the *coefficient of determination*

$$R^2 = \frac{S_{min}^0 - S_{min}^p}{S_{min}^0} = 1 - \frac{\sum_{i=1}^{n} (y_i - \hat{y}_i)^2}{\sum_{i=1}^{n} (y_i - \bar{y})^2}.$$

This quantity is often interpreted as the proportion of the variability of Y explained by the regression on $x_1, \ldots, x_p$. In our example, $R^2 = 0.982$, which says that 98.2% of the variability of Y is accounted for by the independent variables x_1 to x_4. If no linear dependency exists, then R^2 lies near 0; in the case of a strong linear dependency, however, it lies near 1. When interpreting the coefficient of determination, however, caution is advised, because for $n \leqslant p + 1$ one has $\hat{y}_i = y_i$, and thus $R^2 = 1$. Interpreting R^2 is meaningful only when n is considerably larger than p.

The root $R = \sqrt{R^2}$ is called the *multiple correlation coefficient* between Y and $x_1, \ldots, x_p$. R is equal to the correlation coefficient of the pairs $(y_i, \hat{y}_i)$. In our example, $R = 0.991$.

5.8   TESTS OF PARTIAL HYPOTHESES

In the second special case $q = p - 1$, mentioned in Section 5.5, the reduced model is

$$\mu_Y = \beta_0 + \beta_1 x_1 + \cdots + \beta_{p-1} x_{p-1},$$

which is obtained from the full model by imposing the restriction $\beta_p = 0$. For simplicity we again assume that it is the redundancy of the pth variable that needs to be tested. As in testing the overall hypothesis, we compute the two minimum sums of squares S^p_{min} (full model) and S^{p-1}_{min} (reduced model). By means of the ratio

$$F = F(\beta_p = 0) = \frac{S^{p-1}_{min} - S^p_{min}}{S^p_{min}/(n - p - 1)},$$

called the *partial F-statistic*, we test the redundancy of x_p in the regression model. Under the validity of the null hypothesis $\beta_p = 0$ the test statistic is distributed as F with 1 degree of freedom in the numerator and $(n - p - 1)$ degrees of freedom in the denominator.

By comparing the realized F-value with the $(1 - \alpha)$ quantile of the corresponding F-distribution one can thus test the partial hypothesis $\beta_p = 0$. If $F < F_{1-\alpha}(1, n - p - 1)$, we accept the simpler reduced model. It is, however, not possible to conclude from this that x_p has no influence on Y, since the influence of x_p may be represented by some other regressors. The only thing we can say is that the full set of regressors does not describe the linear relationship better than the reduced set.

If several partial F-values are computed, we recommend their use merely for descriptive purposes. In particular, it is not correct to conclude from the nonsignificance of several partial regression coefficients that these may simultaneously be removed from the model. Indeed, the elimination of one single regressor can strongly influence the other coefficients.

Many computer programs give *partial t-statistics* on $n - p - 1$ degrees of

Table 5.5 Standard errors and partial F-statistics in the Hald example

j	b_j	$s(b_j)$	$F(\beta_j = 0)$
0	62.418	71.59	0.760
1	1.551	0.745	4.331
2	0.510	0.724	0.496
3	0.102	0.755	0.018
4	− 0.144	0.710	0.041

freedom rather than partial F-statistics for testing the redundancy of a single variable. The relationship between the two statistics is simple: $F = t^2$, reflecting the fact that F with 1 degree of freedom in the numerator and m degrees of freedom in the denominator is the same as the square of t with m degrees of freedom.

5.9   STANDARD ERRORS OF THE REGRESSION COEFFICIENTS

From the partial F-value the *standard error of b_j* can be estimated as follows:

$$s(b_j) = \frac{|b_j|}{\sqrt{F(\beta_j = 0)}}$$

In our example one can thus supplement the estimated regression equation with a list of partial F-values and standard errors of the partial regression coefficients as shown in Table 5.5. The rather large standard errors (compared to the absolute values of the coefficients), and the small F-values lead one to suspect that the set of variables can be reduced in some way. An approach for eliminating redundant variables will be discussed in the next section.

5.10   SELECTION OF A SUBSET OF REGRESSORS

The selection of a suitable subset of regressors is often quite difficult. Different algorithms may yield different results. It can also happen that different subsets of equal size yield results of practically the same quality. In our example, we could eliminate one of the four independent variables and would obtain for the four reduced models the following coefficients of determination:

Model without	R^2
x_1	0.973
x_2	0.981
x_3	0.982
x_4	0.982

Since none of the models with three regressors results from one of the others through a linear restriction, they cannot be compared to each other by an analysis of variance. According to the coefficient of determination, three of the four models containing three regressors would be about equally good.

Situations such as this are especially likely to occur when the regressors are strongly related to each other. The relations among the x_j are usually described by a correlation matrix, although the values taken by the x_j are considered as fixed for the purpose of least squares estimation.

Because of the noncomparability of models with an equal number of regressors one often uses hierarchical algorithms for selecting a subset of independent variables. We describe here the method of *backward elimination*. Starting with the full model with p variables, we first eliminate the variable with the smallest partial F-value. In the resulting model with $p-1$ regressors we consider again the partial F-values of the remaining variables, i.e. we compare the model with $p-1$ variables with all models which result from elimination of one additional variable. Again, the variable with the smallest partial F-value is eliminated, etc., until in the end all regressors have been eliminated from the model. Applied to our example, the backward elimination yields the following results (where MPF stands for *Minimum Partial F*):

Step 1: Full model

Variable	b_j	$s(b_j)$	$F(\beta_j = 0)$
x_1	1.551	0.745	4.33
x_2	0.510	0.724	0.50
x_3	0.102	0.755	0.02 ← MPF
x_4	−0.144	0.710	0.04
intercept	62.418		

coefficient of determination: $R^2 = 0.982$
standard error of the residuals: $s_r = 2.448$

Step 2: Elimination of x_3

Variable	b_j	$s(b_j)$	$F(\beta_j = 0)$
x_1	1.452	0.117	154.01
x_2	0.416	0.186	5.03
x_4	−0.237	0.173	1.86 ← MPF
intercept	71.648		

$R^2 = 0.982$ $s_r = 2.309$

Step 3: Elimination of x_4

Variable	b_j	$s(b_j)$	$F(\beta_j = 0)$
x_1	1.468	0.121	146.52 ← MPF
x_2	0.662	0.046	208.58
intercept	52.577		

$R^2 = 0.979 \qquad s_r = 2.406$

Step 4: Elimination of x_1

Variable	b_j	$s(b_j)$	$F(\beta_j = 0)$
x_2	0.789	0.168	21.96
intercept	57.424		

$R^2 = 0.666 \qquad s_r = 9.077$

Elimination of x_2 in step 5 finally yields the estimate $b_0 = \bar{y} = 95.423$ and s_r = standard deviation of $Y = 15.044$.

It is now up to the user to make the important decision of how many regressors, and which ones, he wants to include in his model. Most program libraries offer the possibility of indicating a critical value F_{min}. The algorithm is stopped as soon as there is no longer a partial F-value smaller than F_{min}. In the hierarchical sequence of tests it is, however, not possible to consider the partial F-values as independent. We therefore recommend the use of partial F-values only in a descriptive sense for the purpose of determining an ordering among the independent variables. A possible stopping criterion is an abrupt change in R^2. In our example, the coefficient of determination decreases abruptly after three steps (see Fig. 5.2); this sharp bend is an indication that the two regressors eliminated first are redundant. The remaining model is based on x_1 and x_2 only; the regression equation (in brackets standard errors of the b_j) is estimated as

$$\hat{\mu}_Y = 52.577 + 1.468x_1 + 0.662x_2$$
$$(0.121) \qquad (0.046)$$

This model can now be compared with the full model. The analysis of variance table is as shown in Table 5.6. The value of the test statistic

$$F = \frac{9.96/2}{47.945/8} = 0.83$$

lies below the 0.95 quantile of the F-distribution with 2 and 8 degrees of

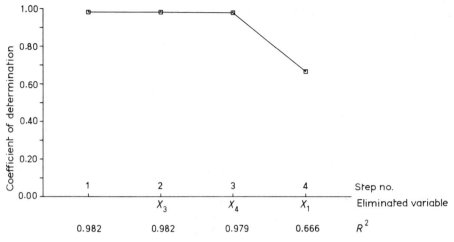

Figure 5.2 Change of the coefficient of determination in backward elimination

Table 5.6 Analysis of variance for redundancy of x_3 and x_4

Model	Minimum sum of squares	Degrees of freedom
$\beta_0 + \beta_1 x_1 + \beta_2 x_2$	57.904	10
$\beta_0 + \beta_1 x_1 + \beta_2 x_2 + \beta_3 x_3 + \beta_4 x_4$	47.945	8
reduction $\beta_3 = \beta_4 = 0$	9.960	2

freedom $[F_{0.95}(2, 8) = 4.46]$. The simplification of the model to 2 regressors appears to be justified.

We would like, however, to emphasize again that the solution thus found need by no means be the only correct one. A model with (x_1, x_4) instead of (x_1, x_2), for example, yields practically the same coefficient of determination. It remains up to the user to decide, based on his knowledge of the subject, which regressors he wants to use to describe the dependent variable.

Moreover, strictly speaking, the test given above is not entirely correct, since it violates the principle that hypotheses should not be generated and tested on the same data.

Table 5.7 gives a list of the y_i, $\hat{y}_i$, and of the residuals $\hat{e}_i = y_i - \hat{y}_i$ for the model with x_1 and x_2. Figure 5.3 depicts the multiple correlation for this model by means of a scatterplot of the pairs $(y_i, \hat{y}_i)$. This figure, at the same time, allows an examination of the residuals: the horizontal (or vertical) distance of $(y_i, \hat{y}_i)$ to the straight line $\hat{y} = y$ (45° line) corresponds precisely to the residual $\hat{e}_i = y_i - \hat{y}_i$. No violation of the assumptions can be detected.

Table 5.7 Fitted values and residuals for the model $\mu_Y(x_1, x_2)$

i	y_i	$\hat{y}_i$	$\hat{e}_i$
1	78.5	80.074	−1.574
2	74.3	73.251	1.049
3	104.3	105.815	−1.515
4	87.6	89.258	−1.658
5	95.9	97.292	−1.393
6	109.2	105.152	4.048
7	102.7	104.002	−1.302
8	72.5	74.575	−2.075
9	93.1	91.275	1.825
10	115.9	114.538	1.362
11	83.8	80.536	3.264
12	113.3	112.437	0.863
13	109.4	112.293	−2.893

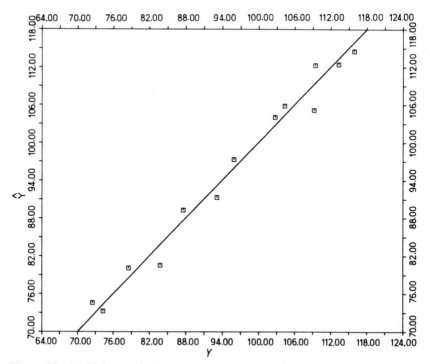

Figure 5.3 Multiple correlation in the model with x_1, x_2

DISCUSSION

Question:

What should one do if the assumptions of the model (normal distribution of the deviations) are not satisfied?

Answer:

In practice, one often encounters problems in which the assumptions for statistical testing are not satisfied. Purely numerically, one can, of course, still compute a 'best fit' hyper-plane, but the statistical tests are no longer correct. Since in this book we consider multiple regression merely as a tool, we refer here to the relevant literature.

Question:

Apart from backward elimination, are there any other procedures for selecting subsets of variables?

Answer:

In statistical program libraries, the following two additional algorithms are often used:

(a) Forward selection

In this method one seeks in step 1 a first variable which, taken alone, yields the highest F-value. In step 2, among all pairs of regressors which contain the already selected variable, one finds the one which maximizes the overall F. Analogously, in step 3 a third variable is added to the two already selected, and so on.

(b) Stepwise regression

This method is a mixture of the two already described. Steps 1 and 2 are as in forward selection; subsequently however, prior to the selection of an additional variable, one always examines the partial F-values of all variables already selected. If such a value falls below a certain limit, the variable in question is again eliminated, whereupon another variable is newly included, and so on. Table 5.8 gives for Hald's example a list of all 15 possible subsets of regressors. On the basis of this table, we can trace all three algorithms:

Step no.	Backward elimination	Forward selection	Stepwise regression
1	$x_1x_2x_3x_4$	x_4	x_4
2	$x_1x_2x_4$	x_1x_4	x_1x_4
3	x_1x_2	$x_1x_2x_4$	$x_1x_2x_4$
4	x_2	$x_1x_2x_3x_4$	x_1x_2
5	–	–	$x_1x_2x_4$

Table 5.8 All subsets regression in the Hald example

Regressors	S_{min}	R^2	Partial regression coefficients					Partial F for the hypothesis			
			$\hat{\beta}_0$	$\hat{\beta}_1$	$\hat{\beta}_2$	$\hat{\beta}_3$	$\hat{\beta}_4$	$\beta_1 = 0$	$\beta_2 = 0$	$\beta_3 = 0$	$\beta_4 = 0$
X_1	1265.7	0.5339	81.48	1.869				12.60			
X_2	906.3	0.6663	57.42		0.789				21.96		
X_3	1939.4	0.2859	110.20			-1.256				4.40	
X_4	883.9	0.6745	117.57				-0.738				22.80
$X_1 X_2$	57.9	0.9787	52.58	1.468	0.662			146.52	208.58		
$X_1 \; X_3$	1227.1	0.5482	72.35	2.313		0.495		5.81		0.31	
$X_1 \quad X_4$	74.8	0.9725	103.10	1.440			-0.614	108.22			159.29
$X_2 X_3$	415.4	0.8470	72.07		0.731	-1.008			36.68	11.82	
$X_2 \quad X_4$	868.9	0.6801	94.16		0.311		-0.457		0.17		0.43
$X_3 X_4$	175.7	0.9353	131.28			-1.200	-0.725			40.29	100.36
$X_1 X_2 X_3$	48.1	0.9823	48.19	1.696	0.657	0.250		68.71	220.54	1.83	
$X_1 X_2 \quad X_4$	48.0	0.9823	71.65	1.452	0.416		-0.237	154.01	5.03		1.86
$X_1 \quad X_3 X_4$	50.8	0.9813	111.68	1.052		-0.410	-0.643	22.11		4.24	208.23
$X_2 X_3 X_4$	73.8	0.9728	203.64		-0.923	-1.448	-1.557		12.42	96.92	41.64
$X_1 X_2 X_3 X_4$	47.9	0.9824	62.38	1.551	0.510	0.102	-0.144	4.34	0.50	0.02	0.04

A comparison between backward elimination and forward selection shows the phenomenon, which is rather rare in practice, that the reversal of forward selection does not produce at all stages the same subset of regressors as backward elimination. For stepwise regression, a critical partial F-value of 2.0 was fixed for elimination. The procedure stops at step 5, since in the next step x_4 would again be eliminated.

In the following, we will always use backward elimination, since at the beginning one performs the overall test. If this test turns out to be nonsignificant, then the decision is that the coefficients $\beta_1, \ldots, \beta_p$ are all zero. In this case, any selection of subsets is unnecessary, whereas in the other procedures, from a number of purely redundant regressors a few can be selected, even though in reality there exists no influence.

Thanks to extremely fast computers it is nowadays also possible to use so-called 'all-subsets-regression' algorithms. If p regressors are available, an exhaustive search implies that $2^p - 1$ subsets have to be analysed – an almost astronomic task for p as small as 10. Of course it is possible to restrict the number of subsets by heuristic considerations, but nevertheless the amount of computation is very large. For an example of all-subsets-regression, see again Table 5.8.

Question:
In backward elimination, can one come up with an automatic stopping criterion that would avoid following through the algorithm to the very end?
Answer:
In most programs for multiple regression this is indeed possible. Backward elimination carried through to the end, however, may provide additional information about the importance of the individual regressors.

Question:
Aren't the assumptions in Hald's example grossly violated? The variables x_1 to x_4, as one can see from the data matrix, are certainly not normally distributed.
Answer:
This is a misconception. You didn't pay attention when we were talking about this point. In the regression model the values of the regressors are fixed numbers, assigned by the researcher. The normality assumption refers only to the deviations e_i.

Question:
How about the numerical accuracy of the results? As is known from experience, the results of various regression programs do not always agree to all decimal digits.
Answer:
The numerical computation of the coefficients consists mainly of the inversion of a matrix. In this connection, certain numerical problems may arise,

especially when the regressors are strongly correlated among each other. It is therefore recommended to analyse one and the same regression problem with different programs. If the results do not agree, a possible way out is to consider, instead of the actual regressors, their principal components (see Chapter 10) as independent variables. This option is provided, for example, in the library BMDP.

Question:
I don't quite understand why you stress the subset selection so much. Why shouldn't we simply use the full model with all p variables included? Why should we make the fit worse by eliminating variables? Since R^2 always increases if we include more variables, it certainly can't hurt if we use all the predictors that are available.

Answer:
From a non-statistical point of view you are right – inclusion of an additional variable will always improve the fit as measured by the coefficient of determination. The statistical question is whether or not the improvement is purely random. There are also other reasons for selecting a subset. For instance, we can argue that a *simple* model is preferable to a *complicated* model, provided that both models work equally well – a rule that is valid not only for statistical models. A very important reason is the *instability* of the parameter estimates if too many variables are included – instability in the sense of both poor numerical accuracy and large standard errors of the parameter estimates. This is clearly visible in the Hald example, if we follow the backward elimination process: in step one, all coefficients are highly unstable (in the sense of high standard errors), while after the elimination of x_3 and x_4 the remaining coefficients are rather stable. This phenomenon occurs typically when the regressors are highly correlated among each other. Subset selection is, admittedly, only one possibility to handle this problem. Another interesting technique is 'ridge regression', which trades the high variability of the parameter estimates for some (hopefully negligible) bias. We would again like to refer the reader to the relevant literature for more detailed information.

Question:
We have discussed the role played by different variables in a regression equation, and we have seen that some variables may be more important for predicting Y than others. Couldn't we do a similar thing for the observations? I mean, is it somehow possible to measure to what extent the regression equation is determined by each observation?

Answer:
Methods for assessing the influence of individual observations on the regression equation have indeed been given much attention in the recent past, as already mentioned in the section on residual analysis. A simple approach is, for instance, to omit observation no. i and recalculate the regression equation

based on the remaining $n - 1$ data points. The influence of the ith observation can then be judged by the changes occurring in the regression coefficients. For a nice introduction to these techniques, see the article by Efron and Gong (1983).

Knowing the background of the data is often helpful to determine which observations need to be looked at more closely for their influence. This is also true for the Hald example, in which the detailed knowledge of the experiment can be used to build an appropriate model and to select observations – see the discussion in Section 9.2 of Daniel and Wood (1980). We would like to repeat here that we used the Hald example simply because it demonstrates various aspects of multiple regression quite nicely with only a small number of observations.

Question:
You said that the coefficient of determination, R^2, should be interpreted only if n is 'considerably larger' than p. What exactly do you mean by that?
Answer:
For interpreting R^2 it may be helpful to take notice of the following theoretical result: under *no* conditions on the x-variables (i.e. their values may be random according to any law, or they may be fixed), and if the random variable Y does not depend on the x-variables, then under rather weak assumptions on the distribution of Y (essentially symmetry and uncorrelatedness of the realizations y_i), the expected value of R^2 is

$$E[R^2] = \frac{p}{n-1}.$$

That is, for a sample size of $n = 21$ and $p = 10$ variables, we can expect R^2 to be about 0.5 by pure chance! So, as a simple rule of thumb, only the proportion of R^2 exceeding the expected value should be interpreted.

By the way, in connection with this result it is also worth noting that the overall F-test of significance (which is functionally closely related to R^2) is valid under similarly weak conditions. This means particularly that the overall F-test does not require exact normality of the residuals, but, broadly speaking, a symmetric distribution. For the partial F-tests it is not known to what extent their correctness depends on strict normality. In general, however, these tests are more reliable the larger the sample size n.

Question:
I have encountered a regression problem with only one regressor x, but the regression function was a quadratic function of x. Can this problem be approached with the linear regression technique?
Answer:
To answer this question, we must first clarify our terminology. In the linear regression model $\mu_y = \beta_0 + \beta_1 x_1 + \cdots + \beta_p x_p$, the word 'linear' refers actually

to the fact that μ_y is a linear function of the *parameters* β_j. The model that you are talking about has the form

$$\mu_y = \beta_0 + \beta x_1 + \beta^2 x_2$$

which can be handled within the framework of linear regression with two regressors, namely $x_1 = x$ and $x_2 = x^2$. On the other hand, the model

$$\mu_y = \beta_0 + \beta x_1 + \beta^2 x_2$$

is not linear in the parameter β, and the linear regression technique can be applied.

FURTHER STUDY

Textbooks

There is probably no other part of statistics for which there exists such a deluge of textbooks as for regression analysis.

A classical textbook is the one of Draper and Smith (1966, expanded 2nd edition 1981). This frequently used work puts great emphasis on stepwise procedures and residual analysis, whereby numerical results are explained by means of computer outputs. Another classic in revised edition is by Daniel and Wood (1980), who present a wealth of examples in computer-oriented representation.

A very detailed, mathematically elementary exposition is given by Younger (1979); this work, which is worth reading, also contains a simple introduction to matrix algebra, as well as guidance for reading the computer output of BMDP and SAS. Belsley, Kuh and Welsch (1980) concern themselves especially with the problem of collinearity, that is, problems induced by high correlations between regressors. Pesaran and Slater (1980) discuss applications of linear regression to time series. Two books well worth reading, and application-oriented, are by Weisberg (1985) and by Montgomery and Peck (1982). A good introduction to the analysis of residuals and influential observations has been written by Cook and Weisberg (1982). Other modern textbooks are by Freund and Minton (1979), by Gunst and Mason (1980) and by Neter, Wasserman and Kutner (1985). The example in this chapter was first discussed by Hald (1952) and is analysed in detail by Draper and Smith (1981, 2nd edition).

Software

Regression programs are those used most frequently and can be found in practically every statistics software package. Most of them print residual plots on computer paper. In the case $p = 1$ or $p = 2$ even a pocket calculator will suffice.

6
Linear combinations

6.1 INTRODUCTION

A basic method for simplifying many multivariate problems consists of considering, in place of the measured variables, linear combinations of them. By a linear combination of the variables $X_1, X_2, \ldots, X_p$ we mean a weighted sum

$$Z = a_1 X_1 + a_2 X_2 + \cdots + a_p X_p,$$

where the a_i are called *weights*, or *coefficients*, of the linear combination. We have already encountered linear combinations with an additional constant term in multiple linear regression. From among the unlimited number of possibilities of forming linear combinations, we shall choose one, or several, that are particularly 'suitable'. What 'suitable' means, will depend on the context of the problem. The application of a given linear combination with coefficients $a_1, a_2, \ldots, a_p$ to multidimensional observations is to be understood in the sense that for each observation $(x_{1i}, x_{2i}, \ldots, x_{pi})$, where $i = 1, 2, \ldots, n$, a value of the variable Z is computed by means of the transformation

$$z_i = a_1 x_{1i} + a_2 x_{2i} + \cdots + a_p x_{pi}.$$

In the next section we shall explain this idea further with a special example.

6.2 A SPECIAL LINEAR COMBINATION

In Chapters 2 and 4 we noticed that the upper and lower margins of the forged notes tend to be too large, relative to the margins of the real ones. Could this be due to too narrow a print image in the forger's production? Would the variables $X_7 = \text{IMAGE} = $ height of the print image possibly be a good variable for discriminating between *Genuine* and *Forged*? Unfortunately, this variable has not been measured. It can be estimated, however, as the difference between the height of the bill and the sum of the marginal widths. In doing so, we use for the height of the bill the arithmetic mean of LEFT and RIGHT. We thus formally define the variable

Table 6.1 Values of $X_7 = $ IMAGE for 10 genuine and 10 forged bills

	Genuine				
	LEFT	RIGHT	BOTTOM	TOP	IMAGE
i	x_{2i}	x_{3i}	x_{4i}	x_{5i}	x_{7i}
1	131.0	131.1	9.0	9.7	112.35
2	129.7	129.7	8.1	9.5	112.10
3	129.7	129.7	8.7	9.6	111.40
4	129.7	129.6	7.5	10.4	111.75
5	129.6	129.7	10.4	7.7	111.55
6	130.8	130.5	9.0	10.1	111.55
7	129.5	129.7	7.9	9.6	112.10
8	129.6	129.2	7.2	10.7	111.50
9	129.4	129.7	8.2	11.0	110.35
10	130.4	130.3	9.2	10.0	111.15
	Forged				
	LEFT	RIGHT	BOTTOM	TOP	IMAGE
i	x_{2i}	x_{3i}	x_{4i}	x_{5i}	x_{7i}
101	130.1	130.3	9.7	11.7	108.80
102	130.5	130.2	11.0	11.5	107.85
103	130.3	130.1	8.7	11.7	109.80
104	130.4	130.6	9.9	10.9	109.70
105	130.2	130.3	11.8	10.9	107.55
106	130.2	130.2	10.6	10.7	108.90
107	130.3	130.1	9.3	12.1	108.80
108	130.1	130.4	9.8	11.5	108.95
109	130.2	129.9	10.0	11.9	108.15
110	130.6	130.8	10.4	11.2	109.10

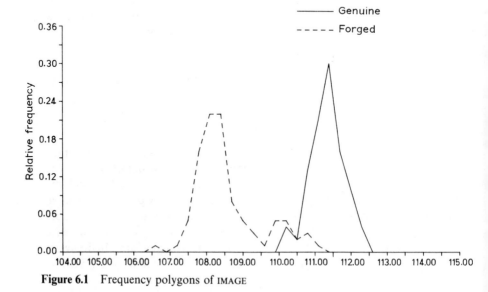

Figure 6.1 Frequency polygons of IMAGE

Table 6.2 Univariate descriptive statistics for IMAGE

Group	Genuine		Forged
mean	111.358		108.583
standard deviation	4696		.9065
mean difference		2.775	
standard distance		3.844	

$$\text{IMAGE} = \tfrac{1}{2}(\text{LEFT} + \text{RIGHT}) - (\text{BOTTOM} + \text{TOP}),$$

or

$$X_7 = \tfrac{1}{2}X_2 + \tfrac{1}{2}X_3 - X_4 - X_5.$$

IMAGE, therefore, is a linear combination of the variables LEFT, RIGHT, BOTTOM and TOP. For each bill we can obtain from the above formula a value of the variable IMAGE. Table 6.1 shows the values of the variables X_2, X_3, X_4, X_5 and X_7 for the first few genuine and forged bills. Figure 6.1 shows the polygons of the frequency distribution of IMAGE in both groups. As shown by the figure, the separation of the two groups by means of IMAGE is better than by means of each of the variables $X_2, X_3, X_4,$ or X_5 alone (see Fig. 2.2 to 2.5). The descriptive statistics for X_7 in both groups are shown in Table 6.2.

6.3   LINEAR COMBINATIONS OF TWO VARIABLES

6.3.1   Arbitrary linear combinations of two variables

In this section, we limit ourselves to linear combinations of two variables only, so that we can rely on geometrical intuition. Figure 6.2 shows a scatterplot of the 100 genuine bills for the variables LEFT and RIGHT.

By projecting the points onto the x- or y-axis, we obtain the familiar one-dimensional frequency distributions of the variables LEFT and RIGHT (Figs 2.2 and 2.3). We now consider the linear combination

$$\text{HEIGHT} = \tfrac{1}{2}(\text{LEFT} + \text{RIGHT}),$$

or

$$X_8 = \tfrac{1}{2}X_2 + \tfrac{1}{2}X_3,$$

i.e. the arithmetic mean of the two heights of the bills. Is it possible to show also the frequency distribution of X_8 in the same plot? In order to answer this question, we argue as follows. A particular value c of the variable X_8 is realized by all pairs (x_2, x_3) whose arithmetic mean is c:

$$\tfrac{1}{2}x_2 + \tfrac{1}{2}x_3 = c.$$

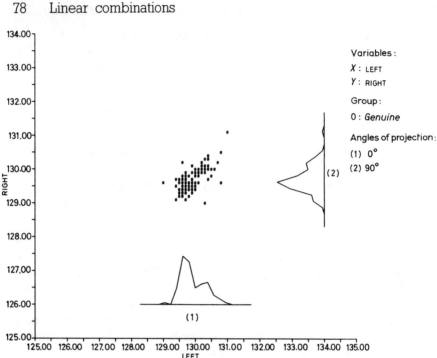

Figure 6.2   Projections of the variables LEFT and RIGHT

Note: Identical pairs of numbers in this and the following figures are represented by a single symbol only. Thus one finds only 68 points in Figure 6.2 instead of 100.

This equation defines a straight line in the (x_2, x_3)-plane. For various values of c, one obtains a family of parallel straight lines, which form an angle of 45° with the y-axis (measured counter-clockwise). Instead of projecting in the direction of the coordinate axis, we now project the point cluster in the direction of the parallel straight lines, and thus obtain – drawn on the perpendicular to the direction of projection – a frequency distribution of X_8. Figure 6.3 illustrates the projection just discussed.

Analogously, for an arbitrary linear combination of two variables X and Y,

$$Z = aX + bY,$$

we can project the points (x_i, y_i) along parallel straight lines of the form

$$ax + by = c$$

and represent the frequency distribution of Z on a perpendicular to the direction of projection.

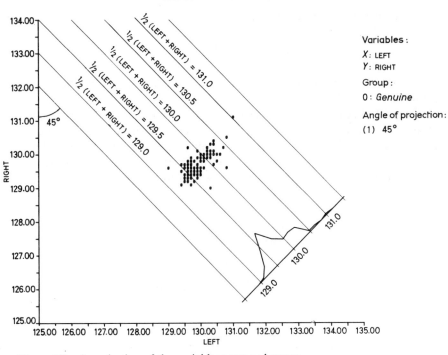

Figure 6.3   A projection of the variables LEFT and RIGHT

6.3.2   Normalized linear combination

If we compare the two linear combinations

$$X_8 = \tfrac{1}{2}X_2 + \tfrac{1}{2}X_3$$

and

$$X_8^* = X_2 + X_3,$$

we note that the direction of projection is the same for both – which is not surprising, since, after all, $X_8^* = 2 \cdot X_8$. In general, two linear combinations,

$$Z_1 = a_1 X + b_1 Y$$

and

$$Z_2 = a_2 X + b_2 Y$$

lead to the same direction of projection, whenever Z_2 is obtained from Z_1 by multiplication with a constant:

$$Z_2 = k \cdot Z_1.$$

This is equivalent to the condition

$$\frac{a_2}{a_1} = \frac{b_2}{b_1} = k,$$

i.e. the ratios of respective coefficients of the two linear combinations are identical.

Obviously, linear combinations with the same direction of projection differ in the unit of measurement, but not in the shape of the distribution, and can therefore be considered as *equivalent* in certain applications. We will therefore characterize each direction of projection by *one* particular linear combination. A linear combination $Z = aX + bY$ will be said to be *normalized*, if

$$a^2 + b^2 = 1.$$

A given non-normalized linear combination with coefficients a and b can be normalized by transforming the coefficients according to

$$a' = \frac{a}{\sqrt{a^2 + b^2}}, \quad b' = \frac{b}{\sqrt{a^2 + b^2}}.$$

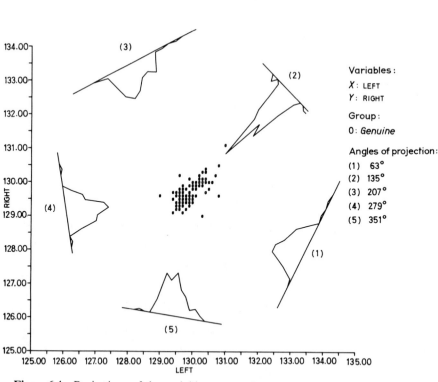

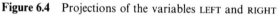

Figure 6.4   Projections of the variables LEFT and RIGHT

The linear combination $Z' = a'X + b'Y$ is then normalized, since

$$a'^2 + b'^2 = \frac{a^2}{a^2 + b^2} + \frac{b^2}{a^2 + b^2} = 1$$

and furthermore,

$$Z' = \frac{1}{\sqrt{a^2 + b^2}} Z,$$

i.e. Z' corresponds to the same direction of projection as Z.

For geometric intuition, normalization offers the following advantages:

1. The scaling of the variable Z corresponds precisely to the scaling of X and Y, i.e. the scale used for the x- and y-axis can be carried over to the z-line.
2. We may interpret the two coefficients of the normalized linear combination as the cosine and sine of an angle ϕ: $a = \cos\phi$, $b = \sin\phi$. The angle ϕ is formed between the direction of projection and the y-axis (measured counter-clockwise). For example, $\phi = 0$ corresponds to a projection onto the x-axis. Every choice of ϕ leads to a normalized linear combination, since, as is well-known, $\cos^2\phi + \sin^2\phi = 1$ for any angle ϕ.

Figure 6.4 shows normalized linear combinations of the variables LEFT and RIGHT for angles of projection ϕ of 63°, 135°, 207°, 279° and 351°.

6.4   LINEAR COMBINATIONS OF SEVERAL VARIABLES

In the case of p variables ($p > 2$), we consider linear combinations of the form

$$Z = a_1 X_1 + a_2 X_2 + \cdots + a_p X_p.$$

In complete analogy to the two-dimensional case we may look at a linear combination as a projection in a particular direction of the p-dimensional space. The linear combination is called normalized, if

$$a_1^2 + a_2^2 + \cdots + a_p^2 = 1.$$

For instance, the normalized linear combination equivalent to the variable IMAGE (as defined in Section 6.2) would be

$$X_7' = \tfrac{2}{5} X_7 = 0.3162 X_2 + 0.3162 X_3 - 0.6325 X_4 - 0.6325 X_5,$$

as is easily checked.

Here too, equivalent linear combinations differ merely in the scaling, but not in the shape of distribution. The description of a normalized linear combination by means of $p - 1$ angles of projection is possible, but not customary, since for $p > 3$ geometric intuition fails.

To conclude this section, we give three examples of normalized linear combinations of all six variables. The examples have been chosen arbitrarily,

Table 6.3 Descriptive statistics for three linear combinations

Linear combination	Group	Mean	Standard deviation	Standard distance
Z_1	Genuine	287.65	0.502	0.349
	Forged	287.83	0.528	
Z_2	Genuine	− 58.50	0.307	3.410
	Forged	− 56.76	0.653	
Z_3	Genuine	56.01	0.508	2.437
	Forged	54.50	0.714	

but are intended to show the multitude of possibilities offered through the construction of linear combinations. The three examples are:

$$Z_1 = 0.5X_1 + 0.4X_2 + 0.4X_3 + 0.3X_4 + 0.3X_5 + 0.5X_6$$
$$Z_2 = 0.1X_1 - 0.4X_2 - 0.3X_3 + 0.7X_4 + 0.5X_5$$
$$Z_3 = -0.25X_1 - 0.17X_2 + 0.02X_3 + 0.24X_4 - 0.15X_5 + 0.91X_6.$$

Even though variable X_6 does not appear in Z_2, we may formally regard Z_2 as a linear combination of all six variables, with a coefficient 0 for X_6.

The descriptive statistics for the three linear combinations are as shown in Table 6.3. Figure 6.5, 6.6 and 6.7 show the frequency distributions of the three linear combinations for both groups. We can see from these figures that different linear combinations of the same variables may be interesting with respect to various questions:

1. We may be interested, for example, in a linear combination which furnishes as large a standard distance as possible between *Genuine* and *Forged*. In this regard, Z_2 and Z_3 would be of interest. The consideration of such linear combinations leads immediately to the problem of discriminant analysis (Chapter 7).
2. We may ask for linear combinations which yield a large difference between the standard deviations of the two groups (e.g. Z_2). We shall consider this question again in the problem of comparing covariance matrices (Chapter 11).
3. If we choose to consider only one group, we may look for a normalized linear combination with a standard deviation as large as possible (e.g. Z_3 for the group *Forged*). This type of problem will lead later to principal component analysis (Chapter 10).

In problems 2 and 3, the mean values do not play any role. For these types of problems, we could without loss of generality shift the origin of the coordinate system in an arbitrary way. For problems of type 3, for example, it is

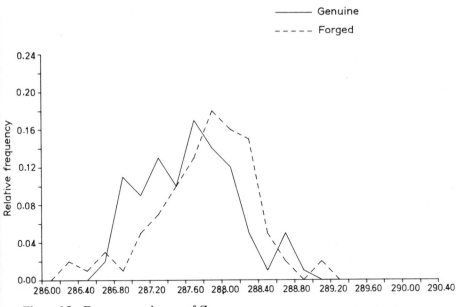

Figure 6.5 Frequency polygons of Z_1

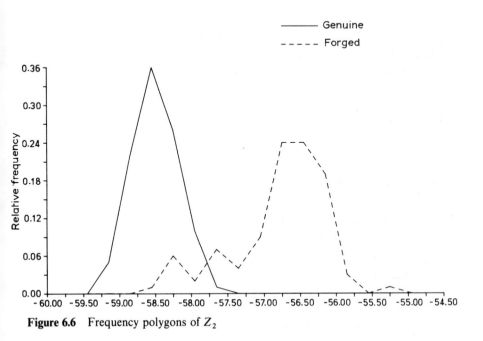

Figure 6.6 Frequency polygons of Z_2

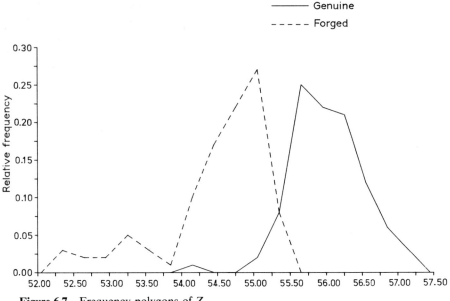

Figure 6.7   Frequency polygons of Z_3

customary to shift the origin of the coordinate system to the mean vector $(\bar{x}_1, \bar{x}_2, \ldots, \bar{x}_6)$. Formally, such a shift means that we subtract from each variable its mean, i.e. the values x_{ji} are transformed according to

$$x'_{ji} = x_{ji} - \bar{x}_j.$$

The new variables X'_j all have mean 0, but the same standard deviations as the X_j, and the same covariance matrix. If we now apply a linear combination

$$Z = a_1 X_1 + a_2 X_2 + \cdots + a_p X_p$$

to the X'_j instead of the X_j, we see from the formulae of the next section that

$$Z' = a_1 X'_1 + a_2 X'_2 + \cdots + a_p X'_p,$$

too, has mean 0, but the same standard deviation as Z. Variances and covariances are not affected by shifting the origin.

6.5   MEAN AND STANDARD DEVIATION OF LINEAR COMBINATIONS

The mean and standard deviation of a (normalized or arbitrary) linear combination

$$Z = a_1 X_1 + a_2 X_2 + \cdots + a_p X_p$$

can be computed by carrying out, for each observation $(x_{1i}, x_{2i}, \ldots, x_{pi})$, the transformation

$$z_i = a_1 x_{1i} + a_2 x_{2i} + \cdots + a_p x_{pi}, \qquad i = 1, 2, \ldots, n,$$

and by subsequently computing $\bar{z}$ and s_z. The same statistics, however, can be computed more simply as follows:

$$\bar{z} = a_1 \bar{x}_1 + a_2 \bar{x}_2 + \cdots + a_p \bar{x}_p = \sum_{j=1}^{p} a_j \bar{x}_j,$$

$$s_z^2 = \sum_{j=1}^{p} \sum_{k=1}^{p} a_j a_k c_{jk},$$

where c_{jk} denotes the covariance between X_j and X_k. (*Note*: c_{jj} is the variance of the variable X_j.) If we denote the variance of X_j by s_j^2, the formula can be written as follows:

$$s_z^2 = \sum_{j=1}^{p} a_j^2 s_j^2 + 2 \sum_{j=1}^{p-1} \sum_{k=j+1}^{p} a_j a_k c_{jk}.$$

Knowing the means of the X_j and the covariance matrix, we can thus determine the mean and variance of every linear combination without actually carrying out the transformation. If, instead of the covariance matrix, the correlation matrix is available, we can use the relationship

$$c_{jk} = s_j \cdot s_k \cdot r_{jk},$$

where r_{jk} = correlation between X_j and X_k, $r_{jj} = 1$. The variance formula then becomes

$$s_z^2 = \sum_{j=1}^{p} a_j^2 s_j^2 + 2 \sum_{j=1}^{p-1} \sum_{k=j+1}^{p} a_j s_j a_k s_k r_{jk}.$$

In our example, the univariate statistics for X_2 and X_3 in the group *Genuine* (cf. Section 2) are:

$$\bar{x}_2 = 129.943 \qquad s_2 = 0.3641$$
$$\bar{x}_3 = 129.720 \qquad s_3 = 0.3553$$

and

$$r_{23} = 0.6639$$

For the linear combination $X_8 = \frac{1}{2} X_2 + \frac{1}{2} X_3$, introduced in Section 6.3., we have thus

$$\bar{x}_8 = \frac{1}{2} \bar{x}_2 + \frac{1}{2} \bar{x}_3 = 129.832$$

and

$$s_8^2 = \frac{1}{4} s_2^2 + \frac{1}{4} s_3^2 + 2 \cdot \frac{1}{2} \cdot \frac{1}{2} s_2 \cdot s_3 \cdot r_{23} = 0.108$$

and

$$s_8 = 0.328.$$

DISCUSSION

Question
What is the interpretation of the various linear combinations in Fig. 6.4?
Answer
Of course not every linear combination has as simple an interpretation as, for instance, IMAGE. Most often, a particular linear combination resulting from a multivariate analysis cannot be interpreted as a quantity that could be measured directly on the objects. Yet the coefficients a_j of a linear combination can be interpreted as in multiple regression: two objects that are identical in all variables except X_j, and differ by 1 in X_j, will differ by a_j in the linear combination.

Question
Does a linear combination have any meaning if the units of measurement of the variables are not all the same?
Answer
In cases of different units of measurement, one sometimes uses the standardized variables in place of the actual variables (cf. Chapter 10). In this way, each value x_{ji} is replaced by

$$z_{ji} = (x_{ji} - \bar{x}_j)/s_j,$$

that is, by its 'signed standard distance' from the mean. A linear combination of standardized variables is then to be considered a weighted sum of such dimensionless 'scores'.

On the other hand, a linear combination of variables with different units of measurement can actually be quite meaningful, for example when the linear combination is interpreted as a separating hyperplane in a classification problem (Section 7.6).

FURTHER STUDY

The theory of linear transformations of random variables plays a central role and is therefore treated in every book on multivariate analysis, although in general in a much more abstract way than in this chapter. Formulae for mean and variance of a linear combination are usually given in matrix form. The Indian statistician S.N. Roy has derived a number of multivariate tests from the principle of simultaneous consideration of all possible linear combinations; his book (Roy (1957)), however, is not easy to read. The technique of Roy has become known in the literature as the 'Union-Intersection Principle', and, although it is quite old, has been given due regard only in the last few years (see, for example, Srivastava and Khatri (1979), Mardia, Kent and Bibby (1979), Seber (1984)). Looking at many different projections has become increasingly popular in the last decade, thanks to fast computers; see Huber (1985) for an excellent review.

7

Linear discriminant analysis for two groups

7.1 INTRODUCTION

In Chapter 2 we compared the (univariate) sample means of the two groups by mean differences and standard distances. If more than one variable is measured on each observation, however, an analysis restricted to single variables may not be sufficiently informative. Moreover, test statistics computed for each variable individually are not independent due to the correlations between the variables. We would therefore like to introduce a method that uses all variables simultaneously. Applied to the bank note example, this means that we would like to characterize the difference in location between genuine and forged notes in such a way that the information from all six variables is used concurrently. This will be achieved by a generalization of the notion of standard distance (cf. Chapter 2). It turns out that this generalization is closely related to a generalization of the well-known two-sample t-statistics and to the multiple regression model, as will be outlined in Sections 7.2 and 7.3.

A second approach to discriminant analysis is given by the following classification problem. Consider two populations in which the same variables are measured. Measurements have been made for a sample from each population (i.e. with known group membership). Now for observations with unknown group membership a decision rule is to be constructed which allows one to allocate the observations to the correct population with high probability. Under certain assumptions concerning the populations, this approach leads to the same method as the generalized standard distance.

7.2 MULTIVARIATE STANDARD DISTANCE

The basic idea for simplifying the problem of analysing differences in location simultaneously in several variables consists of finding suitable linear combinations of all variables. In Section 6.2 we have already seen that the linear combination IMAGE,

$$X_7 = \tfrac{1}{2}X_2 + \tfrac{1}{2}X_3 - X_4 - X_5,$$

seems to separate genuine from forged bills rather well. We could now – as has already been done in Section 6.4 – consider additional linear combinations of all variables. By varying the coefficients we may be able to find a linear combination for which the frequency distributions of both groups overlap as little as possible.

Apart from the exorbitant expense of such a purely heuristic procedure, this would be mathematically unsatisfactory. We therefore define a mathematical optimality criterion that, among all possible linear combinations, singles out a particular one. Using an arbitrary linear combination

$$Z = a_1 X_1 + a_2 X_2 + \cdots + a_p X_p$$

we obtain in both groups a new variable Z, whose mean and standard deviation is denoted by $\bar{z}_G$ and s_G (for genuine bills), and by $\bar{z}_F$ and s_F (for forged bills), respectively. For the linear combination Z we can compute the associated standard distance (cf. Chapter 2)

$$D(Z) = D(a_1, \ldots, a_p) = \frac{|\bar{z}_G - \bar{z}_F|}{s}$$

with

$$s^2 = \frac{(n_G - 1)s_G^2 + (n_F - 1)s_F^2}{n_G + n_F - 2}.$$

(In Section 6.2, this was already done for the variable IMAGE). We can now define the *multivariate standard distance* as the maximum standard distance that can be obtained from any linear combination of X_1 to X_p. Formally,

$$D_p = \max D(a_1, \ldots, a_p)$$

over all possible choices of the coefficients a_1 to a_p. The index p in D_p indicates that the measure of distance is based on p variables. The linear combination for which the maximum is achieved will be called *discriminant function* or *discriminant variable*. Multivariate standard distance is therefore nothing but univariate standard distance for a particular linear combination called the discriminant function.

Is the foregoing definition of multivariate standard distance reasonable? We answer this question with the following two remarks:

1. D_p is always at least as large as any of the univariate standard distances computed for the p variables. This is clear from the fact that variable X_j is itself a linear combination of X_1 to X_p – simply with coefficient $a_j = 1$ and all other coefficients equal to zero. This property is certainly desirable.
2. The linear combinations $Z = a_1 x_1 + a_2 X_2 + \cdots + a_p X_p$ and $Z' = -a_1 X_1 - a_2 X_2 - \cdots - a_p X_p$ yield the same standard distance. More generally, any

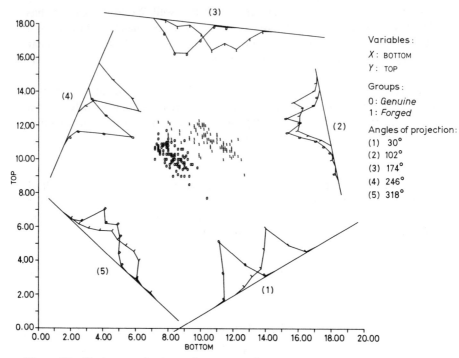

Figure 7.1   Various projections of BOTTOM and TOP

multiple $Z' = kZ$ yields

$$D(Z') = \frac{|k\bar{z}_G - k\bar{z}_F|}{|k|s} = D(Z),$$

i.e. equivalent linear combinations (in the sense defined in Section 6.3) yield the same standard distance. This property is highly desirable, since the measure of distance should not depend on the scale units.

From remark 2 it is clear that we can assume, without loss of generality, that the discriminant function is normalized, that is, the squares of its coefficients a_1 to a_p add up to unity. The a_j are called discriminant function coefficients or simply *discriminant coefficients*.

Before we consider in some detail the general solution of the maximization problem, we want to let intuition guide us in the case $p = 2$. Figure 7.1 shows a scatterplot of all 200 bills in the variables $X_4 = $ BOTTOM and $X_5 = $ TOP. The normalized linear combinations, angles of projection and standard distances corresponding to the projections drawn are given in Table 7.1.

Among the five chosen linear combinations, the fourth has the largest standard distance. The search for the maximum, on the basis of Fig. 7.1, can be envisioned as successively changing the angle of projection in very small steps,

Table 7.1 Linear combinations and standard distances associated with various projection directions (cf. Fig. 7.1)

	Angle of projection		Normalized linear combination	Standard distance
	degrees	radian		
1.	30	0.5236	$0.866X_4 + 0.500X_5$	3.75
2.	102	1.7802	$-0.208X_4 + 0.978X_5$	0.63
3.	174	3.0369	$-0.995X_4 + 0.105X_5$	2.20
4.	246	4.2935	$-0.407X_4 - 0.914X_5$	3.95
5.	318	5.5501	$0.743X_4 - 0.669X_5$	0.99

and then choosing that linear combination which yields the highest value of D.

Figure 7.2 shows, in addition to the projections onto the coordinate axes already known from Chapter 2 (Figs 2.4 and 2.5), the best linear combination in the sense of our criterion,

$$V = -0.6122X_4 - 0.7907X_5,$$

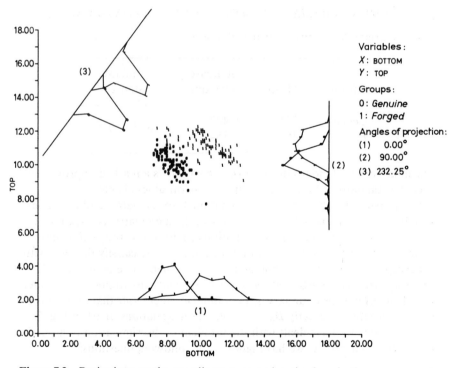

Figure 7.2 Projections on the coordinate axes, and optimal projection

which corresponds to an angle of projection of 232.25 degrees. To simplify, we can change the signs of both coefficients and consider as discriminant function the linear combination $- V$ (corresponding to an angle of projection of 232.25 $- 180 = 52.25$ degrees).

The standard distance of V is 4.63, expressing the fact that the two means in projection 3 are 4.63 standard deviations apart. According to our definition of multivariate standard distance we can now say that the bivariate standard distance for BOTTOM and TOP is $D_2 = 4.63$. Note that this is considerably larger than both univariate standard distances.

From Figs 7.1 and 7.2 we may observe that both the location of the two point clusters in the plane as well as the covariance structure (variances and covariances) have an influence on the optimal projection. With the same means and standard deviations, but positive correlation between BOTTOM and TOP, the multivariate standard distance would be much smaller.

The general solution of the problem in the case of $p \geqslant 2$ variables requires the solution of a system of p linear equations, a task which can be carried out with the help of computer programs. The reader interested in the mathematical solution is referred to Section 13.4 of the Appendix.

In our example, the solution is

$$V = 0.002X_1 + 0.327X_2 - 0.334X_3 - 0.439X_4 - 0.463X_5 + 0.612X_6.$$

The univariate descriptive statistics of V are

Group	Mean	Standard deviation	Standard distance
Genuine	77.855	0.422	$6.95 = D_6$
Forged	75.125	0.354	

The multivariate standard distance $D_6 = 6.95$ shows a marked improvement over the standard distances of the individual variables (Table 2.1).

By applying the above linear combination V to the data we obtain a new variable $X_9 = V$. Table 7.2 shows a section of the data matrix enlarged by X_9. Figure 7.3 shows the frequency distribution of V for both groups. If we draw a boundary line at 76.5 we observe that we can correctly classify the bills, with the exception of one genuine bill, on the basis of their value in the variable V. This way of drawing the boundary, however, depends on extreme values. Later we will determine the boundary in an optimal manner. Note that the means of the two groups are exactly $D_6 = 6.95$ standard deviations apart in Fig. 7.3.

Up to now, we have dealt with the problem of discrimination in a purely descriptive manner, i.e. we have ignored the following questions:

1. If the two groups of observations actually come from the same population (e.g. if all 200 bills were actually genuine), then the optimum linear

Table 7.2 Values of $X_9 = V$ (discriminant variable)

Genuine							
	LENGTH	LEFT	RIGHT	BOTTOM	TOP	DIAGONAL	V
i	x_{1i}	x_{2i}	x_{3i}	x_{4i}	x_{5i}	x_{6i}	x_{9i}
1	214.8	131.0	131.1	9.0	9.7	141.0	77.335
2	214.6	129.7	129.7	8.1	9.5	141.7	78.293
3	214.8	129.7	129.7	8.7	9.6	142.2	78.289
4	214.8	129.7	129.6	7.5	10.4	142.0	78.357
5	215.0	129.6	129.7	10.4	7.7	141.8	78.146
6	215.7	130.8	130.5	9.0	10.1	141.4	77.531
7	215.5	129.5	129.7	7.9	9.6	141.6	78.210
8	214.5	129.6	129.2	7.2	10.7	141.7	78.266
9	214.9	129.4	129.7	8.2	11.0	141.9	77.579
10	215.2	130.4	130.3	9.2	10.0	140.7	76.997
Forged							
101	214.4	130.1	130.3	9.7	11.7	139.8	75.339
102	214.9	130.5	130.2	11.0	11.5	139.5	74.843
103	214.9	130.3	130.1	8.7	11.7	140.2	76.156
104	215.0	130.4	130.6	9.9	10.9	140.3	75.927
105	214.7	130.2	130.3	11.8	10.9	139.7	74.760
106	215.0	130.2	130.2	10.6	10.7	139.9	75.536
107	215.3	130.3	130.1	9.3	12.1	140.2	75.708
108	214.8	130.1	130.4	9.8	11.5	139.9	75.417
109	215.0	130.2	129.9	10.0	11.9	139.4	75.037
110	215.2	130.6	130.8	10.4	11.2	140.3	75.568

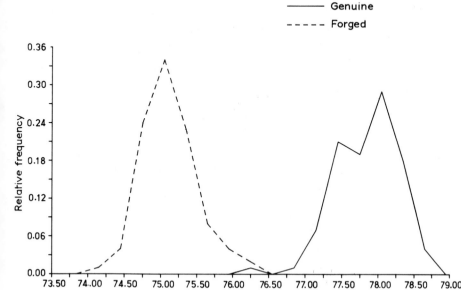

——————— Genuine

– – – – – Forged

Figure 7.3 Distribution of the discriminant variable

combination V found would merely be a product of randomness, and the same would be true for the differences between the sample means in each individual variable. Are we allowed to conclude from the value $D_6 = 6.95$ that the two samples come from different populations?

2. Assuming that question 1 is answered in the affirmative, we can further ask ourselves whether perhaps a simpler linear combination could provide a discrimination that is just as good, or nearly as good. Simpler linear combinations would either be those which are formed by the researcher from his *a priori* knowledge (such as the linear combination IMAGE in Section 6.2), or those which do not include all six variables. Is it possible to remove one or several variables from the linear combination V without loss of information?

To answer these questions, we are now going to introduce an extremely useful relationship between discriminant and regression functions.

7.3   RELATIONSHIP BETWEEN DISCRIMINANT ANALYSIS AND MULTIPLE LINEAR REGRESSION

During the 1930s, different but essentially equivalent approaches to the multivariate two sample problem were developed independently by R.A. Fisher in England, by H. Hotelling in America, and by P.C. Mahalanobis in India. Also, Fisher pointed out the following equivalence between discriminant analysis and multiple linear regression. As the dependent variable in the regression model we take a pseudo-variable (or binary variable) that takes only two values c_1 and c_2, and put

$$W_i = \begin{cases} c_1 & \text{if observation no. } i \text{ comes from group 1} \\ c_2 & \text{if observation no. } i \text{ comes from group 2.} \end{cases}$$

W_i is simply a group code. Often, a coding proposed by Fisher is used which has certain mathematical advantages, namely

$$c_1 = \frac{n_2}{n_1 + n_2}; \qquad c_2 = \frac{-n_1}{n_1 + n_2},$$

where n_1 and n_2 are the two sample sizes. Fisher's idea now consists of estimating the group code by a linear combination of the variables X_1 to X_p, using the least squares method. We thus form the sum

$$S = \sum_{i=1}^{n_1 + n_2} (W_i - \beta_0 - \beta_1 x_{1i} - \cdots - \beta_p x_{pi})^2$$

$$= \sum_{i=1}^{n_1} (c_1 - \beta_0 - \beta_1 x_{1i} - \cdots - \beta_p x_{pi})^2$$

$$+ \sum_{i=n_1+1}^{n_1 + n_2} (c_2 - \beta_0 - \beta_1 x_{1i} - \cdots - \beta_p x_{pi})^2$$

and choose for $\beta_0, \beta_1, \ldots, \beta_p$ those values $b_0, b_1, \ldots, b_p$ for which S becomes minimal. Viewed formally, this is the same approach as multiple linear regression, i.e. we can determine the coefficients with the help of regression analysis. Conceptually, however, the situation is just the other way round, since W_i assumes fixed preassigned values and the X_i are random variables.

Let's apply this to the bank note example. The Fisher code is, in this case,

$$W_i = \begin{cases} c_1 = n_F/(n_G + n_F) = \frac{1}{2} & \text{for genuine bills} \\ c_2 = -n_G/(n_G + n_F) = -\frac{1}{2} & \text{for forged bills.} \end{cases}$$

Estimating the group code by multiple linear regression yields the following linear combination:

$$\hat{W} = -25.897 + 0.0007X_1 + 0.111X_2 - 0.113X_3 - 0.149X_4 \\ - 0.157X_5 + 0.207X_6.$$

If we compare the linear combination $\hat{W}$ with the discriminant variable V of Section 7.2, we observe that the coefficients $b_j (j = 1, \ldots, 6)$ of $\hat{W}$ can be obtained from the coefficients a_j of V of

$$b_j = 0.3385a_j.$$

This means that $\hat{W}$, up to an intercept b_0, is a linear combination equivalent to V:

$$\hat{W} = -25.897 + 0.3385V.$$

Since adding b_0 changes neither the mean difference nor the standard distance, we can regard the variable $\hat{W}$ as being equivalent to V for the purpose of discriminant analysis. Remarkably, this equivalence holds in general – whenever we compute a discriminant function V by maximizing the standard distance, and a regression function $\hat{W}$ by regressing a binary code variable on X_1 to X_p, the relationship

$$\hat{W} = k_0 + k_1 V$$

holds for some constants k_0 and k_1!

This important relation enables us to apply algorithms and programs of multiple linear regression to problems of discriminant analysis. As will be discussed in the following section, the analogy, under certain assumptions, is not limited merely to the computation of the discriminant function, but at the same time allows us to answer the questions raised at the end of Section 7.2.

Due to this equivalence, the standard distance between the two groups is the same for $\hat{W}$ as for V, and the multivariate standard distance D_p can therefore be obtained by applying the regression equation to the data and computing D_p for the 'predicted group code'. There is, however, an easier way of computing D_p. Denoting by R_p^2 (where the index p indicates again that the calculation is based on p variables) the coefficient of determination obtained from the multiple regression, we can compute D_p by

$$D_p = \sqrt{\left[\frac{(n_1 + n_2)(n_1 + n_2 - 2)}{n_1 n_2} \cdot \frac{R_p^2}{1 - R_p^2}\right]}.$$

Through this remarkable relationship it is possible to show that tests used in multiple regression analysis are valid in the discriminant analysis situation, too! We will use this fact in the following section.

7.4 TESTING HYPOTHESES ABOUT THE DISCRIMINANT FUNCTION

Having seen the close formal relationship between discriminant analysis and multiple linear regression, the question naturally arises whether still more elements of regression analysis can be carried over to discriminant analysis. It turns out that, under certain assumptions, the regression F-tests can be employed for testing hypotheses about the discriminant function. The assumptions are:

1. Both groups come from p-dimensional normally distributed populations.
2. The covariance structure is the same in both populations, i.e. they differ only in their means.

For the verification of the second assumption there exist test procedures; one of them is described in Chapter 11.

   Verification of the first assumption, while possible in a number of different ways, is quite complicated in general. In the case of the bank note example, we limit ourselves, for the moment, to observing that up to now no compelling objections against the normal distribution model have been found.

   The most important hypotheses about the discriminant function can now be described in complete analogy to multiple linear regression.

7.4.1 The overall Test of Significance

In analogy to the regression model, we can test the hypothesis that all discriminant coefficients are zero, i.e. $\beta_1 = \beta_2 = \cdots = \beta_p = 0$. This is equivalent to the hypothesis that the two p-variate population means are identical. A third way of putting the overall hypothesis is to say that the standard distance between the two populations is zero.

   For a test of the overall hypothesis we use the statistic

$$F = \frac{(n_1 + n_2 - p - 1)n_1 n_2}{p(n_1 + n_2)(n_1 + n_2 - 2)} D_p^2,$$

which is a simple function of the (sample) standard distance D_p. Under the hypothesis of no mean differences, F has the F-distribution with p degrees of freedom in the numerator and $n_1 + n_2 - p - 1$ degrees of freedom in the denominator. Using the relation between R_p^2 and D_p given at the end of Section 7.3, it is not hard to show that this F-statistic is exactly the same as $F(\beta_1 = \beta_2 = \cdots = \beta_p = 0)$, the overall F-statistic from the regression approach, and even the degrees of freedom associated with the regression test are correct! This provides yet another way of computing the multivariate standard distance, namely

$$D_p = \sqrt{\left[\frac{p(n_1 + n_2)(n_1 + n_2 - 2)}{(n_1 + n_2 - p - 1)n_1 n_2} F(\beta_1 = \cdots = \beta_p = 0) \right]}.$$

Testing the overall null hypothesis $\beta_1 = \cdots = \beta_p = 0$ lets us answer the question whether or not the discriminant function corresponds to a real difference in location (and not just a random one) between the two samples. For $p = 1$, i.e. in the univariate case, the resulting statistic is equivalent to the two-sample t-test; and so the overall test of significance of the discriminant function is a multivariate generalization of the t-test.

Since the dependent variable in the regression approach is not random, it is customary to speak of a *pseudo*-analysis of variance: instead of the variability of a random variable, the *pseudo*-variability of a group code is being decomposed. If the code values are c_1 and c_2, the minimum sum of squares associated with the reduced model is

$$S_{min}^0 = \frac{n_1 n_2}{n_1 + n_2} (c_1 - c_2)^2,$$

which reduces to $n_1 n_2 / (n_1 + n_2)$ in the case of Fisher's code.

In the bank note example, with $c_1 = \frac{1}{2}$ and $c_2 = -\frac{1}{2}$, we get the pseudo-analysis of variance shown in Table 7.3. The overall F-statistic is therefore

$$F = \frac{46.2075/6}{3.7925/193} = 391.9.$$

Table 7.3 Pseudo-analysis of variance table

Model	Minimum sum of squares	Degrees of freedom
reduced model β_0	50.0	199
full model $\beta_0 + \beta_1 X_1 + \cdots + \beta_6 X_6$	3.7925	193
reduction $\beta_1 = \cdots = \beta_6 = 0$	46.2075	6

This is considerably larger than the 95% quantile of the F-distribution with 6 and 193 degrees of freedom:

$$F_{0.95}(6, \ 193) = 2.14.$$

We decide therefore that the differences in location between the two samples are not just random. It is left to the reader to check that the same F is obtained if the formula based on D_p is used instead of the ANOVA table.

It should be noted that the choice of the group codes c_1 and c_2 affects the sums of squares, but not the F-test.

The overall F-test answers the first question raised at the end of Section 7.2.

7.4.2   Testing for redundancy of variables

As with regression analysis, we can ask whether some variables are redundant for discrimination. For simplicity, assume again that the ones to be tested for redundancy are labelled X_{q+1} to X_p. Then the hypothesis of *redundancy* of the last $p - q$ variables (or *sufficiency* of the first q variables) can formally be stated as $\beta_{p+1} = \cdots = \beta_p = 0$. This hypothesis is equivalent to saying that the standard distance between the two populations is the same whether we use all p variables or only the first q ones.

If D_p and D_q denote the (sample) standard distances based on p and q variables, respectively, a statistic for testing the above hypothesis is

$$F = \frac{n_1 + n_2 - p - 1}{p - q} \cdot \frac{D_p^2 - D_q^2}{\dfrac{(n_1 + n_2 - 2)(n_1 + n_2)}{n_1 n_2} + D_q^2}$$

with $p - q$ and $n_1 + n_2 - p - 1$ degrees of freedom.

Again, by the relation between standard distance and coefficient of determination, this is the same F-statistic as the one obtained by the regression approach. Instead of testing for zero coefficients in the discriminant function, it is also possible to test whether some coefficients are in a specified ratio; an example for this will be given in Section 7.5.

For $q = 0$, if we put $D_0 = 0$ by definition, it is clear from the above F-statistic that testing for redundancy of *all* variables in the discriminant function is the same as the overall test of significance.

7.4.3   Partial hypotheses and standard errors of discriminant function coefficients

An important special case of the general test for redundancy occurs if $q = p - 1$, i.e. if we test for redundancy of a single variable. The appropriate F-statistic is

Table 7.4 Standard errors and partial F-statistics

Variable	Coefficient b_j	Standard error of b_j	Partial F-statistic
intercept	− 25.897		
LENGTH	0.001	0.030	0.0005
LEFT	0.111	0.044	6.43
RIGHT	− 0.113	0.040	8.09
BOTTOM	− 0.149	0.010	215.19
TOP	− 0.157	0.017	84.43
DIAGONAL	0.207	0.015	189.57

$$F = (n_1 + n_2 - p - 1)\frac{D_p^2 - D_{p-1}^2}{[(n_1 + n_2 - 2)(n_1 + n_2)]/n_1 n_2 + D_{p-1}^2}$$

with 1 and $n_1 + n_2 - p - 1$ degrees of freedom.

To test a partial hypothesis, we can thus use the partial F-statistic computed by the regression method. Moreover, if the estimated regression coefficient for variable X_j is denoted by b_j and the associated partial F-statistic by $F(\beta_j = 0)$, an estimate of the *standard error* of the jth discriminant function coefficient is given by

$$s(b_j) = |b_j|/\sqrt{[F(\beta_j = 0)]}.$$

This is, of course, exactly the standard error computed in the regression model.

In the bank note example, we obtain the standard errors and partial F-statistics given in Table 7.4.

The large standard error $s(b_1) = 0.030$, relative to the magnitude of the discriminant coefficient $b_1 = 0.001$, and the correspondingly small F-statistic, show that LENGTH is redundant and can be eliminated from the discriminant function.

7.5 SCREENING A DISCRIMINANT FUNCTION

We will now try, through successive backward elimination, to eliminate redundant variables. As already observed in the previous section, the variable LENGTH can be dropped from the discriminant function without loss of information. The complete protocol of the algorithm begins with Table 7.4 (solution with all six variables, supplemented by $R_6^2 = 0.9242$ and $D_6 = 6.95$) as step 1 and continues as shown in Table 7.5.

Let us first look at the partial F-statistics. In the solution with all variables (step 1), LENGTH has a very small value of $F = 0.0005$. In comparison,

Table 7.5 Backward elimination

Variable	Coefficient	Standard error	Partial F-statistic
Step 2: Elimination of LENGTH			
intercept	− 25.809		
LEFT	0.111	0.042	7.00
RIGHT	− 0.113	0.039	8.22
BOTTOM	− 0.149	0.010	223.92
TOP	− 0.157	0.017	85.09
DIAGONAL	0.207	0.015	197.13
$R_5^2 = 0.9242$ $D_5 = 6.95$			
Step 3: Elimination of LEFT			
intercept	− 19.062		
RIGHT	− 0.047	0.031	2.31
BOTTOM	− 0.149	0.010	218.65
TOP	− 0.157	0.017	82.77
DIAGONAL	0.201	0.015	184.69
$R_4^2 = 0.9214$ $D_4 = 6.81$			
Step 4: Elimination of RIGHT			
intercept	− 25.339		
BOTTOM	− 0.154	0.010	258.23
TOP	− 0.164	0.017	95.15
DIAGONAL	0.203	0.115	188.56
$R_3^2 = 0.9205$ $D_3 = 6.77$			
Step 5: Elimination of TOP			
intercept	− 40.637		
BOTTOM	− 0.120	0.011	122.35
DIAGONAL	0.297	0.014	476.72
$R_2^2 = 0.8819$ $D_2 = 5.44$			
Step 6: Elimination of BOTTOM			
intercept	− 54.951		
DIAGONAL	0.391	0.014	836.07
$R_1^2 = 0.8085$ $D_1 = 4.09$			

the 95% quantile of the F-distribution with 1 and 193 degrees of freedom is $F_{0.95}(1, 193) = 3.89$. Surely, LENGTH may be considered redundant. Because the partial F-statistics are not independent, however, we will no longer use critical values of the F-distribution. The partial F-values will be used in a purely descriptive way to find a reasonable subset of variables.

In step 2, LENGTH is eliminated. Now it is LEFT which has the smallest partial F-value (7.00). Elimination of LEFT in the next step produces the interesting phenomenon that the partial F-value of RIGHT drops sharply – from 8.22 in

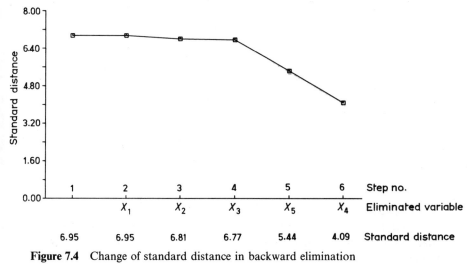

Figure 7.4   Change of standard distance in backward elimination

step 2 to 2.31 in step 3. This means that RIGHT by itself evidently does not contribute much to the discrimination, but does so together with LEFT. If we look at the coefficients of LEFT and RIGHT in step 2, we recognize that the contribution of the two variables is to be found in their difference. In step 4 one eliminates the variable RIGHT, which has now become 'useless'. The three remaining variables all have very high partial F-values. If we nevertheless continue with the algorithm, we observe that elimination of TOP in step 5 causes the partial F-value of BOTTOM to drop sharply – a similar phenomenon as has already been described for LEFT and RIGHT. As last variable in step 6 there remains DIAGONAL

In determining the place where elimination of additional variables should be stopped, we first look at Figure 7.4 which depicts the successive change of the standard distance. According to this curve it seems plausible to stop after step 4 and to accept the linear combination

$$-25.339 - 0.154X_4 - 0.164X_5 + 0.203X_6$$

as a simplified discriminant function. A comparison of the full model with the one reduced to three variables yields the pseudo-analysis of variance shown in Table 7.6. The F-statistic is $F = 3.11$. The critical value of the test distribution is $F_{0.95}(3, 193) = 2.65$. On the basis of a purely statistical criterion (at a significance level of 5%), the reduction to three variables is thus not permitted. Since the F-value is only slightly larger than the critical value, one might also accept the small loss of information in favour of the simpler model. Such considerations are especially important if the variables in question are expensive to measure.

Table 7.6 Testing for redundancy of X_1 to X_3

Model	Sum of squares	Degrees of freedom
reduced model (only X_4, X_5, X_6)	3.9757	196
full model (all variables)	3.7925	193
reduction	0.1832	3

We leave the final decision to the reader, but we want to continue looking for a suitable model in case the restriction to three variables is considered unacceptable. Since stopping after step 3 is then not reasonable, we have to accept the solution with 5 variables. The discriminant function reduced by LENGTH (which we denote now by DF for Discriminant Function) is

$$DF = 25.809 + 0.111X_2 - 0.113X_3 - 0.149X_4 - 0.157X_5 + 0.207X_6$$

A comparison of this model with the full model yields the pseudo-analysis of variance shown in Table 7.7. The associated test statistic is $F = 0.002$ on 1 and 193 degrees of freedom. Theoretically this F-statistic should be identical with the partial F of LENGTH in the full model; the small difference is due to numerical inaccuracy.

Figure 7.5 shows the frequency distribution of DF for both groups. Because of the very small coefficient of LENGTH in the full model, the figure is practically identical with Figure 7.3.

Another appealing possibility of simplifying the discriminant function is offered to us through the variable IMAGE, which was introduced in Chapter 6.

Table 7.7 Testing for redundancy of X_1

Model	Sum of squares	Degrees of freedom
reduced model (X_2 to X_6)	3.79246	194
full model (all variables)	3.79250	193
reduction	0.00004	1

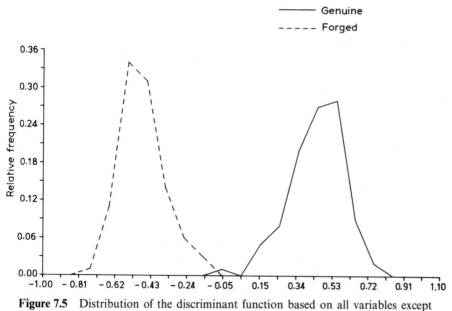

Figure 7.5 Distribution of the discriminant function based on all variables except LENGTH

This variable has been defined as

$$\text{IMAGE} = X_7 = \tfrac{1}{2}X_2 + \tfrac{1}{2}X_3 - X_4 - X_5.$$

We now seek to discriminate between the two groups on the basis of the variables IMAGE and DIAGONAL, i.e. we postulate the model

$$\text{DF}(X_6, X_7) = \beta_0 + \beta_6 X_6 + \beta_7 X_7$$
$$= \beta_0 + \beta_6 X_6 + \beta_7(\tfrac{1}{2}X_2 + \tfrac{1}{2}X_3 - X_4 - X_5),$$

which is to be compared with the model $\text{DF}(X_2, \ldots, X_6)$. Because of the linear relationship between X_7 and X_2 to X_5, the two models can be transformed into one another through a linear restriction. We restrict the model involving X_2 to X_6 by the condition

$$2\beta_2 = 2\beta_3 = -\beta_4 = -\beta_5,$$

which means that the coefficients of the variables X_2 to X_5 are forced to be in a prescribed relationship – the one given by X_7. Expressed differently, this means that for the variables X_2 to X_5 we must estimate only one common parameter β_7. The estimation of this model yields the following coefficients, standard errors and partial F-statistic:

Variable	Coefficient	Standard error	Partial F-statistic
intercept	−49.639		
DIAGONAL	0.231	0.014	268.5
IMAGE	0.156	0.010	224.7

If, instead of $X_7 =$ IMAGE, we substitute again the variables X_2 to X_5, the equation becomes

$$DF(X_6, X_7) = -49.639 + 0.078X_2 + 0.078X_3 - 0.156X_4 - 0.156X_5 + 0.23X_6.$$

For comparison of the two models, we again set up the pseudo-analysis of variance table (Table 7.8). The value of the F-statistic is $F = 11.59$, while the 95% quantile of the F-distribution with 3 and 194 degrees of freedom is $F_{0.95}(3, 194) = 2.65$. The simplification, therefore, cannot be considered permissible. In other words, this means that IMAGE does not contain the complete information about group differences contained in the variables LEFT, RIGHT, BOTTOM and TOP.

Table 7.8 Testing the discriminant function based on IMAGE

Model	Sum of squares	Degrees of freedom
reduced model (X_6 and X_7)	4.4722	197
full model ($X_2, \ldots, X_6$)	3.7925	194
reduction	0.6797	3

7.6 FURTHER USES OF THE COEFFICIENT OF DETERMINATION

Besides the relationship between R_p^2 and D_p displayed at the end of Section 7.3, the coefficient of determination from the regression approach has some other interesting properties. Let c_1 and c_2 denote the two code values and assume, for simplicity, that $c_1 > c_2$. If we apply the regression function to the data, we get two sample means $\bar{y}_1$ and $\bar{y}_2$ which 'estimate' c_1 and c_2 in the sense of least squares. If the two groups are well separated in p-dimensional space, we expect that $\bar{y}_1$ is close to c_1, and $\bar{y}_2$ close to c_2. It turns out that the inequality

$$c_1 > \bar{y}_1 \geqslant \bar{y}_2 > c_2$$

always holds, and the proportion of the interval (c_2, c_1) covered by the interval $(\bar{y}_2, \bar{y}_1)$ is exactly R_p^2. In symbols,

$$R_p^2 = \frac{\bar{y}_1 - \bar{y}_2}{c_1 - c_2}.$$

If the two codes differ by unity, this simplifies to

$$R_p^2 = \bar{y}_1 - \bar{y}_2$$
$$(\text{or } R_p^2 = |\bar{y}_1 - \bar{y}_2| \quad \text{if } c_2 > c_1).$$

Thus the coefficient of determination describes in a very direct way how well the group codes c_1 and c_2 are 'estimated' by the regression function.

Again, if we apply the regression function to the data, we can compute the standard deviation in each group, and a pooled variance s^2 of both groups. By the definition of multivariate standard distance, we know that

$$D_p = \frac{|\bar{y}_1 - \bar{y}_2|}{s},$$

and therefore $s^2 = (D_p^2/(\bar{y}_1 - \bar{y}_2)^2)^{-1}$. Using the relation between R_p^2 and D_p and substituting $(\bar{y}_1 - \bar{y}_2)^2 = (c_1 - c_2)^2 R_p^4$, we get

$$s^2 = \frac{n_1 n_2 (c_1 - c_2)^2}{(n_1 + n_2)(n_1 + n_2 - 2)} R_p^2 (1 - R_p^2).$$

By similar considerations, the formulae

$$\bar{y}_1 = c_1 - \frac{n_2}{n_1 + n_2}(c_1 - c_2)(1 - R_p^2)$$

and

$$\bar{y}_2 = c_2 + \frac{n_1}{n_1 + n_2}(c_1 - c_2)(1 - R_p^2)$$

can be obtained. These show again that, if R_p^2 is close to 1, the group codes c_1 and c_2 will be 'estimated' almost correctly by $\bar{y}_1$ and $\bar{y}_2$. Computing $\bar{y}_1$, $\bar{y}_2$ and the pooled variance s^2 of the discriminant function by the above formulae is of course more convenient than first applying the discriminant function to the data and then computing these quantities in the usual way. We will illustrate this in the following section.

Again, if we use Fisher's code, the formulae become somewhat simpler, thanks to $c_1 - c_2 = 1$.

7.7 CLASSIFICATION OF OBSERVATIONS

In the introductory section of this chapter we already mentioned that besides the generalization of the t-test and the regression approach there exists a third, classification-theoretic approach which, under suitable assumptions, yields a solution equivalent to the discriminant function. The point of departure in this approach are two populations of objects (e.g. genuine and forged bills), from each of which a random sample has been taken. Then a decision rule is to be formulated which allows us to allocate observations of unknown group membership to the correct group with high probability.

We first consider the problem in one dimension, using as example the variable RIGHT. As is shown by Figure 2.3, the histograms of the groups *Genuine* and *Forged* overlap rather strongly. It is evidently not possible to identify a bill as genuine or forged on the basis of its value in X_3.

A simple classification procedure would be as follows. By trial and error, we fix a limit in the following way. Determine the two numbers

$$f_G = \text{number of genuine bills with } X_3 > g$$
$$f_F = \text{number of forged bills with } X_3 < g$$

and choose the limit g in such a way that $f_G + f_F$ becomes minimal. Then we formulate the classification rule:

Allocate a bill to group *Genuine*, if $X_3 < g$;
otherwise allocate it to group *Forged*.

An application of this rule to the two known groups yields the following table of correct and incorrect allocations:

| | | bill comes from group | |
		Genuine	*Forged*
rule allocates bill into group:	*Genuine*	$n_G - f_G$ (correct)	f_F (incorrect)
	Forged	f_G (incorrect)	$n_F - f_F$ (correct)

The number of incorrect allocations would be $f_G + f_F$, i.e. minimal, thanks to the way g was determined.

This method, however, depends heavily on a few values close to g. In order to avoid this, we look at the problem from a more theoretical point of view, i.e. we describe the frequency distribution of the two groups by means of suitable density functions. As in so many other instances, the normal distribution model is particularly suited, for reasons which will be mentioned later in this section. The means μ_G and μ_F of the two models as well as the standard deviations σ_G and σ_F are estimated by the corresponding sample values of RIGHT from Chapter 2:

$$\hat{\mu}_G = 129.720 \qquad \hat{\mu}_F = 130.193$$
$$\hat{\sigma}_G = \quad 0.3553 \qquad \hat{\sigma}_F = \quad 0.2982$$

Figure 7.6 shows the two normal density curves $p_G(x)$ for *Genuine* and $p_F(x)$ for *Forged* with the above estimates as parameters. For these density functions we now try to find the domains in which $p_G(x) > p_F(x)$ or $p_G(x) < p_F(x)$, respectively. This is equivalent to computing the points of intersection of the two density curves. In general, one obtains two points of intersection g_1 and g_2. In our case, omitting technical details, these points are:

$$g_1 = 129.94 \quad \text{and} \quad g_2 = 132.70.$$

The rule of allocation would thus be as follows:

Genuine, if $X_3 < 129.94$ or $X_3 > 132.70$
Forged, otherwise.

As can be seen from Figure 7.6, the limit g_2 lies far to the right, outside of the picture, and plays no role for all practical purposes.

Any two normal density curves can have, in general, two finite intersections. If we assume, however, that the standard deviations in both groups are identical (i.e. the two sample standard deviations differ only randomly), the situation gets simpler: The common variance σ^2 is estimated by pooling the sample variances of both groups (cf. Chapter 2), and there will be only one intersection, namely

$$g = \frac{\bar{x}_G + \bar{x}_F}{2}.$$

In the example of the variable RIGHT, one thus obtains the limit $g = 129.957$.

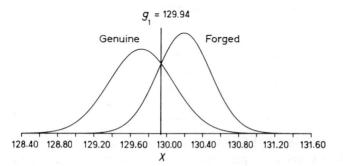

Figure 7.6   Normal density curves for variable RIGHT

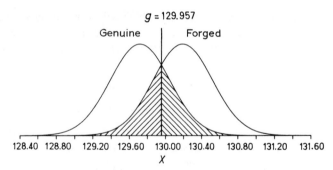

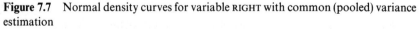

Figure 7.7   Normal density curves for variable RIGHT with common (pooled) variance estimation

Figure 7.7 shows the two density functions under the assumption of equal standard deviations. The simplified classification rule thus becomes:

Genuine, if $X_3 < 129.957$
Forged, otherwise,

and it differs in practice only little from the rule which we have obtained assuming different standard deviations. The probability of a misclassification can now be estimated with the help of a table of the normal distribution by computing the hatched area in Figure 7.7.

We now look at the analogous problem in two dimensions, using for example the variables BOTTOM and TOP. What we seek is a subdivision of the (x_4, x_5)-plane into domains inside which genuine or forged bills, respectively, occur with larger probability. As a suitable statistical model, we assume in both groups a two-dimensional normal distribution. The bivariate normal distribution of two variables can be characterized by the means, the standard deviations, and the correlation coefficient of both variables. For BOTTOM and TOP we use the corresponding estimates from Chapters 2 and 3:

Group	Genuine	Forged
$\bar{x}_4$	8.305	10.530
$\bar{x}_5$	10.168	11.133
s_4	0.6428	1.1320
s_5	0.6490	0.6360
r_{45}	−0.6316	−0.6809

Figure 7.8 shows the two-dimensional normal distribution densities with the above estimates as parameters. The two density functions are denoted by $p_G(x, z)$ for genuine bills, and $p_F(x, z)$ for forged bills. As boundary between the

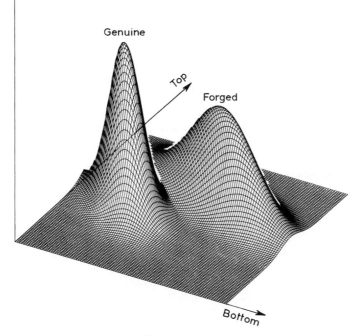

Figure 7.8 Bivariate normal densities for BOTTOM and TOP

domains of association we ask for the points of intersection of the two functions, i.e. pairs of values (x, z) which satisfy the equation $p_G(x, z) = p_F(x, z)$. The general solution of this problem is a curve of the form

$$ax + bz + cx^2 + dz^2 + exz = f.$$

Again, by assuming equal standard deviations of corresponding variables in both groups, as well as equal correlation, the situation simplifies considerably, since all nonlinear terms disappear. One obtains thus a curve of the form

$$ax + bz = f,$$

that is, a straight line.

The assumption of equal standard deviations and correlation coefficients can be formulated somewhat simpler as equality of the two covariance matrices. The common covariance c_{xz}, like the common variance, is estimated as weighted mean of the covariances of the groups *Genuine* and *Forged*. The weights here, too, are the degrees of freedom $n_G - 1$ and $n_F - 1$. The covariance matrix thus estimated identically for both groups is often called the *pooled covariance matrix*. By means of

$$r_{xz} = c_{xz}/s_x s_z$$

the pooled correlation coefficients can then be computed. In our example, the pooled covariance matrix is:

	X_4	X_5
X_4	0.8437	−0.3769
X_5	−0.3769	0.4129

The pooled correlation is $r_{45} = -6371$. Putting this into the density function of the bivariate normal distribution, one then obtains the straight line

$$6.1715x_4 + 7.9705x_5 = 143.01.$$

Figure 7.9 shows this straight line in a scatterplot of BOTTOM and TOP. The equation of the straight line tells us that a new observation (x_{4i}, x_{5i}) is to be allocated to the group *Genuine* or *Forged*, according as the value

$$6.1715x_{4i} + 7.9705x_{5i}$$

is smaller or larger than 143.01, respectively. Thus only the values of the linear

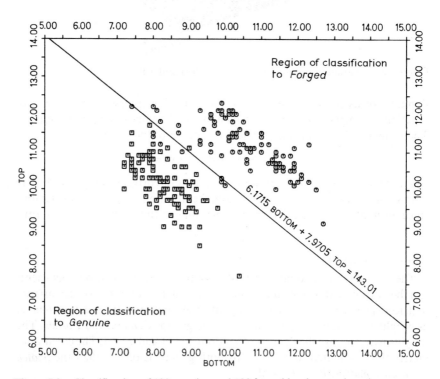

Figure 7.9   Classification of 100 genuine and 100 forged bank notes based on BOTTOM and TOP

combination

$$6.1715X_4 + 7.9705X_5$$

need to be considered. As a comparison with Section 7.2 shows, this linear combination, however, is equivalent to the discriminant variable found there, the factor of proportionality being approximately 10.8.

In complete analogy, we can now carry over the problem to $p > 2$ dimensions. Under the assumption of a normal distribution model with equal covariance structure in both groups, the boundary between the two domains of allocation is an equation of the form

$$b_1x_1 + b_2x_2 + \cdots + b_px_p = f.$$

This equation describes a $(p - 1)$-dimensional hyperplane in p-dimensional space. To classify an observation, we must compute its value in the variable

$$b_1X_1 + \cdots + b_pX_p$$

and compare this value with f. As in the two-dimensional case it turns out that this linear combination is identical, up to a multiplicative factor, with the discriminant variable defined in Section 7.2, and thus, in our terminology, is equivalent to it.

Thanks to this equivalence, we may once again use the regression approach for the classification problem. This entails the following advantages:

1. With the help of the criteria discussed in Section 7.4, one may be able to eliminate variables which are unimportant for classification.
2. The constant f in the equation for the separating hyperplane need not be determined on the basis of the equation $p_G = p_F$. We can rather compute the means and the pooled standard deviation of the discriminant variable obtained via the regression approach and determine the classification boundary on the basis of these univariate statistics. In this way, the multidimensional classification problem is reduced to its one-dimensional analogue.
3. In many applications one observes that, although the assumption of normal distributions in both groups is violated, the discriminant function can be considered as approximately normal. The reason for this lies in the central limit theorem, according to which weighted sums of random variables are, under fairly general conditions, closer to normality than the original variables themselves.

Remark 3 has an interesting consequence: if the distribution of the discriminant variable looks normal (with equal variances) in both groups, it is legitimate to use the normal theory classification procedure, regardless of the distribution of the original variables. We can, however, no longer expect the method to be optimal in this case.

We now apply these considerations to the discriminant variable, found in Section 7.3, which has been reduced by the variable LENGTH,

$$DF = -25.809 + 0.111X_2 - 0.113X_3 - 0.149X_4 - 0.157X_5 + 0.207X_6$$

Either by means of the equations in Section 6.5, or by computing the 200 values of DF, we obtain the following univariate statistics for the discriminant function:

Group	Genuine	Forged
mean	0.4621	−0.4621
standard deviation	0.1427	0.1226

The pooled variance computes to

$$s^2 = (99 \cdot 0.1427^2 + 99 \cdot 0.1226^2)/198 = 0.0177.$$

It is left to the reader to convince himself of the validity of the formulae of Section 7.6 by computing $\bar{y}_1$, $\bar{y}_2$ and s^2 directly from $R_5^2 = 0.9242$. The boundary of the two domains of allocation is $g = 0$, yielding a simple classification rule: bills with positive DF-value are to be classified as genuine, those with negative DF-value as forged. The fact that the boundary falls on zero is a direct consequence of the two groups being of equal size. For different sample sizes, the boundary is in general not zero, unless the intercept b_0 of the regression equation is adapted accordingly.

The probability of erroneously classifying a bill as forged is estimated as $P(Y < g)$, where Y is a normally distributed random variable with mean 0.4621 and standard deviation $\sqrt{0.0177} = 0.1330$:

$$P(Y = 0) = \phi\left(\frac{0 - 0.4621}{0.1130}\right) = \phi(-3.474) \approx 0.0003.$$

It is to be noted, however, that with this method, even when the normality assumptions are satisfied, the probability of a misclassification is generally underestimated, especially for small sample sizes.

If we test the success of the classification rule in the case of the 200 known bank notes, we observe that only one genuine bill (no. 70) would not be classified correctly. Close to the boundary are the following four bills:

	No.	Value of DF
Genuine	10	0.171
	70	−0.077
Forged	103	−0.113
	125	−0.115

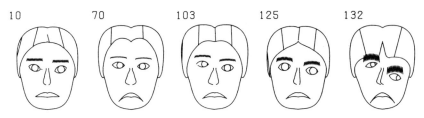

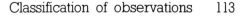

Figure 7.10   Faces of five selected bills

Table 7.9 Data measured on four additional bills

	LENGTH	LEFT	RIGHT	BOTTOM	TOP	DIAGONAL	DF
i	x_{1i}	x_{2i}	x_{3i}	x_{4i}	x_{5i}	x_{6i}	y_i
201	215.2	130.4	130.1	10.1	11.6	139.8	−0.3772
202	214.9	130.4	130.3	10.7	11.6	139.6	−0.5304
203	215.3	130.4	130.4	7.7	12.0	139.8	−0.1169
204	215.1	130.6	130.2	9.2	11.0	138.8	−0.3455

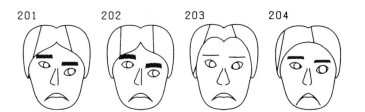

Figure 7.11   Faces of bills 201 to 204

A boundary at -0.1 would thus yield the desired complete separation; this boundary, however, would – as has already been mentioned earlier – be influenced by extreme values. It is quite instructive to consider the above 'critical' bills once again in their representation as faces. The four bills would certainly create difficulties in an attempt to separate the two groups using a graphical method. On the other hand, the forged notes with a negative value of DF (e.g. no. 132 with DF $= -0.754$) can be recognized as forgeries graphically without any trouble. Figure 7.10 shows the faces of the five bills just discussed.

Finally, we apply the classification rule to four additional forged notes which we have not mentioned up to now. Table 7.9 shows the data of these four bills along with their values in the discriminant function. All four bills can be recognized as forged. As an intuitive possibility of classification we could try to compare the faces of these four bills with the means of both groups. Figure 7.12 shows the faces corresponding to the means of *Genuine* and *Forged*, Figure 7.11 the faces of the bills, nos 201 to 204. The classification

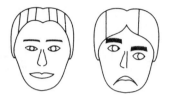

Figure 7.12   Mean faces of both groups of bills

would be least clear for bill no. 203. This bill does indeed show a discriminant value of -0.1169, which is near the boundary.

So far we have discussed classification of items into one of two known groups. With bank notes it may happen, however, that a presumably forged note has been produced by a different forger or a different machine, and it might distinguish itself from the genuine notes in a way that is not necessarily detected by a discriminant function. What we need is therefore a rule which tells us whether a given item (suspicious bill) can be allocated to a known group (genuine bills) or not. Such a procedure, called *identification* analysis, is given in the next chapter. Since identification can be thought of as a special case of discrimination, our reader is advised to make sure that linear discriminant analysis is well understood before going on to Chapter 8.

DISCUSSION

Question:
How does one determine the proportionality factor between the two equivalent solutions (maximizing the standard distance, and multiple linear regression)?
Answer:
The proportionality factor cannot be determined without explicit computation of the regression solution. From the regression equation we can obtain it by normalizing the linear combination, i.e. it corresponds precisely to the normalizing constant.

Question:
Various program libraries offer as multidimensional generalization of the univariate t-test the T^2-statistics of Hotelling. How is T^2 related to discriminant analysis?
Answer:
Hotelling's T^2 is equivalent to the overall F-test. The functional relationship is

$$F_{overall} = \frac{n_1 + n_2 - p - 1}{(n_1 + n_2 - 2)p} T^2.$$

In contrast to the regression approach, however, T^2 does not provide an immediate possibility for testing the redundancy of individual variables.

Question:

Can a variable which, in a univariate approach, does not yield a significant mean difference, be *a priori* omitted from discriminant analysis?

Answer:

No. If the variable in question is correlated with other variables, it can, viewed multidimensionally, indeed contribute significantly to the discrimination. Consider, as an illustration, Figure 7.9, and imagine the point cluster of the group FORGED shifted somewhat towards below.

Question:

How can one test the efficiency of the method, if the assumptions for statistical tests (normal distribution, equality of the covariance matrices) are not satisfied?

Answer:

For the case of unequal covariance matrices there exist procedures (nonlinear discriminant analysis), which, however, cannot be interpreted as intuitively. In addition, such methods are often also based on normality assumptions. This problem was briefly touched upon in Section 7.7.

A useful procedure consists of splitting each group randomly into two parts. On one part of each group a discriminant analysis is carried out, and the discriminant function thus obtained is applied to the remaining observations. On the basis of the distribution of the discriminant variables in the remaining observations, one can then easily check whether the discriminant function is a mere product of randomness, or whether it uncovers genuine group differences.

In the bank note example, we have randomly divided the groups *Genuine* and *Forged* into subgroups *Genuine 1, Genuine 2, Forged 1* and *Forged 2* of 50 bills each. The linear discriminant analysis of the groups *Genuine 1* and *Forged 1* yields the discriminant function shown in Table 7.10.

Figure 7.13 shows the frequency distribution of the discriminant variable in

Table 7.10 Discriminant function based on subgroups *Genuine 1* and *Forged 1*

Variable j	Coefficient b_j	Standard error of b_j	Partial F
intercept	− 34.673		
LENGTH	0.012	0.042	0.08
LEFT	0.120	0.065	3.38
RIGHT	− 0.076	0.059	1.64
BOTTOM	− 0.162	0.015	121.60
TOP	− 0.149	0.028	28.11
DIAGONAL	0.211	0.025	73.89

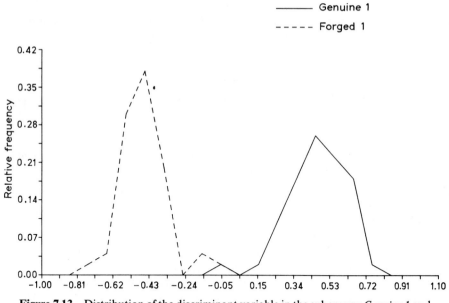

Figure 7.13 Distribution of the discriminant variable in the subgroups *Genuine 1* and *Forged 1*

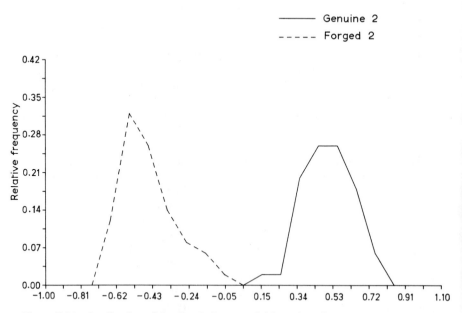

Figure 7.14 Application of the discriminant variable to the subgroups *Genuine 2* and *Forged 2*

the subgroups *Genuine 1* and *Forged 1*. More interesting, however, is now the application of the discriminant function to the subgroups *Genuine 2* and *Forged 2*. For each bill i from *Genuine 2* and *Forged 2* we compute the discriminant value

$$y_i = -34.673 + 0.012x_{1i} + \cdots + 0.211x_{6i}.$$

Figure 7.14 shows the frequency distribution of these 100 y_i-values in the subgroups *Genuine 2* and *Forged 2*. If the discriminant function reflected only random differences in location, then we would expect the two groups to overlap considerably. As the figure shows, however, the linear combination obtained from only part of the data discriminates between the two control groups very well.

Numerically, we can check the discrimination by computing the (univariate) standard distance between *Genuine 2* and *Forged 2* in the discriminant variable based on *Genuine 1* and *Forged 1*. This standard distance is $D = 7.14$; its transformation to a two-sample t-statistic (cf. Chapter 2) yields a highly significant value of $t = 35.72$ on 98 degrees of freedom. Note that we can use the univariate t-test here because the discriminant function is not based on *Genuine 2* and *Forged 2*. (For groups *Genuine 1* and *Forged 1*, this procedure would not be correct.) In this way, the significance of the discriminant function has been unequivocally verified. With respect to the difference in location of the subgroups *Genuine 2* and *Forged 2*, we can of course also apply a nonparametric Wilcoxon (Mann-Whitney) test.

We can moreover check the variability of the individual coefficients of the discriminant function by computing a discriminant function also in the control groups *Genuine 2* and *Forged 2*. The solution is as shown in Table 7.11. The changed sign of LENGTH, in comparison to the first solution, confirms that this variable is redundant. A relatively strong difference is observed for the variable RIGHT with a coefficient of -0.076 in solution 1 and of -0.142 in solution 2. In other variables, there are only slight changes of the coefficients.

Table 7.11 Discriminant function based on subgroups *Genuine 2* and *Forged 2*

Variable j	Coefficient b_j	Standard error of b_j	Partial F
intercept	− 21.865		
LENGTH	− 0.014	0.044	0.10
LEFT	0.116	0.062	3.52
RIGHT	− 0.142	0.054	6.82
BOTTOM	− 0.130	0.014	82.18
TOP	− 0.153	0.022	46.88
DIAGONAL	0.221	0.021	116.38

Similar comments hold for the comparison with the solution based on all 200 bills.

Question:
We have learned that the overall F-test for discriminant analysis of two groups is a generalization of the t-test. Are there also generalizations for the case of several groups?

Answer:
The theory of comparing several means (one-way analysis of variance) can be generalized to the multidimensional case. We then speak of a Multivariate ANalysis Of VAriance (MANOVA). If the researcher is interested in classification rules, then, in general, several discriminant functions must be analysed simultaneously. The difficulty then arises that a variable may be redundant for the comparison of two specific groups, but may be significant in another comparison.

We therefore prefer – at least if the number of groups is not too large – to carry out pairwise discriminant analyses. If we denote by k the number of groups, then $[k(k-1)]/2$ pairs of groups can be formed. For each pair one can thus consider the problem of redundancy separately. The $[k(k-1)]/2$ overall tests, however, are no longer statistically independent. At most $k-1$ independent comparisons can be carried out.

Question:
The described method of obtaining boundaries in classification does not appear to be necessarily meaningful in applications. For example, with a medical diagnosis failure to recognize a disease can be fatal. On the other hand, it is less serious to classify a healthy person as sick and to rectify the misdiagnosis in a second test.

Answer:
Often the two types of misclassifications can indeed not be rated equally important. Imagine, for example, a money changing machine, which measures some lengths on bills that are inserted for change, and which computes a discriminant value. In this case it is important, above all, to recognize a forgery as such. One accepts the risk of refusing a genuine bill as forged. For our discriminant variable this would mean that the boundary would have to be moved to the right (cf Fig. 7.5). If the importance of a misclassification can be measured in terms of costs, then a boundary can be defined which minimizes the costs.

Often, however, the implications of a misclassification cannot be expressed in terms of costs. For example, in medical mass examinations one will want to keep the risk of not diagnosing a sick person as ill as low as possible. The smaller this risk is, however, the greater the probability that a healthy person is mistakenly diagnosed as ill. Figure 7.15 illustrates the two error probabilities in the case that a sick person is to be correctly diagnosed with a probability of

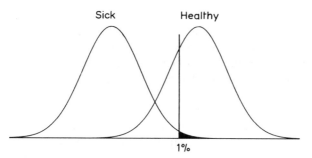

Figure 7.15   Defining a reasonable boundary in a medical problem

99%. The probability of classifying a healthy person mistakenly as sick would in this example be approximately 25%.

Finally, the so-called prior probabilities also play a role in determining the boundary. By these we mean the two numbers

p_1 = probability that a new observation comes from
    population 1

$p_2 = 1 - p_1$ = probability that it comes from population 2

We thus could assume, for example, that in the case of an automaton about every tenth bill is a blossom, i.e. we put $p_G = 0.9$ and $p_F = 0.1$. The costs may be expressed by the following symbols:

$C(G|F)$ = cost of a forged bill being mistakenly
    accepted as genuine

$C(F|G)$ = cost of a genuine bill being mistakenly
    considered as forged

Under these conditions we can give a general method of determining the boundary, which takes into account the costs and the prior probabilities:

$$g = \frac{\bar{y}_G + \bar{y}_F}{2} + \frac{s^2}{\bar{y}_G - \bar{y}_F} \cdot \log \frac{p_F \cdot C(G|F)}{p_G \cdot C(F|G)}.$$

Here, log means the natural logarithm and $\bar{y}_G$, $\bar{y}_F$ and s^2 are the means and pooled variance, respectively, of the discriminant function. This boundary minimizes the expected costs under normality assumptions.

In our example, we can set the costs $C(G|F) = 1000$. If we assume that the owner of the automaton forfeits a profit of Fr 50.00 if a genuine bill is mistakenly refused, then we can put $C(F|G) = 50$. Together with the above assumptions about p_G and p_F we therefore obtain the optimal boundary g = 0.0153, which is not very different from the original boundary 0.

Question:

At the end of Section 7.5 it was pointed out that the discriminant function based on DIAGONAL and IMAGE is worse than the one using variables LEFT to DIAGONAL. Yet one might be satisfied with a discriminant function based on IMAGE and DIAGONAL provided that the groups can be separated completely. Is this the case in our example?

Answer:

Figure 7.16 shows a scatterplot of IMAGE versus DIAGONAL for both groups. Genuine and forged bills can be separated by a straight line. More obvious than this separation, however, is a strong inhomogeneity of the group *Forged*, which appears practically divided into two subgroups. We shall return to this inhomogeneity in Chapter 12.

Question:

In this chapter you have always used Fisher's code in the regression approach to discriminant analysis. Do you recommend to do this in all applications? Under what circumstances would you choose a different code?

Answer:

The Fisher code has some theoretical and computational advantages (cf. Section 7.6). For practical purposes, however, any other code does the job as well, and there is no compelling reason for using the Fisher code. For reasons

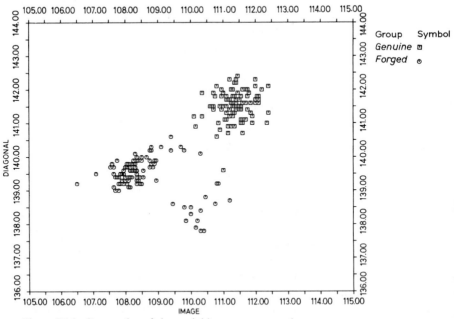

Figure 7.16 Scatterplot of the variables DIAGONAL and IMAGE

of numerical accuracy it is often better to choose c_1 and c_2 such that $|c_1 - c_2|$ is large, especially if the discriminant function coefficients have leading zeros in their decimal representation. For example, a popular code is $c_1 = 0, c_2 = 100$. Then the values y_i of the discriminant function are, in general, sufficiently accurate if they are rounded to integers, the classification boundary is around 50, and the classification rule is easy to remember (e.g. as 'genuine' closer to 0, 'forged' closer to 100).

Question:
I feel somehow uneasy about the normality assumptions. Can you give some more details about the role they play?
Answer:
As in regression analysis, unsatisfied normality assumptions affect the correctness of statistical tests, but not necessarily the usefulness of the discriminant function as a tool for data analysis. The overall F-test is known to be relatively robust against non-normality and against inequality of the covariance matrices, at least asymptotically (i.e. for large samples). Less is known about the partial F-tests, but in general it can still be assumed that these tests are valid for large samples. Methods like the one proposed in one of the preceding questions are especially helpful if the assumptions are doubtful. Two important keywords in this connection are the 'jackknife' and the 'bootstrap' (see the article by Efron and Gong (1983) and references therein) – but beware: the computations may become quite laborious!

Question:
I'd like to ask another question about variable selection. In section 7.5 you said that LENGTH, LEFT and RIGHT can be eliminated without much loss of information. Can this be true? Looking at the univariate distributions of LEFT and RIGHT (Fig. 2.2 and 2.3), for instance, there seems to be quite a lot of information about mean differences in these two variables!
Answer:
Redundancy of variables in a discriminant function does not mean that these variables carry no information. What it means is that they furnish no *additional* information to the group separation than can be obtained using the sufficient (non-redundant) variables alone. It's like guessing the name of a president: knowing that he is Republican is of some value, but once you know that he was a movie star before becoming a politician, the former information becomes redundant.

It is sometimes interesting to analyse how much information the set of redundant variables itself contains. Let's illustrate this on the bank notes, assuming that LENGTH, LEFT and RIGHT are considered as redundant. How well could the two groups be separated using these three variables? To answer this question, we can compute a discriminant function between *Genuine* and *Forged*, using only LENGTH, LEFT and RIGHT. The group codes used here are 0 for genuine bills and 100 for forged bills. The discriminant function, called DFR (R for Redundant) is

$$\text{DFR} = -2452.1 - 42.1\,\text{LENGTH} + 30.1\,\text{LEFT} + 58.8\,\text{RIGHT},$$
$$(7.27) \qquad (11.21) \qquad (9.86)$$

the associated standard distance is $D_3 = 1.789$. This is definitely not *no* information about difference in location, but nevertheless these three variables provide almost no additional information, once BOTTOM, TOP and DIAGONAL have entered the analysis.

Let's illustrate this graphically. A discriminant function based on the set of sufficient variables (BOTTOM, TOP, DIAGONAL) has been given in Section 7.5. If we use the same group code as above (0 = genuine, 100 = forged), we get an equivalent linear combination which we call DFS (S for Sufficient):

$$\text{DFS} = 253.9 + 15.4\,\text{BOTTOM} + 16.4\,\text{TOP} - 20.3\,\text{DIAGONAL}$$
$$(0.96) \qquad (1.68) \qquad (1.48)$$

with $D_3 = 6.77$. Figure 7.17 shows a scatterplot of DFS versus DFR with the means in both groups marked by crosses. The excellent group separation based on DFS is evident. The information contained in LENGTH, LEFT and RIGHT appears in the vertical mean difference, but this difference doesn't

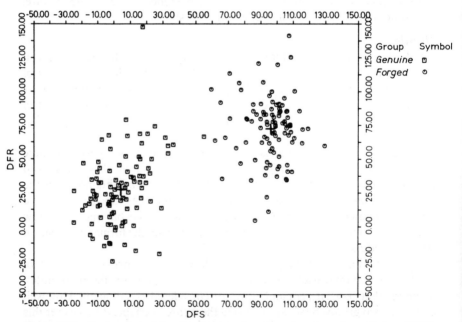

Figure 7.17 Scatterplot of the discriminant functions based on the sufficient (DFS) and the redundant (DFR) sets of variables

contribute significantly to the overall group separation. Figure 7.17 reveals a little surprise, however: there is a genuine bill, no. 1, with an extremely large value of DFR, appearing at the very top of the scatterplot. We will devote more attention to such potential outliers in the next chapter.

FURTHER STUDY

Textbooks

Discriminant analysis is discussed in any multivariate book – see, for instance, Anderson (1984), Mardia *et al.* (1979), Seber (1984), Srivastava and Carter (1983).

For good application-oriented introductions see Morrison (1976) or Johnson and Wichern (1982). Two smaller books devoted exclusively to discriminant analysis are by Tatsuoka (1970) and Lachenbruch (1975).

Articles

Discriminant analysis was introduced by Fisher (1936), and hundreds of papers on discriminant analysis have been published since – see the bibliography in Lachenbruch (1975). The key article on testing hypotheses about discriminant function coefficients was by C.R. Rao (1970). Among the more recent papers, see McCabe (1975) for computational procedures in variable selection, and Flury and Riedwyl (1985) for a discussion of the relationship between regression and discriminant analysis.

Software

Programs for discriminant analysis for the two-group and multiple group case are included in most statistical program libraries. For the two-group case, a program for multiple linear regression suffices.

EXAMPLES

Example 7.1 Skull Dimensions of Voles

Airoldi and Hoffmann (1984) took various skull measurements on two species of voles (small rodents): *Microtus californicus*, and *Microtus ochrogaster*. We are going to use only two subgroups of females who are at least 120 days old (the age is exactly known since the animals were lab-reared). From the total of 48 variables measured by Airoldi and Hoffmann, we used the following six, which can be considered as characterizing the skulls sufficiently well (see Fig. 7.18):

$$L_2 = \text{condylo-incisive length}$$
$$L_9 = \text{length of incisive foramen}$$

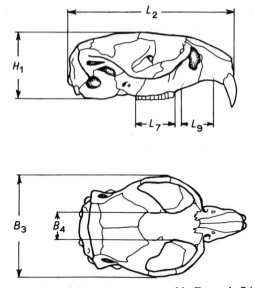

Figure 7.18 Diagram of cranial measurements used in Example 7.1. (This figure was drawn by J.P. Airoldi, University of Berne.)

L_7 = alveolar length of upper molar tooth row
B_3 = zygomatic width
B_4 = interorbital width
H_1 = skull height

The labels of the variables are the same as in Airoldi and Hoffmann (1984). The data are given in Table 7.12. Table 7.13 displays means and standard deviations for both groups as well as univariate standard distances; these range from 1.31 (variable $L2$) to 3.39 (variable $B4$). Good multivariate discrimination should therefore be possible. For all variables except $B4$ the mean is larger in group *M. californicus* than in group *M. ochrogaster*.

We used the regression approach with codes 0 (*M. californicus*) and 100 (*M. ochrogaster*) to obtain the discriminant function given in Table 7.14. The coefficient of determination in the regression with all six variables is $R_6^2 = 0.8685$, yielding a six-variate standard distance of $D_6 = 5.09$. The value of the overall F-statistic (Section 7.4) is $F = 86.9$ on 6 and 79 degrees of freedom, which is highly significant.

Comparing the coefficients of the discriminant function with their standard errors, it appears that two coefficients (those of L_9 and B_3) are highly unstable. A stepwise elimination procedure, using the criterion that each variable remaining in the equation should have a partial F of at least 4 (that is, the absolute value of the coefficient should be at least twice the standard error),

Table 7.12 Skull dimensions of voles. *Age* is in days, all other variables are in 0.1 mm. Data courtesy of J.P. Airoldi, University of Berne.

M. californicus, females ($n_1 = 41$)

AGE	L2	L9	L7	B3	B4	H1
345	304	55	75	168	34	110
127	273	47	69	155	33	108
132	272	42	71	157	38	110
218	289	48	74	165	38	114
189	291	47	75	164	36	114
288	298	52	73	161	32	104
121	280	49	72	156	35	106
188	271	44	67	154	34	107
231	283	52	73	168	35	108
139	285	45	73	158	38	111
126	292	50	80	174	35	117
196	288	50	71	161	33	110
164	285	48	75	163	37	114
181	277	51	73	156	33	106
128	256	44	66	148	32	102
129	268	42	71	159	37	112
166	281	50	68	155	33	107
178	267	48	70	150	36	108
242	288	51	72	165	34	108
189	297	52	73	161	33	109
161	283	49	72	156	34	112
164	288	49	73	156	33	108
163	281	46	70	151	32	105
185	250	39	66	148	33	100
160	284	50	76	162	34	108
165	281	52	71	160	37	108
151	273	56	75	159	35	108
149	277	53	70	161	35	112
249	282	53	72	165	33	113
168	277	49	74	164	35	113
129	274	51	72	159	36	109
129	284	55	74	164	36	110
148	299	56	75	166	34	110
130	303	62	79	177	35	118
296	297	58	77	168	35	115
140	264	50	71	151	37	105
129	262	52	67	152	32	104
129	269	52	73	165	33	107
129	281	56	73	161	33	106
121	293	55	78	168	34	118
129	267	53	68	159	35	103

M. ochrogaster, females ($n_2 = 45$)

AGE	L2	L9	L7	B3	B4	H1
152	265	44	64	144	41	104
183	261	47	64	143	42	103
183	249	43	58	141	42	100
183	245	42	61	145	40	102
183	263	42	63	157	39	103
183	255	47	65	142	41	101
213	273	41	60	155	41	107
213	250	39	60	142	37	98
213	252	39	60	142	37	99
213	265	41	62	147	40	105
213	268	45	63	152	40	103
213	259	44	63	149	39	103
213	268	47	62	151	39	103
213	270	45	66	149	40	105
244	260	39	63	147	40	101
244	269	46	65	148	41	106
244	261	43	63	146	42	103
244	272	43	63	158	40	106
244	277	49	64	158	39	111
244	257	42	67	152	41	104
274	261	44	64	146	40	106
305	268	48	64	157	40	106
305	288	51	67	153	41	109
305	274	46	68	158	39	108
305	262	46	65	151	39	108
305	269	47	63	147	42	106
305	275	43	66	149	39	103
305	277	44	66	145	40	102
335	271	43	64	152	41	102
335	278	49	68	155	38	107
335	274	40	63	157	39	107
365	264	47	64	158	40	102
365	273	48	66	154	42	107
365	274	39	65	159	38	106
365	271	46	66	160	40	108
365	268	50	61	147	40	100
365	274	47	66	159	39	105
365	271	51	66	155	39	103
274	289	42	67	167	41	108
122	254	49	71	143	37	99
122	269	46	66	146	38	107
152	264	45	68	147	40	105
124	263	45	67	138	39	102
138	267	45	64	149	42	107
126	262	43	63	144	41	102

Table 7.13 Univariate basic statistics in the voles example

Variable		Mean	Standard deviation	Standard distance
L_2	cali.	280.829	12.369	1.31
	ochr.	266.644	9.213	
L_9	cali.	50.317	4.574	1.43
	ochr.	44.756	3.120	
L_7	cali.	72.366	3.277	2.80
	ochr.	64.333	2.450	
B_3	cali.	160.244	6.560	1.53
	ochr.	150.311	6.399	
B_4	cali.	34.561	1.747	3.39
	ochr.	39.867	1.375	
H_1	cali.	109.122	4.136	1.36
	ochr.	104.267	2.957	

Table 7.14 Linear discriminant function with six variables in the voles example

Variable	Coefficient	Standard error	Partial F-statistic
intercept	− 27.268		
L_2	0.715	0.316	5.12
L_9	0.089	0.683	0.02
L_7	− 4.991	1.027	23.64
B_3	0.251	0.518	0.24
B_4	9.725	0.974	99.72
H_1	− 1.706	0.953	3.21

yields the following simplified discriminant function:

$$DF = -58.105 + 0.632L_2 - 5.877L_7 + 9.059B_4$$
$$(0.266) \quad (0.822) \quad (0.896)$$

The standard distance is $D_3 = 4.97$. The decrease in standard distance is relatively small, although the three eliminated variables have univariate

standard distances around 1.5. This is again a case where redundancy of
variables does not imply that the redundant variables carry no information
about group separation – but L_9, B_3 and H_1 do not add information to the
discrimination provided by L_2, L_7 and B_4.

Although good discrimination seems possible, given a standard distance of
approximately five, one should be critical of the foregoing analysis: as
Table 7.12 shows, the age distribution is not the same in both groups,
individuals of the species *M. ochrogaster* being on the average older than those
of the species *M. californicus*. Since these animals tend to grow during their
whole lifetime, the discriminant function might reflect age differences rather
than differences in the shapes of the skulls, and hence it might be worthless for
the classification of new specimens. To answer this criticism, a scatterplot of
the discriminant function versus the age of the animals was constructed; see
Fig. 7.19. The different age distributions are clearly visible, but there is almost
no correlation between *Age* and the discriminant function.

Of course one might not be so lucky, and a linear discriminant function
might indeed reflect mostly differences in the size of the specimens that are due
to age variation. One might then, for instance, try a discriminant analysis
where the variables are replaced by their residuals of the regression on age.
However, in most cases the age of the specimens would probably not be known

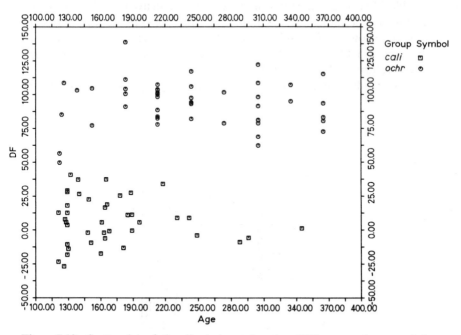

Figure 7.19 Scatterplot of the discriminant function (DF) versus the age of the
animals

(recall that the animals used in this example were lab-reared). It may then be appropriate to estimate so-called 'growth-invariant' discriminant functions; see Reyment *et al* (1984, p. 135) for references. We will briefly return to this problem in Example 10.3.

Some details of the analysis have been omitted here and are left to the reader; see Exercise 13 in Chapter 12.

Example 7.2 Analysis of differences between two machines producing electrodes

This application of linear discriminant analysis to quality control is due to Kreuter (1975, pp. 44–50). The productions of two machines that produce the same items (in this case, electrodes) are to be compared. Figure 7.20 shows a cross section of an item, with five variables marked. X_1, X_4 and X_5 are diameters, while X_3 and X_4 are lengths. The data of two samples of 50 each from the two machines are given in Table 7.15. All measurements were in mm $\cdot 10^{-3}$, but for reasons of secrecy the data were transformed by subtracting suitable constants from the variables. (This corresponds to a shift of the coordinate system in p-dimensional space, which does not affect discrimination).

Table 7.16 displays univariate basic statistics for all five variables. The fourth variable has a rather large standard distance of 4.19, so the univariate approach shows already substantial differences between the two machines. There are also differences between the standard deviations of the two groups; we will return to this point in Example 11.1.

The linear discriminant function, obtained by the regression approach with

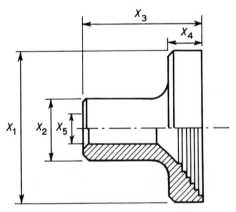

Figure 7.20 Cross-section through an electrode, describing variables X_1 to X_5 of Example 7.2. (Courtesy of U. Kreuter, Consult AG, Berne.)

Table 7.15 Measurements taken on electrodes produced by two machines. See text and Fig. 7.20 for a description of the variables. Data courtesy of U. Kreuter, Consult AG, Berne.

Machine 1

X_1	X_2	X_3	X_4	X_5
40	58	31	44	64
39	59	33	40	60
40	58	35	46	59
39	59	31	47	58
40	60	36	41	56
45	60	45	45	58
42	64	39	38	63
44	59	41	40	60
42	66	48	20	61
40	60	35	40	58
40	61	40	41	58
40	58	38	45	60
38	59	39	46	58
42	59	32	36	61
40	61	45	45	59
40	59	45	52	59
42	58	38	51	59
40	59	37	44	60
39	60	35	49	59
39	60	37	46	56
40	58	35	39	58
39	59	34	41	60
39	60	37	39	59
40	59	42	43	57
40	59	37	46	60
43	60	35	38	62
40	59	29	41	60
40	59	37	41	59
40	60	37	46	60
40	58	42	45	61
42	63	48	47	64
41	59	37	49	60
39	58	31	47	60
42	60	43	49	61
42	59	37	53	62
40	58	35	40	59
40	59	35	48	58
39	60	35	46	59
38	59	30	47	57
40	60	38	48	62
44	60	36	44	60
40	58	34	41	58
38	60	31	49	60
38	58	29	46	60
39	59	35	43	56
40	60	37	45	59
40	60	37	44	61
42	62	37	35	60
40	59	35	44	58
42	58	35	43	61

Table 7.15 (Continued)

Machine 2

X_1	X_2	X_3	X_4	X_5
44	58	32	25	57
43	58	25	19	60
44	57	30	24	59
42	59	36	20	59
42	60	38	29	59
43	56	38	32	58
43	57	26	18	59
45	60	27	27	59
45	59	33	18	60
43	58	29	26	59
43	59	39	22	58
43	59	35	29	59
44	57	37	19	58
43	58	29	20	58
43	58	27	8	58
44	60	39	15	60
43	58	35	13	58
44	58	38	19	58
43	58	36	19	58
43	58	29	19	60
43	58	29	21	58
42	59	43	26	58
43	58	26	20	58
44	59	22	17	59
43	59	36	25	59
44	57	33	11	59
44	60	25	10	59
44	58	22	16	59
44	60	36	18	57
46	61	39	14	59
42	58	36	27	57
43	60	20	19	60
42	59	27	23	59
43	58	28	12	58
42	57	41	24	58
44	60	28	20	60
43	58	45	25	59
43	59	35	21	59
43	60	29	2	60
44	59	22	11	59
44	58	46	25	58
43	60	28	9	60
43	59	38	29	59
43	58	47	24	57
42	58	24	19	59
43	60	35	22	58
45	60	28	18	60
43	57	38	23	60
44	60	31	22	58
43	58	22	20	57

Table 7.16 Univariate basic statistics for Example 7.2

Variable		Mean	Standard deviation	Standard distance
X_2	machine 1	40.36	1.575	2.33
	machine 2	43.32	0.868	
X_2	machine 1	59.54	1.555	0.70
	machine 2	58.60	1.107	
X_3	machine 1	36.80	4.472	0.78
	machine 2	32.34	6.736	
X_4	machine 1	43.66	5.255	4.19
	machine 2	19.88	6.077	
X_5	machine 1	59.54	1.809	0.60
	machine 2	58.68	0.913	

code values 0 (machine 1) and 100 (machine 2) is

$$DF = 434.29 + 5.77X_1 - 6.75X_2 + 0.22X_3 - 2.67X_4 - 2.53X_5,$$
$$\quad\quad\quad\quad (1.48) \quad\quad (1.40) \quad (0.35) \quad\quad (0.24) \quad\quad (1.34)$$

where the numbers in brackets are standard errors. The multivariate standard distance is $D_5 = 5.387$. This standard distance is so large that we can expect complete or almost complete separation of the two groups in the discriminant variable. It is left to the reader to verify this by computing the values of the discriminant function for all 100 observations; see Exercise 14 in Chapter 12. For a given item, it would be possible to predict with high probability by which machine it was produced.

Since the univariate standard distance of X_4 is so large, it is interesting to ask how well the two groups can be separated if X_4 is omitted. The discriminant function based on X_1, X_2, X_3 and X_5 turns out to be

$$DF_4 = 78.97 + 18.40X_1 - 5.44X_2 - 1.56X_3 - 7.17X_5$$
$$\quad\quad\quad\quad (1.40) \quad\quad (2.10) \quad\quad (0.47) \quad\quad (1.92)$$

the associated standard distance is $D_4 = 3.23$. So, even without X_4, the two machines differ quite substantially. Comparing the two discriminant functions DF and DF_4, it can be seen that variables X_3 and X_5, which are redundant in DF, play a significant role if X_4 is omitted. This illustrates that the

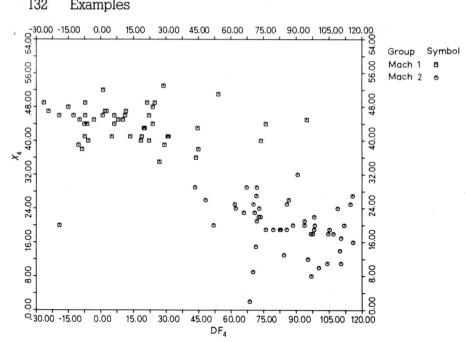

Figure 7.21   Scatterplot of DF_4 (the discriminant function obtained without variable X_4) versus X_4

redundancy problem depends crucially on the set of variables on which the analysis is based.

Figure 7.21 shows a scatterplot of DF_4 (the discriminant function obtained without X_4) versus variable X_4. It is clear from this scatterplot that X_4 alone carries more information about differences between the two machines than the four remaining variables combined. Some of the items produced by machine 1 appear as outliers in Fig. 7.21, and the investigator might wish to check the correctness of the respective measurements.

What are the practical consequences of this analysis? If it is desirable that the productions of the two machines do not differ, one would probably first try to adjust the mean of X_4 (as was already suggested by the univariate analysis). Since adjusting one variable may influence the others, it might then be necessary to obtain new samples of items from one or from both machines.

Example 7.3 Discriminant analysis in a medical investigation

The data of this example consist of six variables recorded on 40 patients who were surgically treated for renal hypertension. After one year, 20 patients were classified as improved and 20 as unimproved, and these were taken as samples from two multivariate populations. The data, which were kindly provided by

Table 7.17 Data for Example 7.3. (Courtesy of W. J. Krzanowski, University of Reading)

Group 1:

C1	C2	C3	B1	B2	B3
45.0	72.0	180.0	0	0	0
1.5	3.0	190.0	1	0	1
4.0	15.6	190.0	0	0	1
27.0	49.0	160.0	0	0	1
48.0	15.0	210.0	1	1	1
51.0	24.0	160.0	0	0	1
67.0	3.0	200.0	1	1	1
41.0	83.0	162.0	0	1	0
43.0	38.0	285.0	0	1	0
47.0	203.0	170.0	0	1	0
53.0	3.0	200.0	0	1	0
36.0	108.0	160.0	0	1	0
56.0	48.0	200.0	0	1	0
59.0	59.0	207.0	1	1	1
55.0	120.0	170.0	0	1	1
54.0	12.0	217.0	0	1	0
52.0	36.0	170.0	0	1	0
36.0	83.0	290.0	0	1	0
45.0	36.0	186.0	1	0	1
37.0	3.0	220.0	0	0	0

Group 2:

C1	C2	C3	B1	B2	B3
40.0	13.0	146.0	0	0	1
39.0	187.0	160.0	0	1	0
60.0	149.0	200.0	1	1	0
56.0	15.0	240.0	1	0	1
34.0	44.0	160.0	0	0	1
42.0	106.0	150.0	1	1	1
17.0	264.0	150.0	0	1	0
56.0	103.0	220.0	0	0	0
18.0	42.0	150.0	0	0	0
35.0	5.0	190.0	1	1	0
57.0	61.0	160.0	1	0	1
29.0	360.0	200.0	0	1	0
43.0	189.0	185.0	0	0	0
45.0	27.0	170.0	0	0	1
39.0	63.0	160.0	1	1	0
52.0	125.0	200.0	1	1	0
60.0	66.0	260.0	0	1	0
56.0	42.0	182.0	1	1	0
40.0	240.0	155.0	0	1	0
68.0	60.0	180.0	1	1	0

Note: The original data set consisted of six continuous and three binary variables. Among the continuous variables, only the first three (C_1 to C_3) are reported here.

W.J. Krzanowski, are displayed in Table 7.17. There are three continuous variables, labeled C_1 to C_3, and three binary variables B_1 to B_3 which indicate presence (1) or absence (0) of certain characteristics.

We leave the computation of univariate and bivariate descriptive statistics as an exercise to the reader and proceed directly to discriminant analysis. The linear discriminant function, obtained from the regression approach with group codes 0 and 100 is as follows (standard errors in brackets):

$$DF = 78.368 + 0.477C_1 + 0.285C_2 - 0.251C_3$$
$$ (0.519) \quad (0.103) \quad (0.218)$$
$$+ 46.532B_1 - 44.456B_2 - 34.492B_3.$$
$$(16.604) \quad (18.359) \quad (18.326)$$

The multivariate standard distance is $D_6 = 1.51$, indicating a relatively poor group separation. The overall F-test gives $F = 3.32$ on 6 and 33 degrees of freedom, which is significant at the 2% level. Hence we conclude that there are indeed differences in location between the two groups, but they are too small for reliable prediction of group membership.

Figure 7.22 shows a plot of the frequency distribution of the discriminant function (DF) in both groups. With a classification boundary at the value 50 of DF, seven individuals would be classified incorrectly, yielding an 'apparent error rate' of $7/40 = 17.5\%$. Because the two samples are relatively small, this estimate of the true error rate may be far too optimistic. To obtain a more reliable estimate, it would be better to use a 'holdout' or 'jackknife' method; see, for example, Section 10.6 in Johnson and Wichern (1982) for a good introduction to this technique. We will return to this problem in Exercise 15 of Chapter 12.

Two additional critical remarks are in order regarding this application of discriminant analysis. First, since three variables are binary, the data can clearly not be multivariate normal. In such a situation, the linear discriminant

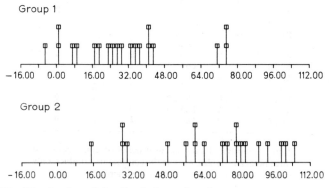

Figure 7.22 Distribution of the discriminant function

function is theoretically not satisfactory, although it may perform well in practical situations. It is beyond the scope of this book to introduce special methods of discrimination in mixed binary-continuous situations; the interested reader is referred to Krzanowski (1975) or to Chapter 12 in the recent book by the same author (Krzanowski, 1988).

The second critical remark refers to the use of discriminant analysis in situations like the one described here. Actually in this example the two groups were not pre-determined, and group membership itself is a binary random variable. In such cases the investigator may be mostly interested in estimating the probability of 'improvement' or 'no improvement', respectively, given the data of a person. Although this can be done using discriminant analysis techniques, a more appealing solution is provided by the so-called method of *logistic regression*. Both discriminant analysis and logistic regression tend to give similar results in practice, but the latter enjoys the advantage of being less affected by non-normality. Let p_i denote the probability of improvement (or recovery) of the ith person, and $1 - p_i$ the probability of no improvement. Then logistic regression estimates the so called log-odds

$$h_i = \log \frac{p_i}{1 - p_i}$$

as a linear function of the measured variables. See, for example Chapter 12 of Afifi and Clark (1984) for an easily readable introduction to logistic regression.

8

Identification analysis

8.1 INTRODUCTION

As observed at the end of the preceding chapter, the properties of forged bills are usually not known beforehand. A discriminant function which is optimal for certain groups of forgeries may be completely worthless for detecting the blossoms of another forger. What we need, then, is a method which is aimed at the 'unknown enemy': a bill is to be compared with the standard found on genuine bills and, on the basis of this comparison, is to be associated with the group of genuine bills, or else to be rejected. This procedure is called identification.

Let us first consider the univariate case and denote by $\bar{x}$ and s the mean and standard deviation, respectively, of a sample of size n. Let x denote the value of a new, additional observation. Then a reasonable criterion for allocation of x to the sample, or rejection of x, may be based on the difference between x and $\bar{x}$. By the same arguments as in Chapter 2 we prefer to use the *standard distance*

$$D = |x - \bar{x}|/s,$$

which gives the absolute difference in units of the standard deviation. We may then reject the new observation if D exceeds some critical level.

Under normality assumptions, a possible criterion is to reject the new observation if

$$|t| = D \cdot \sqrt{\frac{n}{n+1}}$$

exceeds the $(1 - \alpha/2)$-quantile of the t-distribution with $n - 1$ degrees of freedom. This rule is simply a t-test for samples of size $n_1 = n$ and $n_2 = 1$.

The key idea behind identification should now be clear from these univariate considerations: look at the identification problem as a special case of comparing two means or mean vectors – with one sample consisting of only one observation!

8.2   IDENTIFICATION ANALYSIS AS A SPECIAL CASE OF DISCRIMINANT ANALYSIS

The definition of the p-variate standard distance between an observation and the mean vector of a sample is completely analogous to that given in Chapter 7. Define D_p as the maximum (univariate) standard distance that can be obtained from any linear combination of the p variables. The particular linear combination that maximizes the distance is simply a discriminant function for the case $n_1 = n$ and $n_2 = 1$. We will call it the *identification function* (or identification variable) and denote it by

$$IDF = b_0 + b_1 X_1 + \cdots + b_p X_p.$$

All results of Chapter 7 can be carried over to the identification function, but some formulae can be simplified due to $n_2 = 1$. The Fisher code, for instance, is $c_1 = 1/(n+1)$ for the n elements of the sample, and $c_2 = -n/(n+1)$ for the additional observation, but again, there is no compelling reason why this code should be preferred over any other code that seems convenient to the user. Two convenient codes are $c_1 = 0$, $c_2 = 1$ and $c_1 = 0$, $c_2 = 100$.

Since the tests for redundancy of variables given in Chapter 7 are valid for any n_1, n_2, we can again use regression F-tests for testing the redundancy of variables. If the additional observation is rejected rather than allocated to the sample, the regression technique easily gives more information about the importance of variables or combinations of variables for the rejection. We will illustrate this in Section 8.4.

Here are the simplified formulae for identification analysis. The p-variate standard distance is computed from the coefficient of determination R_p^2 as

$$D_p = \sqrt{\left(\frac{n^2 - 1}{n} \cdot \frac{R_p^2}{1 - R_p^2} \right)}.$$

The overall test of significance is based on the statistic

$$F = \frac{n(n - p)}{p(n^2 - 1)} D_p^2,$$

which is distributed as F with p and $n - p$ degrees of freedom under the null hypothesis that the additional observation is from the same population as the sample. The test for redundancy of $p - q$ variables is based on

$$F = \frac{n - p}{p - q} \cdot \frac{D_p^2 - D_q^2}{(n^2 - 1)/n + D_q^2},$$

with $p - q$ and $n - p$ degrees of freedom. Again, these F-statistics are exactly identical with those obtained from the regression approach.

Denoting by $\bar{y}$ the sample mean, by y the value of the additional observation, and by s^2 the variance of the identification variable, we get furthermore the equalities

$$R_p^2 = \frac{y - \bar{y}}{c_2 - c_1}$$

$$s^2 = \frac{n}{n^2 - 1}(c_1 - c_2)^2 R_p^2 (1 - R_p^2)$$

and

$$\bar{y} = c_1 - \frac{1}{n+1}(c_1 - c_2)(1 - R_p^2)$$

$$y = c_2 + \frac{n}{n+1}(c_1 - c_2)(1 - R_p^2).$$

These formulae are especially simple if the two code values differ by unity. This is the case, for instance, for Fisher code, but another extremely simple code is $c_1 = 0$ and $c_2 = 1$.

8.3   MORE ABOUT STANDARD DISTANCE

Before turning to applications of identification analysis, we would like to compare the notion of standard distance with the more familiar Euclidean distance, and then discuss further properties of standard distance. As before, we will first consider the two-dimensional case in order to let geometric intuition help us to understand things more clearly.

Denote the coordinates of a plane by x and z, and let $P_1 = (x_1, z_1)$ and $P_2 = (x_2, z_2)$ be two arbitrary points in the plane. The *Euclidean distance* between P_1 and P_2 is then

$$D_{\text{Euclid}} = \sqrt{(x_2 - x_1)^2 + (z_2 - z_1)^2}.$$

Now let (x_0, z_0) be a fixed point. All points (x, z) having the same distance c from (x_0, z_0) satisfy the equation

$$(x - x_0)^2 + (z - z_0)^2 = c^2.$$

This is the equation of a circle with radius c about the center (x_0, z_0). Figure 8.1 shows a scatterplot of the genuine bills in the variables BOTTOM and TOP. A cross indicates the bivariate mean

$$(\bar{x}_4, \bar{x}_5) = (8.305; \; 10.168)$$

of the scatterplot. The circles trace points of equal distance to the centre, $(\bar{x}_4, \bar{x}_5)$. Let us take a special look at bill no. 5 with the values $(x_{45}, x_{55}) = (10.4; 7.7)$. This bill stands out by the fact that it lies rather far away from the mean, yet in the direction of the main axis of the elliptically shaped point cluster.

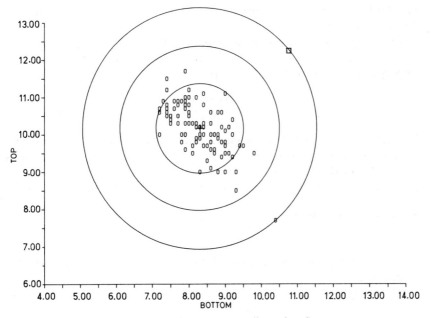

Figure 8.1 Euclidean distance to the mean (two-dimensional)

According to the above formula, the Euclidean distance of this point to the mean is

$$D_{\text{Euclid}} = \sqrt{(10.4 - 8.305)^2 + (7.7 - 10.168)^2} = 3.237.$$

The outermost cricle in Fig. 8.1 describes all points which have the same Euclidean distance 3.237 to the centre. Suppose we now imagine a new bill whose pair of values (x_4, x_5) also lies on the circle, but not in the direction of the main axis of the ellipse described above. It is marked in Fig. 8.1 with a square. This new fictitious bill also has the same Euclidean distance to the centre as does bill no. 5. Nevertheless, we will hardly be willing to count it among the group of genuine bills, because in some sense it is further away from the centre than bill no. 5.

From these considerations it is now clear that a statistically adequate measure of distance must somehow respect the standard deviations and the correlation between the two variables. This is exactly what distinguishes standard distance from Euclidean distance. From the definition of multivariate standard distance we know that it is obtained from a projection that maximizes the univariate standard distance. In Fig. 8.1 the approximate direction of this projection for the fictitious note is quite clear, and obviously the fictitious bill will have a larger bivariate standard distance than bill no. 5.

For the two-dimensional case it is possible to give an explicit formula for the standard distance, which we are going to use for illustrating the relationship to Euclidean distance.

For simplicity of notation we denote the bivariate mean by $(\bar{x}, \bar{z})$ Furthermore, s_x^2, s_z^2 and c_{xz} denote the variances and the covariance, respectively. For a point (x, z) the bivariate standard distance from $(\bar{x}, \bar{z})$ is then

$$D_2 = \sqrt{\left[\frac{(x - \bar{x})^2 s_z^2 - 2(x - \bar{x})(z - \bar{z})c_{xz} + (z - \bar{z})^2 s_x^2}{s_x^2 s_z^2 - c_{xz}^2}\right]}$$

The distance of bill no. 5 to the mean, using the appropriate statistics from Tables 2.1 and 3.3, thus computes to $D_2 = 3.96$. The distance of the fictitious note becomes $D_2 = 8.23$, which is remarkably larger. We now examine the distance formula a little more closely, and make the following observations:

1. In the special case $s_x = s_z = 1$ and $c_{xz} = 0$ the formula simplifies to

$$D_2 = \sqrt{[(x - \bar{x})^2 + (z - \bar{z})^2]} = D_{\text{Euclid}}$$

   In this special case, the standard distance is identical with the Euclidean distance.

2. If we only assume $c_{xz} = 0$ (uncorrelatedness), then the formula becomes

$$D_2 = \sqrt{\left[\left(\frac{x - \bar{x}}{s_x}\right)^2 + \left(\frac{z - \bar{z}}{s_z}\right)^2\right]}.$$

   In this case, the standard distance can be interpreted as the Euclidean distance for standardized variables.

3. From the two preceding remarks one can see that the essential change over the Euclidean distance measure lies in accounting for the correlation.

We can now ask for the set of all points which, for given means and given covariance matrix, have the same standard distance

$$D_2 = c \text{ (constant)}$$

from the mean.

Rewriting the above definition of D_2, we thus get

$$\frac{s_z^2}{s_x^2 s_z^2 - c_{xz}^2}(x - \bar{x})^2 - 2\frac{c_{xz}}{s_x^2 s_z^2 - c_{xz}^2}(x - \bar{x})(z - \bar{z}) + \frac{s_x^2}{s_x^2 s_z^2 - c_{xz}^2}(z - \bar{z})^2 = c^2$$

This is the equation of an ellipse. Figure 8.2 shows the same point cluster as Fig. 8.1, but this time with concentric ellipses indicating different standard distances to the centre. It is quite obvious that this way of measuring distances deals better with the situation than does the Euclidean distance. In particular, the fictitious note is now far outside the ellipse passing through bill no. 5.

The generalization to $p > 2$ dimensions, in the case of the Euclidean distance, leads to spheres and hyperspheres as the sets of all points with a fixed

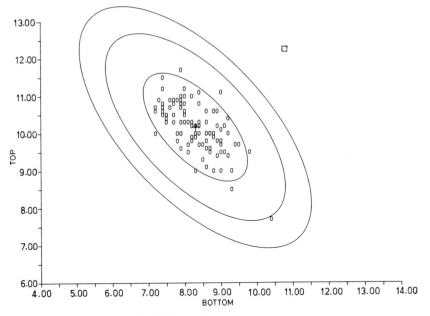

Figure 8.2   Bivariate standard distance from the mean

distance to a given point. While the equation of a spherical surface is very simple in higher dimensions, the p-dimensional standard distance can practically no longer be represented without the help of matrix algebra. To the ellipse in the two-dimensional case there corresponds for $p = 3$ an ellipsoid. In higher dimensions we speak of hyperellipsoids.

The notion of standard distance can be applied numerically to any multivariate data, but the foregoing considerations show that it is especially appropriate for data that appear elliptical in p-dimensional space. Indeed, in multivariate statistical theory, the so-called elliptical distributions play an important role. If we denote the density function of a p-variate distribution by $f(x_1, \ldots, x_p)$, then an elliptical distribution is characterized by the fact that sets of constant density c, i.e. sets defined by the equation $f(x_1, \ldots, x_p) = c$, are ellipsoids. The most prominent member of the family of elliptical distributions is – what a surprise! – the multivariate normal. As an illustration, go back to Fig. 7.8 and chop off the top of a 'mountain' by a horizontal cut. The resulting plane is elliptically shaped.

For the multivariate normal distribution we know the following useful result on the distribution of D_p: The squared standard distance D_p^2 of an observation from the mean is distributed approximately as chi square with p degrees of freedom. This is an asymptotic result, i.e. the approximation is better the larger the sample size n. Since the expected value of a chi squared variable on p degrees of freedom is p, we get a very simple rule of thumb for identification analysis: the standard distance of an observation is expected to be around $\sqrt{p}$, and only standard distances considerably above $\sqrt{p}$ will indicate potential outliers. For large n, we may also base a decision on the comparison of D_p^2 with quantiles of the chi square distribution instead of using the overall F-test. The two criteria are asymptotically equivalent.

The squared standard distance D_p^2 usually bears the name *Mahalanobis distance* in the multivariate literature, in honour of the famous Indian statistician. Although D_p and D_p^2 are mathematically equivalent, we prefer D_p since it seems closer to our everyday notion of distance than its square.

A final remark on standard distance concerns discriminant analysis. The classification rule described in Section 7.6 is equivalent to the rule that an observation is to be allocated to the group to whose mean it has the smaller standard distance. This fact is especially helpful in the case of nonlinear discriminant analysis, since we do not need to compute the quadratic equation which defines the two classification areas.

8.4 IDENTIFICATION OF A BANK NOTE

The following six measurements are those of another bill whose genuineness is doubtful. We assign the number 205 to this bill. The measured values are:

No.	LENGTH	LEFT	RIGHT	BOTTOM	TOP	DIAGONAL
205	214.9	130.5	130.2	8.4	11.6	138.4

We perform an identification analysis of bill no. 205 versus the 100 genuine bills, using the regression technique. With the code $c_1 = 0$ (for the real notes) and $c_2 = 100$ (for note no. 205), we obtain the identification function shown in Table 8.1. From the formulae in Section 8.2, we get the following statistics for

Table 8.1 Identification function of bill no. 205

Variable	Coefficient	Standard error	Partial F
(intercept)	1575.67		
LENGTH	− 0.12	2.51	0.002
LEFT	− 2.37	3.37	0.50
RIGHT	1.43	3.28	0.19
BOTTOM	1.13	2.02	0.31
TOP	1.32	2.00	0.44
DIAGONAL	− 10.24	1.76	33.79

$R_6^2 = 0.3330$ $D_6 = 7.065$

the identification function: $\bar{y} = 0.660$ (mean of the genuine notes), $y = 33.96$ (value of bill no. 205), and $s = 4.713$ (standard deviation of the identification function). Bill no. 205 is 7.065 ($= D_6$) standard deviations away from the mean of the genuine notes.

Either by the analysis of variance table of the regression program, or by the formula of Section 8.2, we get the statistic $F = 7.82$ for the overall test. The 95%

Table 8.2 Backward elimination in the identification analysis of no. 205 vs 100 genuine bills

Variable	Coefficient	Standard error	Partial F
Step 2: elimination of LENGTH			
(intercept)	1559.99		
LEFT	−2.40	3.29	0.53
RIGHT	1.41	3.21	0.19
BOTTOM	1.11	1.98	0.32
TOP	1.31	1.97	0.44
DIAGONAL	−10.26	1.71	35.83
$R_5^2 = 0.3330$ $D_5 = 7.065$			
Step 3: elimination of RIGHT			
(intercept)	1629.68		
LEFT	−1.59	2.71	0.34
BOTTOM	1.28	1.94	0.44
TOP	1.43	1.94	0.54
DIAGONAL	−10.23	1.71	35.98
$R_4^2 = 0.3317$ $D_4 = 7.045$			
Step 4: elimination of LEFT			
(intercept)	1415.29		
BOTTOM	0.75	1.71	0.19
TOP	0.94	1.75	0.29
DIAGONAL	−10.11	1.69	35.90
$R_3^2 = 0.3293$ $D_3 = 7.007$			
Step 5: elimination of BOTTOM			
(intercept)	1456.52		
TOP	0.44	1.32	0.11
DIAGONAL	−10.32	1.61	41.05
$R_2^2 = 0.3279$ $D_2 = 6.984$			
Step 6: elimination of TOP			
(intercept)	1486.15		
DIAGONAL	−10.50	1.51	48.14
$R_1^2 = 0.3272$ $D_1 = 6.973$			

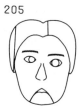

205

Figure 8.3   Face of bill no. 205

quantile of the F-distribution with 6 and 94 degrees of freedom is 2.2, and so the decision clearly is to reject the new bill.

The high partial F-value of DIAGONAL already leads one to suspect that the main reason for rejection comes from this variable. In order to corroborate this suspicion, we perform a backward elimination, which yields the results in Table 8.2. The successive behaviour of R_p^2 and D_p shows clearly, that for the rejection of bill no. 205 the variable DIAGONAL suffices. As identification function we can in this case, of course, simply take $IDF = X_6$.

Now a question of interest is whether perhaps bill no. 205 comes from the same forger as the bill nos. 101 to 200. An identification analysis of no. 205 against the group of forged bills yields the identification function

$$IDF = 204.85 - 1.01X_1 + 3.24X_2 - 0.96X_3 - 1.53X_4 - 0.72X_5 - 1.87X_6$$
$$(3.21) \quad (5.36) \quad (4.49) \quad (1.45) \quad (2.31) \quad (2.17)$$

where the numbers in brackets are the standard errors of the respective coefficients. The overall F is 0.90 with 6 and 94 degrees of freedom. On the basis of this F-value there is thus no reason to assume that bill no. 205 would come from a different forger.

Figure 8.3 shows the face of bill no. 205. A comparison with the mean faces of the two groups (Fig. 7.12) once again shows the strong deviation from the group of genuine bills in the variable DIAGONAL (mouth, fairness of the hair).

8.5   ANALYSIS OF OUTLIERS

In histograms, scatterplots and face plots we have occasionally paid attention to extreme values, and we have been asking whether these observations should be considered as outliers. We have also remarked that it would not necessarily be correct to declare an observation as an outlier merely because of an extreme value in one variable. The notion of multivariate standard distance now gives us a tool for measuring the deviation of an observation from the mean in several variables simultaneously. The identification function, on the other hand, can be used to describe with respect to which variables an observation is extreme.

Of course, a large standard distance does not strictly prove that the

Table 8.3 Identification analyses of bills no. 1, 5, 40 and 70 vs the remaining 99 genuine bills

Variable	Analysis of no. 1		Analysis of no. 5		Analysis of no. 40		Analysis of no. 70	
	coeff.	std. error	coeff.	std. error	coeff.	std. error	coeff.	std. error
(intercept)	−617.99		309.28		1196.11		1348.54	
LENGTH	−6.36	(2.67)	0.35	(2.81)	−7.87	(2.69)	−0.24	(2.74)
LEFT	4.92	(3.60)	−3.97	(3.78)	15.11	(3.63)	−4.57	(3.69)
RIGHT	12.53	(3.50)	1.92	(3.68)	−10.89	(3.53)	5.27	(3.58)
BOTTOM	−2.59	(2.16)	2.81	(2.27)	−1.86	(2.18)	−0.46	(2.21)
TOP	−4.27	(2.14)	−3.97	(2.24)	−2.99	(2.15)	0.59	(2.19)
DIAGONAL	−1.50	(2.19)	−0.70	(2.30)	−0.05	(2.21)	−9.82	(2.25)
R_6^2	0.2479		0.1701		0.2368		0.2116	
D_6	5.71		4.50		5.54		5.15	

questionable observation stems from a different population. Analysing the identification function, however, may give us some hints about possible causes for the large distance. We are going to illustrate this by examples.

From among the hundred genuine bills we pick the numbers 1, 5, 40 and 70, which have caught our attention in the chapter on face plots, and we perform an identification analysis of each of them against the 99 remaining genuine bills. Since we did not know before inspecting the data that these four bills would look 'suspicious', it would be unwise to analyse them in the sense of a statistical test for allocation or rejection. The analyses are therefore carried out in a purely descriptive sense. Table 8.3 gives the identification function (with standard errors of the coefficients in brackets) for each of these four notes, together with the coefficients of determination and the standard distances. In all four analyses the regression approach was used with $c_1 = 0$ and $c_2 = 100$. A quick glance at the table shows that most of the identification function coefficients are unstable in the sense of high standard errors. In a stepwise elimination procedure the identification function of no. 5 can be reduced without much loss of information to either variable TOP or BOTTOM. The univariate standard distance of no. 5 in TOP is 4.14, which is not much smaller than the multivariate distance $D_6 = 4.50$. The location of no. 5 in the scatterplot of BOTTOM and TOP (Fig. 3.13) shows that the position of the print image within this note is very high.

Similarly, the distance $D_6 = 5.15$ of bill no. 70 is mostly due to variable DIAGONAL, with a univariate standard distance of 4.78.

It is left to the reader to verify the above statements about bills no. 5 and 70 by performing the two identification analyses, using a regression program and the stepwise elimination procedure.

The analyses of bills no. 1 and 40 are more interesting and will now be given in more detail. Figure 8.4 depicts the change of standard distance in a backward elimination procedure for the identification function of no. 1. If we stop in step 5, we get the simplified identification function for no. 1,

$$\text{IDF}_1 = -421.90 - 6.46 \text{ LENGTH} + 13.97 \text{ RIGHT},$$
$$\qquad\qquad (2.57) \qquad\quad (2.80)$$

with $R_2^2 = 0.2058$ and $D_2 = 5.06$. Evidently the variables RIGHT and LENGTH are mainly responsible for the large standard distance of $D_6 = 5.71$. Why LENGTH? The value of no. 1 in LENGTH is 214.8, which is close to the mean! In the scatterplot of LENGTH and RIGHT (Fig. 3.2), however, the importance of LENGTH becomes clear if we draw the ellipses of equal standard distance.

In contrast to LENGTH, variable LEFT is eliminated from the identification function (in step 4), even though no. 1 appears extreme when viewed in LEFT alone. As Fig. 3.6 shows, the reason for this lies in the fact that the point $(x_{21}, x_{31}) = (131.0, 131.1)$ is located close to the main axis of the elliptically shaped point cluster. In this situation the value of LEFT yields almost no

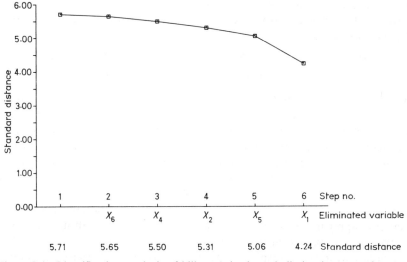

Figure 8.4   Identification analysis of bill no. 1, backward elimination procedure

additional information, given that the value of RIGHT is known. We conclude that no. 1 was cut too wide, and since the values of the other variables (especially LENGTH) are not extraordinarily large, we can probably exclude a systematic error in the measurement of this bill.

For the identification analysis of no. 40 versus the remaining 99 genuine bills, Fig. 8.5 shows the change of standard distance in a stepwise elimination

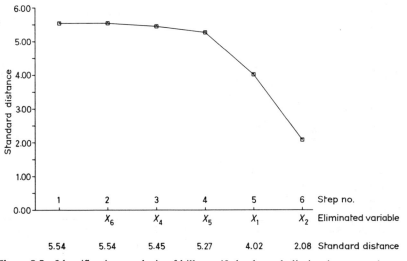

Figure 8.5   Identification analysis of bill no. 40, backward elimination procedure

procedure. The decline in steps 5 (elimination of LENGTH) and 6 (LEFT) is striking. If we decide to stop after step 4, we get the simplified identification function for no. 40,

$$IDF_{40} = 1448.12 - 8.12 \text{ LENGTH} + 13.62 \text{ LEFT} - 11.34 \text{ RIGHT},$$
$$(2.61) \qquad\qquad (3.38) \qquad\qquad (3.47)$$

with $R_3^2 = 0.2193$ and $D_3 = 5.27$. The decline of the standard distance in step 6 can be explained by the location of bill no. 40 in the scatterplot of LEFT and RIGHT (Fig. 3.6), where it appears rather far away from the main axis of the point cluster. This is an example of an observation which turns out to be very extreme only when viewed in several dimensions: a bill that came out too short, and was cut obliquely. We do not know whether a measurement error may also have occurred.

Sometimes it is helpful to look at an identification function more closely by actually applying it to the data and plotting the resulting frequency distribution. It may occur that some observations are close to the 'outlier', in which case we might be suspicious of a subgroup instead of just a single outlier. In our example, we apply the simplified identification functions IDF_1 and

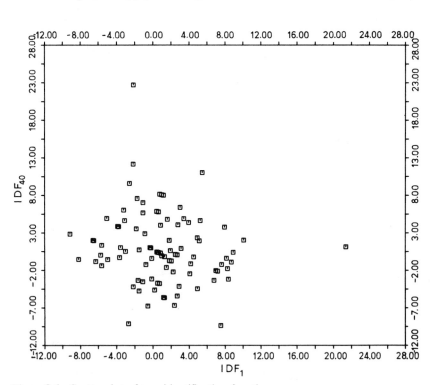

Figure 8.6 Scatterplot of two identification functions

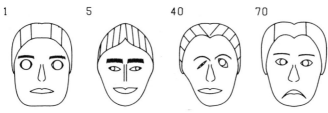

Figure 8.7   Four suspicious faces

IDF_{40} to the data and show the bivariate distribution of these two variables for all 100 genuine bills in form of a scatterplot (Fig. 8.6). Both bills (no. 1 and no. 40) are clearly 'standing out' with no close neighbours. Moreover, IDF_1 and IDF_{40} are almost uncorrelated, thus showing that bills no. 1 and 40 are distant observations in different directions of the six-dimensional space.

Finally, a comparison of the above interpretations with the face plots in Chapter 4 shows that we were able to corroborate the observations made there. Figure 8.7 once again shows the faces of the four bills.

DISCUSSION

Question:
Can one always assume that the additional observation to be identified comes from a model with the same covariance matrix as the known sample?
Answer:
The assumption of equality of both covariance matrices cannot be checked here, since from a sample of size 1 we do not obtain estimates of variances and covariances, i.e. the method relies only on the covariance matrix of the known group. However, there is no reason to worry about this point. A large standard distance simply indicates that the questionable observation may not come from the same population or model as the known sample. It doesn't matter whether the population it comes from has a different mean vector or larger variability.

Question:
In the identification analysis of bill no. 205 against the 100 genuine bills, is the variable DIAGONAL solely responsible for rejection? Could the negative decision be derived also from the five remaining variables?
Answer:
To answer this question, we must carry out an identification analysis of no. 205 against the group *Genuine* without the variable DIAGONAL. This analysis yields the identification function

$$IDF_{205} = 327.78 - 3.16X_1 + 0.71X_2 + 1.35X_3 + 3.79X_4 + 5.38X_5$$
$$\phantom{IDF_{205} = 327.78 - }(2.84)\quad(3.85)\quad(3.80)\quad(2.28)\quad(2.17)$$

with an overall F of 1.95, $R_5^2 = 0.0933$ and $D_5 = 3.21$. Clearly, variable DIAGONAL is mostly responsible for the large distance of $D_6 = 7.065$, and a rejection could not be based on X_1 to X_5 alone.

Question:
When we talked about regression, you promised to tell us what 'leverage' is in the chapter on identification analysis!?

Answer:
Sorry, we almost forgot! The leverage is a measure of *potential influence* of an observation on the parameter estimates, and it is computed from the regressors alone (i.e. the dependent variable is not used for determining leverage). Leverage is related to standard distance as follows:

$$v_i = \frac{1}{n} + \frac{D_p^2(i)}{n-1},$$

where v_i is the leverage of the ith observation, $D_p(i)$ is the p-variate standard distance of the ith observation (using the p regressors), and n is the sample size. Clearly, leverage is mathematically equivalent to standard distance.

Question:
Why did you always use the code $c_1 = 0$ and $c_2 = 100$ in this chapter, and not, for instance, Fisher's code or $c_1 = 0$ and $c_2 = 1$?

Answer:
If we use $c_1 = 0$, $c_2 = 1$, then all identification function coefficients would be smaller by a factor of 100, which means that we would need to give them to four decimal digits after the decimal point. With the code used in this chapter, the identification functions are somehow more 'readable'.

FURTHER STUDY

The book by Hawkins (1980) entitled *Identification of Outliers* contains a chapter on multivariate outliers, the overall F-test being given in the equivalent form of the T^2-criterion. Hawkins discusses also applications of principal component analysis to the analysis of outliers. Gnanadesikan (1977) proposes interesting graphical methods. See also the review article by Bekman and Cook (1983). Identification analysis as discussed in this chapter has first been proposed by Riedwyl and Kreuter (1976).

Software

To our knowledge, there is no special software for identification analysis. Any good program for multiple regression can be used.

Table 8.4 Five variables measured on 50 switch drums. See text and figure 8.8 for a description of the variables. Data courtesy of U. Kreuter, Consult AG, Berne.

X_1	X_2	X_3	X_4	X_5
20	8	13	9	7
20	12	17	12	11
15	7	9	7	2
16	12	14	13	8
20	12	16	13	9
16	10	15	10	8
16	10	12	10	5
20	11	15	11	8
18	10	14	12	9
19	11	14	11	7
21	7	11	7	4
17	10	12	10	6
19	10	14	10	8
18	12	14	12	7
15	10	12	12	7
14	10	12	11	6
21	10	14	10	7
19	10	13	11	7
17	9	13	9	6
19	11	15	11	9
17	8	13	9	7
17	11	14	11	8
18	7	13	8	7
19	11	15	11	9
16	9	11	9	6
15	11	16	12	9
17	10	16	11	11
20	9	12	10	7
18	13	15	14	10
20	12	15	14	10
16	10	12	10	6
20	11	15	13	9
17	11	13	12	7
18	11	13	13	8
16	10	15	11	8
18	6	12	8	6
19	14	16	16	13
17	12	16	13	12
18	13	16	14	12
17	8	13	10	10
15	8	11	10	8
22	9	13	9	8
18	10	13	12	9
17	13	15	14	12
16	10	12	10	8
20	12	17	12	12
20	11	15	12	11
19	11	14	11	8
20	11	14	12	11
18	11	14	12	10

EXAMPLES

Example 8.1 Quality inspection of switch drums

This application of identification analysis to quality control is due to Kreuter (1975, pp. 71–73). Five variables have been measured on a lot consisting of 50 switch drums. The data are given in Table 8.4. As in the electrodes example at the end of Chapter 7, all measurements are in $mm \cdot 10^{-3}$, and the raw data have been transformed by subtracting suitable constants from the measurements. Figure 8.8 describes the variables X_1 to X_5 on a cross-section of a switch drum. We will refer to the 50 items of Table 8.4 as the 'reference sample', and compare two new items with it.

Table 8.5 displays univariate and bivariate summary statistics for the

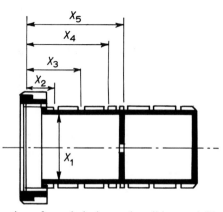

Figure 8.8   Cross-section of a switch-drum, describing variables X_1 to X_5 used in Example 8.1 (Courtesy of U. Kreuter, Consult AG, Berne.)

Table 8.5 Summary statistics for the sample of 50 switch drums, and data of two additional items

Variable	Mean	Standard deviation	Correlation matrix					Data of two additional items no. 51	no. 52
X_1	17.96	1.86	1.00	0.14	0.35	0.08	0.27	18	13
X_2	10.30	1.71	0.14	1.00	0.73	0.91	0.69	12	9
X_3	13.76	1.71	0.35	0.73	1.00	0.68	0.82	15	12
X_4	11.08	1.87	0.08	0.91	0.68	1.00	0.76	13	12
X_5	8.26	2.21	0.27	0.69	0.82	0.76	1.00	12	7

reference sample, as well as the data taken on two additional switch drums that were produced later. We will compute an identification function for each of these two additional items versus the reference sample.

The two identification functions (with standard errors of the coefficients given in brackets) are as follows.

Item no. 51:

$$IDF_{51} = 18.50 - 0.29X_1 + 2.49X_2 - 2.84X_3 - 2.45X_4 + 3.51X_5.$$
$$(1.19) \quad (3.29) \quad (2.42) \quad (3.15) \quad (1.88)$$

Item no. 52:

$$IDF_{52} = 23.05 - 1.82X_1 - 6.72X_2 + 1.37X_3 + 6.77X_4 - 1.64X_5.$$
$$(1.05) \quad (2.87) \quad (2.24) \quad (2.73) \quad (1.78)$$

The multivariate standard distances based on all five variables are $D_5 = 2.24$ for item no. 51, and $D_5 = 3.93$ for item no. 52. The overall F-statistics are $F = 0.90$ (item no. 51) and $F = 2.79$ (item no. 52). For comparison, the 95% quantile of the F-distribution with 5 and 45 degrees of freedom is 2.43. So, at a significance level of 5%, we would reject item no. 52. Item 51, on the other hand, would clearly be accepted. Indeed, its standard distance $D_5 = 2.24$ is almost exactly what one would expect from the rule of thumb given in Section 8.3: if the additional observation comes from the same population as the reference sample, then its multivariate standard distance would roughly be expected around $\sqrt{p}$, where p is the number of variables.

Although the identification function of item 51 must be regarded as pure noise, we can use it to illustrate a phenomenon that may look paradoxical at first sight. Figure 8.9 shows a scatterplot of IDF_{51} versus IDF_{52}. Item 52, marked by a triangle, appears quite distant from the reference sample, as was to be expected. But also item 51, marked by a black dot, appears at the very margin of the point cluster. This seems to be a contradiction to the former statement that the standard distance of item no. 51 is about average. To solve the paradox, let us make some short remarks on high dimensional geometry. Imagine, for instance, a cube in p-dimensional space. If p equals 2, the cube is a square and the number of corners is 4. For $p = 3$, the number of corners is 8, and it doubles with each additional dimensions. So, in our five-dimensional case, the number of corners of the five dimensional cube is 32. Suppose now that we have a set of 32 five-dimensional observations, each of them corresponding exactly to a corner of a five-dimensional cube. Obviously, each of the 32 points is at the margin of the five-dimensional scatterplot. If we make an appropriate projection into one-dimensional space (i.e. compute an identification function), we should not be surprised to find that the respective point looks relatively extreme. In our case, we have 50 instead of 32 points in five-dimensional space, but nevertheless these considerations should give

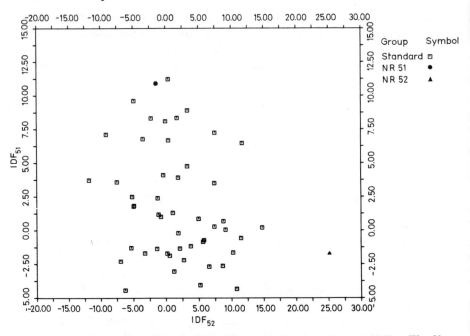

Figure 8.9   Scatterplot of the two identification functions IDF$_{51}$ and IDF$_{52}$. The 50 items of the reference sample are marked by squares. Items no. 51 and 52 are marked by a black dot and by a triangle, respectively

some intuition why just looking at the identification function (without a formal statistical test) may be misleading.

Let us return to a more detailed analysis of item no. 52. Three of the five identification function coefficients in IDF$_{52}$ have relatively large standard errors, so the elimination procedure was used to identify those variables which are mostly responsible for the rejection. After elimination of X_3 and X_5, the simplified identification function is

$$IDF_{52} = 36.34 - 1.94X_1 - 5.84X_2 + 5.43X_4,$$
$$\quad\quad\quad (0.95)\quad\;\; (2.51)\quad\;\; (2.26)$$

with a standard distance of $D_3 = 3.78$. The next variable to be eliminated is X_1, with a partial F of 4.14. The identification function based on X_2 and X_4 alone is then

$$IDF_{52} = 4.56 - 7.23X_2 + 6.46X_4,$$
$$\quad\quad\quad (2.49)\quad\;\; (2.28)$$

with a standard distance of $D_2 = 3.01$. Looking back to the data of item no. 52 in Table 8.4, this is a rather surprising result. Indeed, the values of item 52 in variables X_2 and X_4 are close to the respective means, the univariate standard distances being 0.76 and 0.49. The large bivariate standard distance is explained by the strong correlation between X_2 and X_4; see exercise 16 in Chapter 12. On the other hand, the value of item 52 in variable X_1 is 13, which corresponds to a univariate standard distance of 2.67. Nevertheless, the joint contribution of the two 'unsuspicious' variables X_2 and X_4 is larger than the univariate contribution of X_1. This demonstrates again the advantage of the multivariate approach to the identification of outliers.

9

Specification analysis

9.1 STANDARD DISTANCE BETWEEN A SAMPLE AND A HYPOTHETICAL MEAN VECTOR

In Chapter 7 we presented a method for analysing differences in location between two samples. In certain situations, however, especially in quality control, we may wish to compare the mean of a single sample with a pre-specified hypothetical mean (called specification). From univariate analysis such a method is well known: the one-sample t-test. Let $\bar{x}$ and s denote the (univariate) mean and standard deviation of a sample of size n, and let μ_0 be the specification. Then the familiar one-sample t-statistic for testing the hypothesis that μ_0 is the population mean is

$$t = \frac{\bar{x} - \mu_0}{s}\sqrt{n}.$$

If the hypothesis is true, and under normality assumptions, this statistic is distributed as t with $n-1$ degrees of freedom.

As in Chapter 2, we describe the difference between $\bar{x}$ and μ_0 by the *standard distance*

$$D = \frac{|\bar{x} - \mu_0|}{s},$$

which is related to t by $|t| = D.\sqrt{n}$. Obviously this definition of standard distance is formally the same as in identification analysis – with the extra observation x replaced by μ_0! (The transformation to a t-statistic, however, is not the same.)

For the multivariate case, we need a vector of p specified values, $\mu_0 = (\mu_{01}, \mu_{02}, \ldots, \mu_{0p})$, which is also called the *hypothetical mean vector*. The multivariate standard distance D_p between μ_0 and the sample mean vector is then defined as the maximum (univariate) standard distance that can be obtained from any linear combination of the p variables. The particular linear combination for which the maximum is attained is called the *specification function*, and we will denote it by

$$Y(\text{or SPF}) = b_0 + b_1 X_1 + \cdots + b_p X_p.$$

The specification function is in fact the same as the identification function for the point μ_0, but we name it differently in order to stress the fact that μ_0 is a hypothetical, fixed point in p-dimensional space rather than an observation.

Thanks to this analogy to identification analysis we can again use the multiple regression technique for computing D_p and the specification function, the values of μ_0 being formally the $(n + 1)$th observation. The n observations in the sample are labelled with the code c_1, while the specification vector is coded as c_2. Again we 'estimate' the code by linear regression. The regression function coefficients thus obtained define a linear combination which is equivalent to the specification function. With R_p^2 denoting the coefficient of determination from the regression approach, we can use the relationship

$$D_p = \sqrt{\left[\frac{n^2 - 1}{n} \cdot \frac{R_p^2}{1 - R_p^2} \right]}$$

to compute the multivariate standard distance between the sample mean vector and the specification vector. By applying the specification function to the sample, we get n values $y_1, \ldots, y_n$, whose mean and variance we denote by $\bar{y}$ and s^2. Furthermore, applying the specification function to the hypothetical mean vector μ_0 yields a value

$$y_0 = b_0 + b_1 \mu_{01} + \cdots + b_p \mu_{0p}.$$

In complete analogy to identification analysis, the following equalities hold:

$$R_p^2 = \frac{y_0 - \bar{y}}{c_2 - c_1}$$

$$s^2 = \frac{n}{n^2 - 1}(c_1 - c_2)^2 R_p^2 (1 - R_p^2)$$

and

$$\bar{y} = c_1 - \frac{1}{n + 1}(c_1 - c_2)(1 - R_p^2)$$

$$y_0 = c_2 + \frac{n}{n + 1}(c_1 - c_2)(1 - R_p^2).$$

Again, for 'simple' codes like $c_1 = 0$, $c_2 = 1$ or $c_1 = 0$, $c_2 = 100$, these formulae are especially simple.

To test the hypothesis that the specification vector μ_0 is the population mean vector, we can use

$$F = \frac{n(n - p)}{p(n - 1)} D_p^2.$$

(Note that this F-statistic differs from the corresponding F in identification analysis by a factor $1/(n + 1)$). Under normality assumptions, this statistic is distributed as F with p and $n - p$ degrees of freedom if the hypothesis is true. Sometimes an equivalent of the F-statistic is used,

$$T^2 = \frac{p(n-1)}{n-p}F = nD_p^2,$$

as was originally proposed by the eminent statistician H. Hotelling. Since tables of the F-distribution are readily available, we prefer to use the F-statistic. Hotelling's T^2 is of course the multivariate equivalent of the (squared) univariate t-statistic.

The test for redundancy of variables is based on

$$F = \frac{n-p}{p-q} \cdot \frac{D_p^2 - D_q^2}{\dfrac{n-1}{n} + D_q^2},$$

with $p - q$ and $n - p$ degrees of freedom.

Since the regression F-tests are correct for the identification analysis case, they can obviously no longer be correct here. Nevertheless, once the standard distances D_p and D_q have been calculated, it is very easy to compute the correct F-statistics by the above formulae.

Alternatively, correct F-statistics can be computed from those obtained with the regression approach (called F_{reg} from now on) as follows: for the overall test of significance, the relation is simply

$$F = (n+1)F_{\text{reg}}.$$

The correction for the test for redundancy of $p - q$ variables is

$$F = \frac{n+1}{nR_q^2 + 1}F_{\text{reg}},$$

where R_q^2 is the coefficient of determination associated with the model with q variables. Both formulae follow from a comparison of the correct F-statistics with those given in Section 8.2. It is worth noting that the degrees of freedom associated with the F_{reg}-statistics are the same as those of the correct F-statistics, although F_{reg} itself needs to be modified.

These correction formulae can easily be built into an existing regression program, or the corrections can be done with a pocket calculator. If R_q^2 is not directly available (as is normally the case for partial F-statistics, i.e. for $q = p - 1$), it can be obtained from the associated F_{reg} as

$$R_q^2 = R_p^2 - \frac{(p-q)(1-R_p^2)}{n-p}F_{\text{reg}}.$$

The R_q^2 thus obtained is then put into the correction formula for F.

If a regression program with uncorrected partial F-statistics is used, the forward selection and backward elimination procedures still yield a correct order or selection. The stopping criterion, however, must generally be modified.

In addition to the partial F-statistics, the standard errors of the specification function coefficients need to be corrected, too. Once the corrected partial Fs have been obtained, the easiest way of computing corrected standard errors is by the formula (cf. Section 5.9).

$$s(b_j) = \frac{|b_j|}{\sqrt{[F(\beta_j = 0)]}},$$

i.e. the absolute value of the coefficient divided by the square root of its partial F.

9.2 SPECIFICATION ANALYSIS OF THE BANK NOTES

We are now going to apply the methodology of Section 9.1 to the real bank notes. What is the hypothetical mean vector? From the artist's design of the bill, the specifications were obtained and are listed in the first row of Table 9.1.

The specification for DIAGONAL follows from the specifications of the width and height of the inner print image (cf. Fig. 1.1), which are 126 and 66, respectively. By the Pythagorean theorem we have thus $\sqrt{(126^2 + 66^2)} =$ 141.354 as the specification for DIAGONAL. Figure 9.1 shows the face of the hypothetical mean. It looks quite similar to many of the real faces.

The univariate standard distances between specification and sample mean range between 0.080 (LENGTH) and 1.081 (BOTTOM), as is shown in the last row of Table 9.1. To compute the multivariate standard distance, we used the regression technique with the code values $c_1 = 0$ (for the 100 genuine bills) and $c_2 = 100$ (for the specification). Table 9.2 shows the results thus obtained. Additional columns to the regression output show the correction factors for each partial F, the corrected partial F-statistics and the corrected standard errors.

From $R_6^2 = 0.0227$ we compute the multivariate standard distance D_6 $= 1.52$. The overall F from the regression approach is multiplied by the factor $n + 1 = 101$ to obtain the correct overall $F = 36.68$ on 6 and 94 degrees of freedom. This value is highly significant, and we conclude therefore that the mean of the production process deviates from the specification given in the artist's design.

Which variables are mainly responsible for the significance of the specification function? To answer this question we used a backward elimination procedure, starting with the full model (Table 9.2) as step 1. Table 9.3 gives the numerical results for steps 2 to 6. Only the corrected partial Fs and the corrected standard errors are listed, but not their uncorrected counterparts.

Table 9.1 Specifications and univariate standard distances for the real bank notes

Variable	LENGTH	LEFT	RIGHT	BOTTOM	TOP	DIAGONAL
Specification	215	130	130	9	10	141.354
Sample mean	214.969	129.943	129.720	8.305	10.168	141.517
Standard deviation	0.3876	0.3641	0.3553	0.6428	0.6490	0.4470
Standard distance	0.080	0.157	0.788	1.081	0.259	0.365

Table 9.2 Specification function of the genuine bank notes

Variable	Output of the regression program			Additional computations			
	Specification fct. coeff.	Standard error	Partial F_{reg}	R_5^2	Correction factor	Partial F, corrected	Standard error, corrected
(intercept)	223.90						
LENGTH	−0.89	3.03	0.0854	0.0218	31.80	2.72	0.537
LEFT	−2.79	4.07	0.4685	0.0178	36.36	17.03	0.676
RIGHT	2.90	3.96	0.5350	0.0171	37.29	19.95	0.648
BOTTOM	2.53	2.43	1.0797	0.0114	47.14	50.90	0.355
TOP	1.24	2.42	0.2615	0.0199	33.74	8.82	0.417
DIAGONAL	−0.56	2.49	0.0507	0.0221	31.44	1.59	0.444

$R_6^2 = 0.0227$ $D_6 = 1.522$

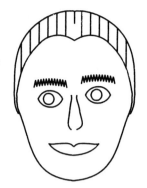

Figure 9.1   Face of the specification

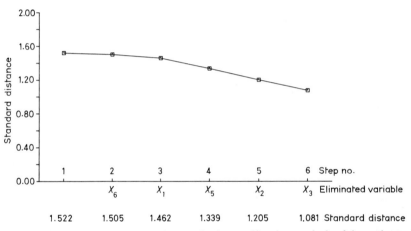

Figure 9.2   Change of standard distance in the specification analysis of the real notes

Figure 9.2 illustrates the decrease of the standard distance during the elimination procedure. This figure as well as the corrected partial Fs suggest that we should stop in step 3 and use the simplified specification function

$$\text{SPF(real)} = -5.26 - 2.84\,\text{LEFT} + 2.63\,\text{RIGHT} + 2.51\,\text{BOTTOM} + 1.32\,\text{TOP}$$
$$\phantom{\text{SPF(real)} = }(0.62)\qquad(0.62)\qquad\quad(0.31)\qquad\qquad(0.38)$$

where the numbers in brackets are the corrected standard errors. To compare the models with six variables and with four variables, respectively, we can use the F-statistic from Section 9.1 and get $F = 2.8$ on 2 and 94 degrees of freedom. Since this is smaller than the corresponding 95% – quantile (approximately 3.1), we conclude that the reduction in standard distance from 1.522 to 1.462 is not significant, and regard LENGTH and DIAGONAL as redundant in the specification function.

Table 9.3 Backward elimination in the specification analysis of the real notes

Variable	Coefficient	Standard error, corrected	Partial F, corrected
Step 2: elimination of DIAGONAL			
(intercept)	151.02		
LENGTH	-1.01	0.52	3.76
LEFT	-2.63	0.66	15.85
RIGHT	2.87	0.64	20.16
BOTTOM	2.62	0.33	61.70
TOP	1.38	0.39	12.59
$R_5^2 = 0.0221$ $D_5 = 1.505$			
Step 3: elimination of LENGTH			
(intercept)	-5.26		
LEFT	-2.84	0.62	20.63
RIGHT	2.63	0.62	17.96
BOTTOM	2.51	0.33	59.16
TOP	1.32	0.38	11.97
$R_4^2 = 0.0209$ $D_4 = 1.462$			
Step 4: elimination of TOP			
(intercept)	-114.29		
LEFT	-2.12	0.58	13.61
RIGHT	2.92	0.56	27.32
BOTTOM	1.53	0.22	48.78
$R_3^2 = 0.0176$ $D_3 = 1.339$			
Step 5: elimination of LEFT			
(intercept)	-208.29		
RIGHT	1.52	0.43	12.75
BOTTOM	1.44	0.20	50.40
$R_2^2 = 0.0143$ $D_2 = 1.20$			
Step 6: elimination of RIGHT			
(intercept)	-12.83		
BOTTOM	1.66	0.15	116.90
$R_1^2 = 0.0116$ $D_1 = 1.081$			

Figure 9.3 shows the distribution of variable SPF for all 100 genuine bills. Mean and variance of the specification function can either be computed from the 100 values of SPF, or more directly by the formulae of Section 9.1. We get $\bar{y} = 0.969$ (sample mean of the 100 genuine notes), $s^2 = 2.051$ (variance of the specification function), and $y_0 = 3.064$ (value of the hypothetical mean in the specification function). The latter is marked with an arrow in Fig. 9.3. Although it is well within the range covered by the real notes, the sample mean is almost $1\frac{1}{2}$ standard deviations away from the specification ($D_4 = 1.46$).

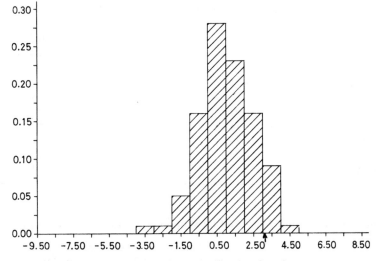

Figure 9.3 Frequency distribution of the specification function

A closer look at the specification function sheds some light on possible causes of the fact that the mean of the production does not match the specification exactly. The main reason seems to be that the mechanism used to cut the notes produces, on the average, a height that is smaller than the specified value of 130. This would also explain the fact that the sum of the two margin widths (BOTTOM + TOP) is, on the average, smaller than its specification – provided that the size of the print image was reproduced with high accuracy.

Some care should be taken, however, in interpreting the specification function. As was noticed in Chapter 2, for the majority of the genuine bills LEFT is larger than RIGHT, and we cannot completely exclude the possibility of a small systematic error in measuring the bank notes. (Recall that the measurements were actually taken on enlarged projections.) Nevertheless, the fact that LEFT is most often larger than RIGHT, while the specification claims that both should be equal, is nicely represented by the fact that the two variables appear in the specification function essentially in the form of their difference. This reflects the fact that the 'typical' bill has a negative value of RIGHT − LEFT.

How good is the forger's production, compared with the specification? Well, let's see! A short glance at the forged mean vector (Table 2.1) and the specified values (Table 9.1) shows that for some variables the forged notes are quite far off. Using the regression approach with code values 0 and 100 we obtained the specification function listed in Table 9.4.

The multivariate standard distance is indeed very large: $D_6 = 7.34$. Since the coefficient of LENGTH, LEFT and RIGHT seem rather unstable, we used again an

Table 9.4 Specification function of the forged notes

Variable	Coefficient	Standard error, corrected	Partial F, corrected
(intercept)	214.01		
LENGTH	− 1.86	1.58	1.38
LEFT	− 2.09	2.65	0.62
RIGHT	− 4.18	2.18	3.66
BOTTOM	− 5.73	0.41	192.97
TOP	− 8.29	0.76	119.77
DIAGONAL	8.27	0.66	155.62

$R_6^2 = 0.3502$ $D_6 = 7.34$

elimination procedure. The resulting simplified specification function is

$$\text{SPF(forged)} = -259.36 - 5.74\,\text{RIGHT} - 5.48\,\text{BOTTOM} - 8.03\,\text{TOP}$$
$$\qquad\qquad\quad (1.61)\qquad\quad (0.38)\qquad\quad (0.74)$$
$$+\,8.28\,\text{DIAGONAL}$$
$$(0.58)$$

with $R_4^2 = 0.3434$ and $D_4 = 7.23$. It is left to the reader to compute the F-statistic for redundancy of LENGTH and LEFT, based on the values of D_6 and D_4.

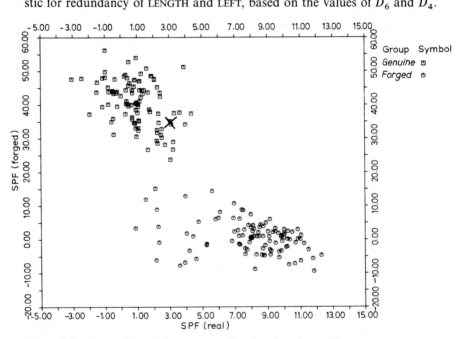

Figure 9.4 Scatterplot of the two specification functions. The group means are marked by black dots and the specification is marked by a cross

Obviously the forger's production doesn't match the specification too well. This is surprising, since we got a rather good impression of the forger's art so far. The reason for this seeming contradiction is probably that the specifications of the real notes are *not* the ones actually used by the forger! What specifications did he use then? We don't know the answer to this question, but most probably he just copied an arbitrary genuine bill as accurately as possible, and it may well have happened that this bill was actually a rather extreme one within the set of genuine notes. In this sense it is 'unfair' to compare the forged bills with the same specifications as the real bills.

Figure 9.4 shows a scatterplot of the variables SPF(real) and SPF(forged) for all 200 bills. The means of both groups as well as the position of the specification are marked in this plot. It is clearly visible that the hypothetical mean lies well within the group of real notes, but far outside the group of forged notes. This explains also why the specification function of the forged notes is so similar to the two-group discriminant function found in Section 7.5.

9.3 CONFIDENCE REGIONS FOR A MEAN VECTOR

In the specification analysis of the genuine notes we have seen that they do not match their specification (μ_0) too well. It is therefore natural to ask *which* specifications the data would fit. In other words, the question is: for which values of μ_0 would the overall F-test tell us to accept the hypothesis that μ_0 is the population mean vector?

Let us first repeat the univariate case. In a two-sided t-test, the hypothesis that μ_0 is the population mean is accepted if

$$|t| = \frac{|\bar{x} - \mu_0|}{s}\sqrt{n}$$

does not exceed $t_{1-\alpha/2}$, the upper $\alpha/2$-quantile of the t-distribution with $n-1$ degrees of freedom. The hypothesis would thus be accepted for all μ_0 such that

$$|\mu_0 - \bar{x}| \geqslant t_{1-\alpha/2}\cdot\frac{s}{\sqrt{n}}.$$

The set of all numbers μ_0 satisfying this condition is the so called *confidence interval*

$$(\bar{x} - t_{1-\alpha/2}s/\sqrt{n} \ , \ \bar{x} + t_{1-\alpha/2}s/\sqrt{n}).$$

That is, the acceptance region of the hypothesis is an interval of length $2t_{1-\alpha/2}s/\sqrt{n}$ symmetric to $\bar{x}$. Another interpretation of the interval is that it covers the true population mean with probability $1-\alpha$.

For generalizing the univariate confidence interval to the multivariate case we proceed analogously, but use the overall F-statistic of Section 9.1 instead of the t-statistic. The overall F-test accepts the hypothesis that μ_0 is the population mean vector if

$$F = \frac{n(n-p)}{p(n-1)} D_p^2$$

does not exceed $F_{1-\alpha}$, the $(1-\alpha)$ quantile of the F-distribution with p and $n-p$ degrees of freedom. In other words, the hypothesis would be accepted for all vectors μ_0 with a sufficiently small standard distance D_p from the sample mean vector, i.e. with

$$D_p \leqslant \sqrt{\left[\frac{p(n-1)}{n(n-p)} F_{1-\alpha} \right]}.$$

From Section 8.3 we know that the set of all points having a fixed standard distance from the sample mean vector is a hyperellipsoid, or an ellipse in the bivariate case. Thus the above inequality defines a region of elliptical shape, centered at the sample mean! This elliptical *confidence region* covers the true population mean vector with probability $1-\alpha$.

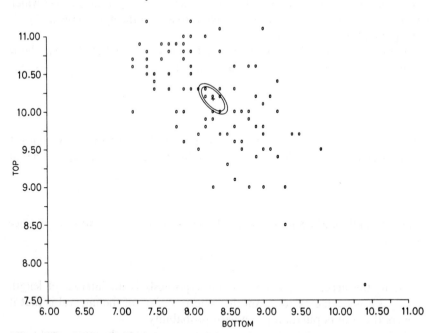

Figure 9.5   95% and 99% confidence ellipses for the mean of BOTTOM and TOP, real notes

Let us illustrate this for the bivariate case. Figure 9.5 shows a scatterplot of the 100 genuine bank notes in variables BOTTOM and TOP. For a 95% confidence region, for instance, we need the 95% quantile of F with 2 and 98 degrees of freedom: $F_{0.95}(2, 98) = 3.09$. The 95% confidence region is the set of all points in two-dimensional space with a standard distance smaller than $\sqrt{((2 \cdot 99 \cdot 3.09)/(100 \cdot 98))} = 0.250$. Similarly, from $F_{0.99}(2,98) = 4.83$ we can obtain a 99% confidence region, which is bounded by the standard distance 0.312. These 95% and 99% confidence regions are marked in Fig. 9.5 by two ellipses. The specification (9, 10) of BOTTOM and TOP is clearly far outside even the larger ellipse.

Since hyperellipsoids are geometrically more complicated objects than intervals, the question naturally arises whether there is any advantage of the multivariate approach over univariate confidence intervals. To answer this question, suppose that in the example of Fig. 9.5 two univariate 99% confidence intervals were used instead of the 99% confidence ellipse. Since the 99.5% quantile of the t-distribution with 99 degrees of freedom is approximately 2.63, the confidence intervals are (8.136, 8.474) for BOTTOM and (9.997, 10.339) for TOP. These two intervals, considered simultaneously, define a rectangular area in the plane. This area is shown in Fig. 9.6 together with the 99% confidence ellipse. From Fig. 9.6 we can now clearly see the shortcomings of the univariate approach. First, the rectangular area is *not* a 99% confidence

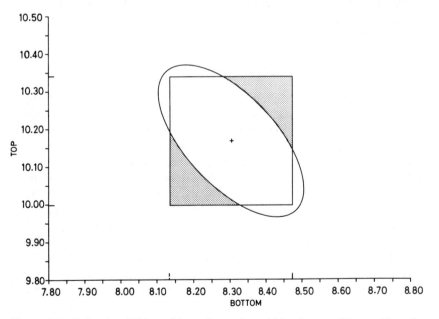

Figure 9.6 Univariate 99% confidence intervals and bivariate confidence ellipse for the means of BOTTOM and TOP, real notes

region. If the two variables were independent, then the rectangular area would cover the true population mean with probability $(0.99)^2 = 98.01\%$, but for correlated variables this is not true. Second, the univariate approach does not reflect the fact that the variables – and thus their sample means – are correlated!

The advantage of the multivariate approach is greater the higher the variables are correlated, because the confidence ellipse tends to become quite narrow with increasing correlation. The area covered by the rectangle, but not by the ellipse (the shaded area in Fig. 9.6) may then become rather large. This leads to the fact that points that would not be suspicious in univariate analyses may well be far outside the elliptical confidence region obtained from the multivariate approach. In our example with variables BOTTOM and TOP, the point (8.4, 10.3), for instance, is outside the 99% confidence ellipse, but inside both univariate 99% confidence intervals.

These considerations reflect the fact that in the presence of dependencies between the variables multivariate tests are in general more powerful than univariate tests. In particular it is important to know about the 'shaded area' in Fig. 9.6: if p specified values lie all within their confidence intervals, they may still lie far outside the p-variate confidence region! For quality control this has the consequence that controlling each of p variables individually may not be sufficient. It is also intuitively clear that this effect is more distinct the higher p, the dimension, is: for p highly correlated variables the 'shaded area' may actually cover most of the p-dimensional rectangular region defined by the univariate confidence intervals.

9.4   A MORE GENERAL MODEL*

As we have seen in the preceding sections, specification analysis is surprisingly similar to identification analysis – in fact, the two methods are computationally identical, except for the corrections that need to be applied to the F-statistics and standard errors. Thus the question naturally arises whether these two methods are merely special cases of a more general technique. This is indeed the case! To explain the more general model, let us go back to the two-sample case, with samples of size n_1 and n_2. In contrast to the usual two-groups situation as it was treated in Chapter 7, we assume now that in sample 2 the raw data got lost, and everything that is left is the sample mean vector and the sample size (n_2). This means essentially that no information about variability is available from the second group. Yet we can still compute a discriminant function and a standard distance between the two samples by using the same approach as in identification or specification analysis, with the additional

---

*This section may be skipped at the first reading

observation replaced by the mean vector of sample 2! Using R_p^2, the coefficient of determination from the regression, we can thus compute a multivariate standard distance as

$$D_p = \sqrt{\left(\frac{n_1^2 - 1}{n_1} \cdot \frac{R_p^2}{1 - R_p^2}\right)}.$$

This is, of course, the same formula as the one given in Section 9.1, with n replaced by n_1.

It is again possible to construct tests for significance of variables in the discriminant function, based on standard distance. The statistic for the overall hypothesis of equality of the two population mean vectors is

$$F = \frac{n_1 n_2 (n_1 - p)}{p(n_1 - 1)(n_1 + n_2)} D_p^2,$$

and its distribution under the null hypothesis is F with p and $n_1 - p$ degrees of freedom. For the test of redundancy of $p - q$ variables, the appropriate statistic is

$$F = \frac{n_1 - p}{p - q} \cdot \frac{D_p^2 - D_q^2}{\dfrac{(n_1 + n_2)(n_1 - 1)}{n_1 n_2} + D_q^2},$$

the associated degrees of freedom being $p - q$ and $n_1 - p$. Both statistics are based on the assumptions of multivariate normality and equality of the covariance matrices in both populations.

Why is this a more general model than both identification and specification analysis? Well, identification analysis is obviously a special case of the above model, namely for $n_2 = 1$. And if we consider the hypothetical mean vector μ_0 as the sample mean of an 'infinite' sample, then specification analysis is again a special case, namely for $n_2 = \infty$. It is left to the reader to verify that the F-statistics given above reduce indeed to the respective statistics from Sections 8.2 and 9.1, if we put $n_2 = 1$ or $n_2 = \infty$, respectively.

As for specification analysis, the F-statistics computed with the regression approach have the correct number of degrees of freedom, but need to be multiplied with a correction factor. Let F_{reg} denote a regression F-statistic for redundancy of $p - q$ variables, then the correction formula is

$$F = \frac{(n_1 + 1)n_2}{n_1 + n_2 + n_1(n_2 - 1)R_q^2} F_{reg}.$$

For the overall test, the correction factor simplifies to $(n_1 + 1)n_2/(n_1 + n_2)$. It is again left to the reader to check that the correction factor is exactly 1 in the case $n_2 = 1$ (identification analysis), and identical with the correction factor given in Section 9.1 in the case $n_2 = \infty$ (specification analysis).

Using the corrected partial F-statistics, corrected standard errors can again be obtained by the formula

$$s(b_j) = \frac{|b_j|}{\sqrt{[F(\beta_j = 0)]}}.$$

Since in the bank note example the raw data from both samples are available, the general method of this section has no direct application, but we will illustrate it by an anthropometric example at the end of this chapter.

Let us summarize the facts that our reader should memorize from this section: even if the raw data from one of two samples are not available, it is still possible to compute a discriminant function and to test hypotheses about it. While the general situation of 'only the mean available in one group' is not likely to occur very often in practice, the general model has considerable theoretical importance, since it covers identification analysis and specification analysis as the special cases $n_2 = 1$ and $n_2 = \infty$, respectively. The importance of these two methods justifies the names 'identification function' and 'specification function' that we have given to the discriminant function in these two special cases.

9.5 SPECIFICATION FACES

Since specification analysis is especially useful in quality control, we would like to close this chapter with an application of face plots to quality control. In contrast to specification analysis, faces are rather apt to detect individual outliers than differences between means, and in this sense face plots are closer to identification analysis than to specification analysis. The reason for presenting this application here is a rather interesting way of using the specified values. The basic idea is to use symmetry such that an item which is close to the specifications appears as symmetric. This is realized by plotting each face with one face half being entirely defined by the specifications, while the second face half shows the actual measurements taken on an item. The 'specification halves' of all faces are thus identical.

In the bank note example we used the specification vector (215, 130, 130, 9, 10, 141.354) to draw the right face halves. The ranges (a_j, b_j) to be mapped to the standard interval (0, 1) were chosen for each variable as specification ± 1. For variable LENGTH, for instance, the range is 214 to 216, and so on. The standard face defined by $z_j = 0.5$ for all parameters corresponds therefore exactly to the specifications.

Figure 9.7 shows the assignments of variables to face parameters. As in Chapter 4, related variables were assigned to related parts of the face – for instance, BOTTOM and TOP are mapped to the hair, LEFT and RIGHT to the eyes. The assignments are, however, not identical with those of Chapter 4.

Figure 9.8 shows the specification faces of the first 25 real and forged notes.

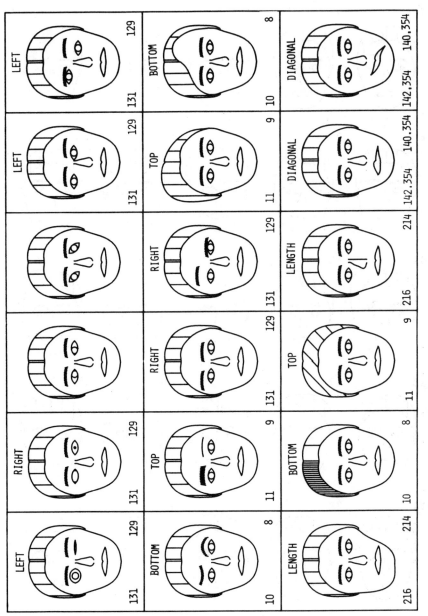

Figure 9.7 Assignments of variables to face parameters for the specification faces

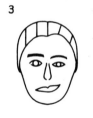
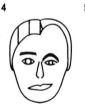

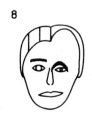
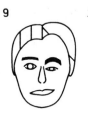

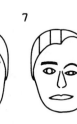

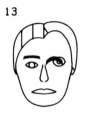
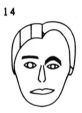
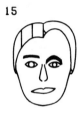
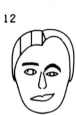

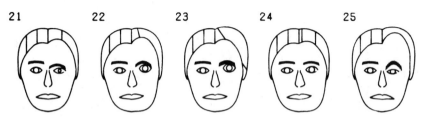

Figure 9.8 Specification faces of 25 real and 25 forged bank notes

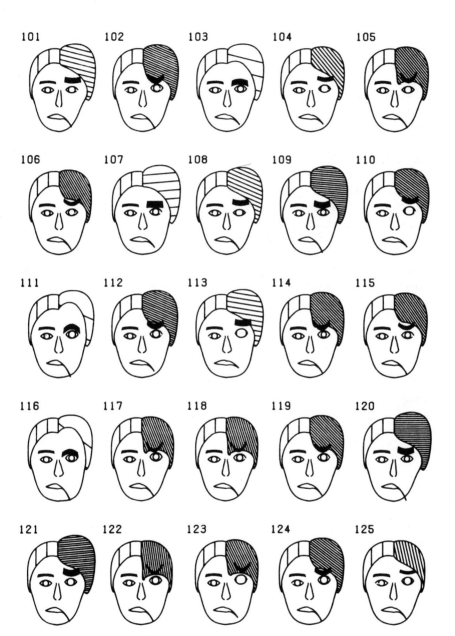

While the forged notes appear all very unsymmetric, there are also some suspicious guys among the real ones, such as no. 5. The typical real face has a rather unsymmetric haircut, due to the fact that the lower margin (BOTTOM) is most often too narrow. Faces no. 8 and 13, which have not appeared as extreme so far, are particularly asymmetric. Indeed, they take the values -1.49 and -1.96, respectively, in the specification function. That is, they appear in the left tail of the distribution of SPF(real) – see Fig. 9.3.

Specification faces might be a useful tool in quality control. An industrial production process could be supervised by one or several faces drawn permanently on a screen. Simultaneous changes in the production process would then appear simultaneously in the face, and a trained supervisor could easily detect 'unfamiliar' faces and identify potential causes for the trouble.

For defining the standard ranges in the face plot, we need, of course, some idea what variability is 'normal' for each variable. This brings us to an aspect that we have not yet considered sufficiently: the covariance structure of the data. In a production process, one would normally like the variability to be as small as possible. So far we have been looking at linear combinations that tell us about mean differences and standard distances. It is now time to turn to linear combinations that give us more information about the covariance structure of the p variables – for instance projections with very large or very small variance. This will be done in the following chapter.

FURTHER STUDY

The overall test for the hypothesis that the specification vector μ_0 is the mean vector of a population appears in the multivariate literature as T^2-test for the one sample case; see any multivariate textbook. The test for redundancy of variables is probably due to Rao (1970); see also Mardia, Kent and Bibby (1979, Section 3.6). The model of Section 9.4, as well as applications of multiple regression to T^2-tests, have been discussed by Flury and Riedwyl (1985).

Software

The standard statistical program libraries can be used to compute the overall T^2-statistic. Since, to our knowledge, no special software for the specification function is available, we recommend use of a regression program.

EXAMPLES

Example 9.1 Cork deposits on trees

The data used in this example are taken from Rao (1948). The four variables N, E, S and W denote measurements of the thickness of cork deposits in four directions, taken on $n = 28$ trees. The raw data are displayed in the first four columns of Table 9.5. An interesting question is, whether the trees grow, on the average, equal amounts of cork in all four directions. We will therefore test the hypothesis

$$H_0: \mu_N = \mu_E = \mu_S = \mu_W.$$

Notice that this null hypothesis implies that the four means are equal, without specifying their common value.

This testing problem can be attacked with specification analysis as follows: the hypothesis H_0 is true exactly if the three equalities $\mu_N = \mu_E, \mu_E = \mu_S$ and $\mu_S = \mu_W$ hold simultaneously. Taking differences between pairs of variables, H_0 can be stated equivalently as

$$H_0': \mu_E - \mu_N = \mu_S - \mu_E = \mu_W - \mu_S = 0.$$

Table 9.5 Data matrix of the cork example. The last column contains the code used as the dependent variable. The last row contains the three hypothetical mean differences. See text for a description of the variables. Source of raw data: Rao (1948).

N	E	S	W	DIFF$_1$	DIFF$_2$	DIFF$_3$	Code
72	66	76	77	−6	10	1	0
60	53	66	63	−7	13	−3	0
56	57	64	58	1	7	−6	0
41	29	36	38	−12	7	2	0
32	32	35	36	0	3	1	0
30	35	34	26	5	−1	−8	0
39	39	31	27	0	−8	−4	0
42	43	31	25	1	−12	−6	0
37	40	31	25	3	−9	−6	0
33	29	27	36	−4	−2	9	0
32	30	34	28	−2	4	−6	0
63	45	74	63	−18	29	−11	0
54	46	60	52	−8	14	−8	0
47	51	52	43	4	1	−9	0
91	79	100	75	−12	21	−25	0
56	68	47	50	12	−21	3	0
79	65	70	61	−14	5	−9	0
81	80	68	58	−1	−12	−10	0
78	55	67	60	−23	12	−7	0
46	38	37	38	−8	−1	1	0
39	35	34	37	−4	−1	3	0
32	30	30	32	−2	0	2	0
60	50	67	54	−10	17	−13	0
35	37	48	39	2	11	−9	0
39	36	39	31	−3	3	−8	0
50	34	37	40	−16	3	3	0
43	37	39	50	−6	2	11	0
48	54	57	43	6	3	−14	0
				0	0	0	100

Hence we can consider the three variables

$$DIFF_1 = E - N$$
$$DIFF_2 = S - E$$
$$DIFF_3 = W - S$$

and test whether the means of these three variables are zero! (Of course one might prefer another triple of differences, for instance $N - S$, $E - W$ and $N - W$. This problem will be discussed as an exercise in Chapter 12).

The fifth to seventh columns of Table 9.5 show the values of the three newly defined variables, on which the analysis is to be performed. Also, a 29th row has been added to the data matrix, containing the values $(0, 0, 0)$ of the hypothetical mean vector. Since we are using the regression approach, the data matrix contains also an eighth column with the values of the code variable: 0 for the trees, 100 for the hypothetical mean vector. The specification function thus obtained is given in Table 9.6, together with the corrected standard errors and corrected partial F-statistics computed from the formulae of Section 9.1. The overall F_{reg} from the regression approach is 0.2208. Multiplied by the correction factor $n + 1 = 29$, this yields a corrected overall F of 6.4 with 3 and 25 degrees of freedom, which is significant at the 1% level. The standard distance is $D_3 = 0.86$.

A closer look at Table 9.6 gives some additional information: the coefficient of $DIFF_2$ is relatively small, compared to the other two coefficients as well as to its standard error. After elimination of $DIFF_2$, the following specification function is obtained (corrected standard errors are given in brackets)

$$SPF = 5.5167 + 0.2242 \ DIFF_1 + 0.2590 \ DIFF_3.$$
$$(0.0998) \qquad (0.1027)$$

The standard distance is now $D_2 = 0.7826$. Writing $DIFF_1$ and $DIFF_3$ in terms of the original variables N, E, S and W, the specification function can also be written as

$$SPF = 5.5167 + 0.2242E + 0.2590W - 0.2242N - 0.2590S.$$

Table 9.6 Specification analysis of the cork data

Variable	Specification function coeff.	Partial F, uncorrected	Standard error, corrected	Partial F, corrected
(intercept)	5.9400			
$DIFF_1$	0.3761	0.3320	0.1413	7.08
$DIFF_2$	0.1803	0.1125	0.1262	2.04
$DIFF_3$	0.3496	0.3862	0.1191	8.61

Coefficient of determination: $R_3^2 = 0.0258$
Standard distance: $D_3 = 0.86$

The closeness of the coefficients suggests another simplification: if the coefficients of $DIFF_1$ and $DIFF_3$ were equal, then the specification function would simply be the contrast

$$DIFF_4 = DIFF_1 + DIFF_3 = (E + W) - (N + S),$$

that is, a comparison between the east-west axis and the north-south axis. The univariate standard distance of $DIFF_4$ is $D_1 = 0.7804$. Since equating two coefficients is a linear restriction, $D_2 = 0.7826$ and $D_1 = 0.7804$ can be compared using the F-test for redundancy given in Section 9.1. This yields $F = 0.057$ on 1 and 26 degrees of freedom, which is clearly not significant.

In conclusion, it appears that the cork deposits differ between the four directions. Since the sample mean of the contrast $E + W - N - S$ is 8.86, we conclude that the cork deposits along the north–south axis tend to be larger than those along the east–west axis.

We will return to this example in Exercise 17 of Chapter 12.

Example 9.2 Anthropometric measurements taken on two ethnic groups in Tibet

In 1966, Prince Peter of Greece and Denmark published a report on anthropometrical studies he had performed during an expedition to central Asia (Peter, 1966). The honourable Prince reported means of several anthropometric variables taken on individuals of different ethnic groups in Tibet. However, being unaware of multivariate statisticians' needs, Prince Peter did not publish the raw data, nor did he compute variances or correlations. Hence we are left without information about variability. The different ethnic groups in Prince Peter's report can be compared only in a purely descriptive manner, unless we are willing to make assumptions regarding the variances and covariances.

Nonetheless, if we wish to compare means or mean vectors from Prince Peter's study with a sample for which full information (i.e. the raw data) is available, we are in the situation of the general model of Section 9.4! We are now going to illustrate this using data collected by Mullis (personal communication, 1982) on $n_1 = 44$ adult men from central Tibet. This sample will be compared with the vector of means reported by Peter (1966) for $n_2 = 51$ adult males of the north-eastern race Amdo. The five variables used are stature (ST), length of the head (LH), width of the head (WH), width of the zygomatic arch (WZA), and morphological facial height (MEH). The data of Mullis are given in Table 9.7. Table 9.8 displays summary statistics for both samples. The largest univariate standard distance is attained for variable WZA.

To compute a discriminant function between the two groups, the mean vector from Prince Peter's sample was added to Table 9.7 as a 45th row. The regression approach with code values 0 (sample 1) and 100 (mean vector of sample 2) gave the results displayed in Table 9.9. Corrected partial F-statistics and corrected standard errors were obtained using the formulae of Section 9.4.

Table 9.7 Five anthropometrical variables measured on 44 male adult Tibetans. All measurements are in cm. See text for a description of the variables. Data courtesy of M.L. Mullis-Glowatzki, University of Berne.

ST	LH	WH	WZA	MFH
164.7	19.3	15.3	14.6	12.4
154.6	19.2	15.8	15.7	12.2
179.4	20.0	14.9	14.4	13.1
165.9	18.8	16.4	15.1	12.9
163.8	19.3	15.2	15.0	11.9
166.1	19.5	15.7	15.2	12.3
169.8	18.8	15.7	14.9	12.8
168.2	19.1	15.2	14.5	12.6
171.4	20.1	15.3	14.6	12.8
163.8	19.7	14.3	14.2	12.9
170.6	20.1	14.5	14.2	13.0
175.1	19.7	14.5	14.2	13.7
166.3	19.6	15.8	14.8	12.2
166.9	19.1	15.7	14.7	12.0
165.4	19.1	14.5	14.2	12.6
159.7	19.3	14.5	14.3	12.1
168.0	19.5	15.8	14.8	13.2
159.1	19.4	15.6	14.5	12.5
162.3	19.2	14.6	14.1	11.9
165.5	19.3	15.3	14.6	12.5
167.2	19.0	15.4	14.3	11.4
159.6	19.0	15.4	14.3	13.5
174.3	19.4	16.2	15.8	12.9
169.0	19.1	16.2	15.0	12.1
154.5	17.8	14.9	14.3	11.3
175.4	19.3	16.2	15.4	11.8
167.1	19.2	15.8	14.6	13.0
161.2	18.8	15.1	14.2	10.9
161.2	19.7	16.0	15.2	12.5
147.5	18.2	15.5	14.6	12.5
163.1	19.3	16.3	15.5	12.1
160.9	18.8	16.0	14.7	13.0
156.9	18.4	15.3	13.9	12.6
162.1	19.0	15.9	14.6	12.6
167.9	19.7	15.6	15.3	13.6
166.0	18.8	15.8	14.6	12.2
166.1	18.8	15.1	13.8	14.1
162.9	19.2	15.5	14.5	11.6
156.8	18.6	14.6	14.0	11.2
162.7	18.6	14.6	13.6	11.7
156.1	19.5	14.8	14.5	12.6
164.3	19.6	15.2	14.8	12.4
166.4	19.7	15.7	14.4	13.5
171.0	20.1	15.8	15.2	13.7

Table 9.8 Summary statistics for Example 9.2

Variable	Correlation matrix[†]					Mean[†]	Standard[†] deviation	Mean[‡]	Univariate standard distance
ST	1	0.600	0.132	0.209	0.358	164.70	6.106	166.68	0.32
LH	0.600	1	−0.015	0.296	0.437	19.22	0.494	19.08	0.28
WH	0.132	−0.015	1	0.749	0.089	15.40	0.564	15.07	0.59
WZA	0.209	0.296	0.749	1	0.073	14.63	0.493	14.07	1.14
MFH	0.358	0.437	0.089	0.073	1	12.51	0.708	12.11	0.56
	ST	LH	WH	WZA	MFH				

[†] Data from Mullis (personal communication)
[‡] Data from Peter (1966)

Table 9.9 Computation of the discriminant function in Example 9.2

	Regression output			Additional computations		
Variable	Coefficient	Partial F	Degrees of freedom	Correction factor for partial F	Partial F, corrected	Standard error, corrected
(intercept)	46.22					
ST	0.29	0.3400	1,39	12.04	4.10	0.14
LH	0.81	0.0123	1,39	11.03	0.14	2.16
WH	3.15	0.1944	1,39	11.57	2.25	2.10
WZA	−8.37	1.0081	1,39	14.83	14.95	2.16
MFH	−2.65	0.4830	1,39	12.55	6.06	1.08

Coefficient of determination: $R_5^2 = 0.05169$
Multivariate standard distance: $D_5 = 1.548$

From the coefficient of determination, $R_5^2 = 0.0517$, the standard distance is computed as $D_5 = 1.548$. The overall F-statistic for equality of both mean vectors is $F = 10.3$ on 5 and 39 degrees of freedom; equality is therefore clearly rejected.

Looking at the corrected partial F-statistics in Table 9.9, it appears that length and width of the head (LH, WH) do not contribute much to discrimination. Eliminating these two variables, we get the following simplified discriminant function (corrected standard errors are given in brackets):

$$DF = 62.37 + 0.31 \text{ ST} - 5.54 \text{ WZA} - 2.40 \text{ MFH}.$$
$$\quad\quad\quad (0.11) \quad\quad (1.10) \quad\quad\quad (0.95)$$

The multivariate standard distance based on these three variables is $D_3 = 1.467$. Comparing this with $D_5 = 1.548$, using the F-statistic for redundancy of variables, we get $F = 1.20$ on 2 and 39 degrees of freedom. Hence the reduction to three variables is reasonable.

In conclusion, the null hypothesis of equality of the mean vectors can be rejected, although the standard distance between the two groups is not very large.

It should be noted that in interpreting the numerical results in this example we tacitly assumed equality of the covariance matrices of both populations. This assumption seems reasonable, considering the nature of the data. Moreover, this assumption becomes less important the larger n_2 is, since for n_2 'very large' we are in the case of specification analysis.

10

Principal component analysis

10.1 INTRODUCTION

If the p variables in a multivariate data set are highly correlated, it is often desirable to replace them by p' variables that contain 'almost all' information given in the data set, but p' being (hopefully) much smaller than p. In doing this there will in general occur some loss of information, but we will try to keep this loss as small as possible. The most important way of dealing with this problem is *principal component analysis*, which essentially transforms the correlated variables into uncorrelated ones. Principal component analysis is also helpful for analysing the covariance structure of a data set and for finding directions of large or small variability (cf. the remark at the end of Section 9.5). In addition, principal component analysis has considerable theoretical importance, due to its relationship to elliptical distributions and to standard distance.

As an analysis of the covariance structure, principal component analysis is independent of the location parameters. We will assume therefore that all variables considered have mean 0 – otherwise we shift variable X_j according to $X'_j = X_j - \bar{x}_j$ and continue to work with X'_j. The covariance matrix is not changed by this. Geometrically, this transformation corresponds to a shift of the coordinate origin to the p-variate mean $(\bar{x}_1, \ldots, \bar{x}_p)$. This is illustrated in Fig. 10.1 for the bivariate case, using the forged notes and variables BOTTOM and TOP.

As in the preceding chapters, we look now at linear combinations, seeking for a particular one that 'summarizes' the p-dimensional scatterplot best. From Fig. 10.1 it is intuitively clear that a projection onto the longer axis of the point cluster (along which the variance is relatively large) would be a good candidate. The basic idea is thus to find a linear combination that has as large a variance as possible.

In symbols, we define a new variable

$$U_1 = b_{11}X_1 + b_{12}X_2 + b_{13}X_3 + \cdots + b_{1p}X_p,$$

that is, a linear combination with coefficients b_{11}, $b_{12}, \ldots, b_{1p}$. We need double indexes here because we will eventually consider several linear

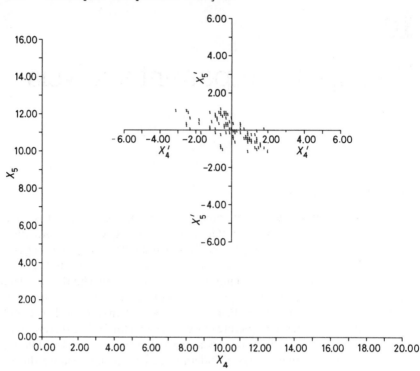

Figure 10.1   Shifting the origin of the coordinate system to the mean

combinations. As a general rule, the first index refers to the transformation (U_h), while the second index refers to the original variable (X_j).

As stated above, the coefficients b_{1j} are to be determined such that U_1 has maximum variance. In this general form, however, the problem is clearly not well defined: the variance of U_1 could be made arbitrarily large by simply increasing the values of the b_{1j}. To avoid this, we introduce a constraint on the b_{1j}, namely

$$b_{11}^2 + b_{12}^2 + \cdots + b_{1p}^2 = 1.$$

In the terminology of Chapter 6 this means that we consider only normalized linear combinations. The transformation U_1 can thus be described as the projection of the p-dimensional point cluster onto that particular straight line on which there results the greatest variability. U_1 is called the *first principal component* of the variables $X_1, \ldots, X_p$.

Suppose U_1 has been found. We now look for a second linear combination

$$U_2 = b_{21}X_1 + b_{22}X_2 + \cdots + b_{2p}X_p,$$

which again is to have maximum variance, but this time under the constraint that U_2 is uncorrelated with U_1, and U_2 must again be normalized. Geometrically, this means that the second direction of projection must be perpendicular to the first one.

The procedure is then continued analogously. The hth step $(2 \leqslant h \leqslant p)$ can be formulated in general as follows. We wish to determine the coefficients of a linear combination

$$U_h = b_{h1}X_1 + b_{h2}X_2 + \cdots + b_{hp}X_p$$

such that U_h has maximum variance among all linear combinations which are uncorrelated with $U_1, U_2, \ldots, U_{h-1}$. This constraint implies that the hth direction of projection is perpendicular to all the preceding ones. U_h is called the hth principal component.

When does this procedure stop? We can distinguish 2 cases:

Case 1

The observations, considered as points in p-dimensional space, lie in a subspace of dimension $p' < p$. The simplest way to visualize this case is to take $p = 3$ and $p' = 2$, i.e. all points lie in a two-dimensional plane. The process stops after p' principal components have been determined, from which the p variables can be reconstructed. This case is called *singular*.

Case 2

There is no subspace of dimension less than p which contains all the points. This is – certainly for $n > p$ – the 'normal case', which is called nonsingular. The process stops only after all p principal components have been determined.

From the construction of the principal components we see that there are two ways of looking at principal component analysis:

1. Thanks to the constraint of pairwise uncorrelatedness of all U_h, principal component analysis can be viewed as a transformation of p correlated variables to p' uncorrelated ones. *All U_hs are pairwise uncorrelated.*
2. Through the maximization of the variance in the hth step one tries to catch as much as possible of the variability that still remains after extraction of U_1 to U_{h-1}. In favourable cases a small number q of principal components is sufficient to reproduce the p-variate data without much loss of information. Principal component analysis can therefore be viewed as a method for approximating high dimensional data in lower dimensions.

Before discussing the properties of principal components in more detail, we are now going to illustrate the method thoroughly for the bivariate case, both mathematically and graphically. This will be helpful for understanding the underlying ideas clearly.

10.2 PRINCIPAL COMPONENTS OF TWO VARIABLES

Let us consider, as an example, the variables $X_4 =$ BOTTOM and $X_5 =$ TOP in the group *Forged*. The descriptive statistics of these variables are

$$\bar{x}_4 = 10.530 \qquad \bar{x}_5 = 11.133$$

$$s_4 = 1.132 \qquad s_5 = 0.636$$

$$r_{45} = -0.6809$$

First, we transform the two variables according to

$$X_4' = X_4 - \bar{x}_4, \qquad X_5' = X_5 - \bar{x}_5$$

and we will drop in the following the prime on the variable. The standard deviations s_4 and s_5 and the correlation r_{45} are not affected by this transformation.

The problem now consists of finding a normalized linear combination

$$U_1 = b_{14}X_4 + b_{15}X_5$$

with maximum variance. The variance of U_1 computes according to Section 6.5 to

$$s^2(U_1) = b_{14}^2 s_4^2 + b_{15}^2 s_5^2 + 2b_{14}b_{15}s_4 s_5 r_{45}$$

$$= 1.2813b_{14}^2 + 0.4045b_{15}^2 - 0.9804b_{14}b_{15}.$$

The coefficients b_{14} and b_{15} are to be chosen, under the constraint $b_{14}^2 + b_{15}^2 = 1$, such that $s^2(U_1)$ becomes maximal. The solution is

$$b_{14} = -0.91286, \qquad b_{15} = 0.40827,$$

so that we obtain

$$U_1 = -0.91286X_4 + 0.40827X_5$$

as the first principal component. For our mathematically trained reader it shouldn't be very hard to verify this result. The variance of U_1 is $s^2(U_1) = 1.5005$.

Since U_1 is a normalized linear combination, we can think of it as a projection associated with an angle ϕ_1. The coefficients b_{14} and b_{15} of the projection depend on the angle ϕ_1 according to

$$b_{14} = \cos \phi_1; \qquad b_{15} = \sin \phi_1.$$

Figure 10.2 shows, as well as the two projections onto the coordinate axes, the first principal component U_1, corresponding to an angle of projection of $\phi_1 = 155.904°$. We note that the variance of U_1 is larger than that of X_4 or X_5.

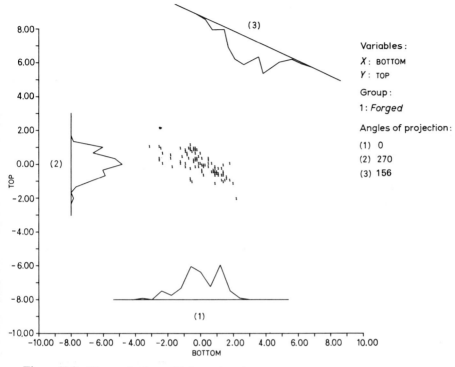

Figure 10.2   The projection with largest variance

Now we look for a second normalized linear combination

$$U_2 = b_{24}X_4 + b_{25}X_5,$$

which has the largest variance among all linear combinations which are uncorrelated with U_1. As can be shown, the condition of uncorrelatedness is precisely equivalent to the condition that the direction of projection ϕ_2, which corresponds to the linear combination U_2, is perpendicular to the direction of projection ϕ_1 of U_1, i.e.

$$\phi_2 = \phi_1 \pm 90°.$$

The two possibilities for choosing ϕ_2 differ by 180°, i.e. they yield equivalent linear combinations that differ only in sign. This, of course, eliminates the need for maximization, and we obtain as second direction of projection, for example,

$$\phi_2 = \phi_1 - 90° = 65.904°.$$

The coefficients of the linear combination U_2 are thus

$$b_{24} = \cos \phi_2 = 0.40827$$
$$b_{25} = \sin \phi_2 = 0.91286.$$

The principal components of the variables BOTTOM and TOP in group *Forged* are therefore

$$U_1 = -0.91286X_4 + 0.40827X_5$$

and

$$U_2 = \quad 0.40827X_4 + 0.91286X_5,$$

with standard deviations $s(U_1) = 1.2249$ and $s(U_2) = 0.4305$. Figure 10.3 shows the projections corresponding to these two linear combinations.

We can now look at the principal components of two variables from a different point of view. Actually we have projected the data points onto two new, orthogonal axes, i.e. we can consider the principal component transformation as a rotation of the entire coordinate system by an angle ϕ. As is shown by Figure 10.4, the U_1-axis is obtained from the X_5-axis through rotation of the coordinate system by $\phi_2 = 65.904°$; in the same way, the

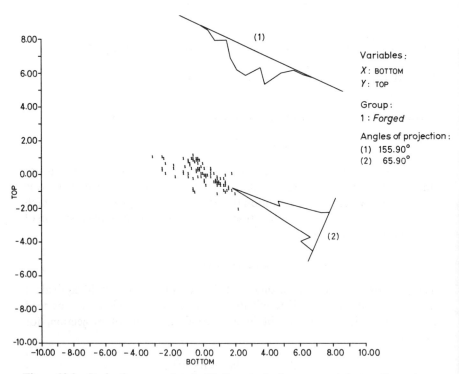

Figure 10.3   Projections associated with the principal components in two dimensions

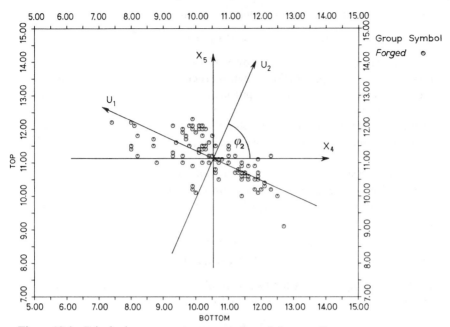

Figure 10.4 Principal components as a rotation of the coordinate system

U_2-axis is obtained from the X_4-axis. Whether we consider ϕ_1 or ϕ_2 as angle of rotation is irrelevant, since the two angles differ by 90°.

By applying the linear combinations U_1 and U_2 to the data, each pair of measurements (x_{4i}, x_{5i}) can now be transformed to a pair (u_{1i}, u_{2i}), which indicates the location of the point in the rotated coordinate system. Conversely, we can transform a pair (u_{1i}, u_{2i}) back to (x_{4i}, x_{5i}) by solving the equations defining U_1 and U_2 for X_4 and X_5:

$$X_4 = -0.91286U_1 + 0.40827U_2$$
$$X_5 = 0.40827U_1 + 0.91286U_2$$

In this way we have achieved the goal of replacing the variables X_4 and X_5 by two uncorrelated variables without loss of information.

How well does the first principal component reproduce the original data? To answer this question, let us first define a simple measure of simultaneous variability of all variables involved: the sum of the variances, called the *total variance*. In our bivariate case, we get

$$s_{\text{total}}^2 = s^2(X_4) + s^2(X_5)$$
$$= 1.132^2 + 0.636^2 = 1.686$$

Variable X_4 has a proportion of 76.01% of the total variance. Interestingly enough, for the principal components U_1 and U_2 one obtains the same sum of variances (except for differences due to rounding), that is

$$s^2(U_1) + s^2(U_2) = s^2(X_4) + s^2(X_5) = s_{total}^2.$$

In the principal components, however, U_1 has a proportion of 89.0% of the total variance. This proportion depends crucially on the correlation between the variables under analysis, and approaches 100% if the correlation lies near 1 in absolute value. As a general rule, one can say that the first principal component reproduces the data well if its proportion of the total variance is sufficiently large, e.g. larger than 80% or 90% or some other value specified by the user.

A special case of importance in applications occurs when both variables are standardized, i.e. have standard deviation 1. In our example with the variables BOTTOM and TOP in group *Forged* we transform the variables X_4 and X_5 according to

$$Z_4 = X_4/s_4 = X_4/1.132$$
$$Z_5 = X_5/s_5 = X_5/0.636.$$

In this case, the solution for two variables can be given quite simply and explicitly. The variance for the normalized linear combination

$$b_{14}Z_4 + b_{15}Z_5$$

becomes

$$b_{14}^2 + b_{15}^2 + 2b_{14}b_{15}r_{45},$$

since the covariance between the standardized variables is equal to the correlation coefficient. If we write the two coefficients as cosine and sine of the angle of projection ϕ_1, the variance of the linear combination becomes

$$\cos^2 \phi_1 + \sin^2 \phi_1 + 2r_{45} \sin \phi_1 \cos \phi_1 = 1 + r_{45} \sin(2\phi_1)$$

Since in our example r_{45} is negative, the variance is maximal when $\sin 2\phi_1$ is minimal, i.e., for $2\phi_1 = \frac{3}{2}\pi$, or $\phi_1 = \frac{3}{4}\pi = 135°$. The coefficients of U_1 are therefore

$$b_{14} = \cos \phi_1 = -\frac{1}{\sqrt{2}}; \quad b_{15} = \sin \phi_1 = \frac{1}{\sqrt{2}},$$

and the variance of U_1 becomes

$$s^2(U_1) = 1 + r_{45} \sin \tfrac{3}{2}\pi = 1 - r_{45}.$$

The direction of projection orthogonal to ϕ_1 is $\phi_2 = \pi/4 = 45°$; and the coefficients of U_2 are thus

$$b_{24} = \cos \frac{\pi}{4} = \frac{1}{\sqrt{2}}; \quad b_{25} = \sin \frac{\pi}{4} = \frac{1}{\sqrt{2}}.$$

The variance of U_2 becomes $s^2(U_2) = 1 + r_{45}$.

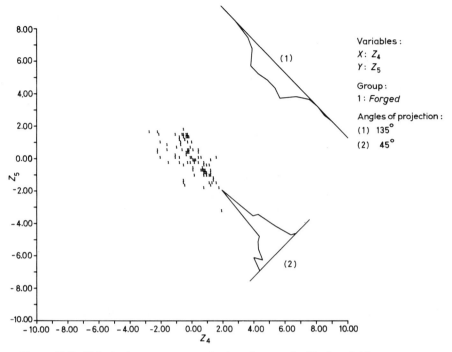

Figure 10.5   Principal component projections for standardized variables

The sum of the variances of the two principal components is exactly 2, thus equal to the sum of the variances of Z_4 and Z_5. If r_{45} were positive, the two angles of projection ϕ_1 and ϕ_2 would simply be exchanged.

Figure 10.5 shows the linear combinations corresponding to the angles of projection of 135° and 45°, respectively:

$$U_1 = -\frac{1}{\sqrt{2}}Z_4 + \frac{1}{\sqrt{2}}Z_5$$

$$U_2 = \frac{1}{\sqrt{2}}Z_4 + \frac{1}{\sqrt{2}}Z_5,$$

with the standard deviations $s(U_1) = \sqrt{(1 - r_{45})} = 1.2965$ and $s(U_2) = \sqrt{(1 + r_{45})} = 0.5649$.

Finally, from the variance formulae we also obtain information about the following two special cases:

1. If the correlation between the two standardized variables is zero, then the variance of every normalized linear combination becomes $1 + 0 \cdot \sin 2\phi = 1$. In this case we could choose two arbitrary orthogonal directions of projection, the method, of course, losing its purpose. In the non-

standardized case, zero correlation results in exactly the original variables being the principal components.

2. If $r = 1$, the angle of projection $\phi_1 = \pi/4$ gives rise to a variance of $1 + 1 \cdot \sin \pi/2 = 2$ for the first principal component. Determining the second principal component becomes unnecessary in this case, since it would have variance 0, i.e. it would be constant. This is the singular case already mentioned in Section 10.1. For $r = -1$ one obtains the same with $\phi_1 = \frac{3}{4}\pi$.

These considerations show that principal component analysis is particularly useful in cases where the variables are highly correlated. For only weakly related variables principal component analysis makes little sense.

How do the principal components obtained from standardized variables and those based on unstandardized variables differ? Are they in some sense equivalent? To answer this question, we substitute $Z_4 = X_4/s_4$ and $Z_5 = X_5/s_5$ in the equations defining the principal components of the standardized variables and get

$$U_1 = -0.707Z_4 + 0.707Z_5 = -0.625X_4 + 1.112X_5$$
$$U_2 = 0.707Z_4 + 0.707Z_5 = 1.112X_4 + 0.625X_5.$$

These two linear combinations of X_4 and X_5 are uncorrelated, but they do *not* correspond to the same projections as the principal components of X_4 and X_5, nor do they define an orthogonal rotation of the coordinate system in the (X_4, X_5)-space. This shows that principal component analysis is a *scale-dependent* method: the choice of the unit of measurement influences the result. We will return to this point later.

10.3 PROPERTIES OF PRINCIPAL COMPONENTS IN THE MULTIDIMENSIONAL CASE

If $p > 2$, it is no longer possible, except in special cases, to solve the problem of principal components in an elementary way. The relationships developed in the two-dimensional case, however, are valid also for $p > 2$. In the following we discuss only the nonsingular case.

According to the construction described in Section 9.1, the p principal components are linear combinations of the p variables:

$$U_1 = b_{11}X_1 + b_{12}X_2 + \cdots + b_{1p}X_p$$
$$U_2 = b_{21}X_1 + b_{22}X_2 + \cdots + b_{2p}X_p$$
$$\vdots$$
$$U_p = b_{p1}X_1 + b_{p2}X_2 + \cdots + b_{pp}X_p$$

The transformation from the variables X_j to the principal components U_h can be viewed as a rotation of the p-dimensional coordinate system in such a way that the new variables U_h are mutually uncorrelated. The coefficients b_{hj} are usually printed by computer programs in form of a matrix:

$$
\begin{array}{cccc}
 & X_1 & X_2 & \cdots & X_p \\
U_1 & b_{11} & b_{12} & \cdots & b_{1p} \\
U_2 & b_{21} & b_{22} & \cdots & b_{2p} \\
\vdots & & & & \\
U_p & b_{p1} & b_{p2} & \cdots & b_{pp}
\end{array}
$$

Each row of this matrix contains the coefficients for one principal component. Some computer programs may also print the matrix in its transposed form, i.e. the coefficients of each principal component being arranged in a column rather than a row.

If the p linear combinations are applied to an observation $(x_{1i}, x_{2i}, \cdots, x_{pi})$, there results a vector $(u_{1i}, u_{2i}, \cdots, u_{pi})$ which can be considered as the ith observation of p uncorrelated variables U_h $(h = 1, \cdots, p)$. In this way, we can replace the p variables X_j by p uncorrelated variables U_h. In statistical computer packages the u_{hi} are usually called 'factor scores', but we prefer to call them 'values of the principal components' or 'principal component scores'. Similarly, the coefficients of the principal component transformation are often called 'factor score coefficients', a terminology that we tend to avoid.

The mathematical treatment of principal component analysis consists mainly in the computation of the so-called *eigenvalues* of the covariance matrix (or correlation matrix). The p eigenvalues of the covariance matrix turn out to be precisely the variances of the p principal components and are often denoted by $\lambda_h (h = 1, \cdots, p)$. Although this notation appears frequently in the multivariate literature, we prefer to denote the eigenvalues as l_h (to indicate that they are sample statistics rather than population parameters), or as $s^2(U_h)$ to stress their interpretation as variances.

With this notation, we have in analogy to the two-dimensional case

$$
s_{\text{total}}^2 = \sum_{i=1}^{p} s_i^2 = \sum_{h=1}^{p} l_h.
$$

The l_h form, by construction of the principal components, a decreasing sequence $l_1 \geqslant l_2 \geqslant \cdots \geqslant l_p$. The proportion of the total variance associated with the hth principal component can be expressed by l_h / s_{total}^2.

As in the bivariate case, the variables X_j can be considered as linear combinations of the principal components U_h. For this inverse transformation, there holds a remarkable fact: the same coefficients b_{hj} of the coefficient matrix can be used, only the matrix must now be read *columnwise* rather than rowwise. The variable X_j is thus obtained from the principal components $U_1, \cdots, U_p$ by

$$
X_j = b_{1j}U_1 + b_{2j}U_2 + \cdots + b_{pj}U_p.
$$

The normalization condition for computing principal components is:

$$b_{h1}^2 + b_{h2}^2 + \cdots + b_{hp}^2 = 1,$$

i.e. the sum of the squares in a row of the coefficient matrix is always equal to 1. The same, however, is true also for the columns of the matrix:

$$b_{1j}^2 + b_{2j}^2 + \cdots + b_{pj}^2 = 1,$$

i.e. the variables X_j can be considered as normalized linear combinations of the principal components.

Instead of the actual principal components one often computes the standardized principal components, which we denote by F_h. These are defined by

$$F_h = U_h/\sqrt{l_h} = \frac{b_{h1}}{\sqrt{l_h}} X_1 + \frac{b_{h2}}{\sqrt{l_h}} X_2 + \cdots + \frac{b_{hp}}{\sqrt{l_h}} X_p.$$

Instead of the coefficients b_{hj} we can also arrange the coefficients $b'_{hj} = b_{hj}/\sqrt{l_h}$ in a matrix. The F_h, however, are no longer normalized linear combinations of $X_1, \cdots, X_p$. This has the consequence that the coefficients b'_{hj} cannot be used directly for the inverse transformation.

10.4 PRINCIPAL COMPONENT ANALYSIS OF THE GENUINE BANK NOTES

Let us now apply principal component analysis to the real bank notes. The analysis is based on the covariance matrix given in Table 3.3. Table 10.1 shows the matrix of coefficients of the principal component transformation. The coefficients are reproduced to four decimal digits, although for almost all practical purposes two digits are sufficient. Each row of the matrix defines one principal component; for instance,

$$U_1 = 0.06X_1 + 0.01X_2 + 0.04X_3 + 0.70X_4 - 0.71X_5 + 0.11X_6.$$

Table 10.2 shows for each principal component its variance (eigenvalue) and

Table 10.1 Coefficients of the principal component transformation

	X_1	X_2	X_3	X_4	X_5	X_6
U_1	0.0613	0.0127	0.0374	0.6970	−0.7055	0.1060
U_2	0.3784	0.5066	0.4543	0.3577	0.3648	−0.3643
U_3	0.4715	0.1013	0.1963	−0.1075	0.0738	0.8438
U_4	−0.7863	0.2441	0.2807	0.2421	0.2434	0.3543
U_5	0.1114	−0.3584	−0.4812	0.5599	0.5483	0.1161
U_6	0.0114	−0.7381	0.6659	0.0510	0.0626	−0.0716

Table 10.2 Variances of the principal components

Principal component	Variance (eigenvalue) l_h	Standard deviation $\sqrt{l_h}$	Proportion of the total variance	Cumulative proportion
U_1	0.6891	0.8301	0.4774	0.4774
U_2	0.3593	0.5994	0.2490	0.7264
U_3	0.1856	0.4308	0.1286	0.8550
U_4	0.0872	0.2953	0.0604	0.9154
U_5	0.0802	0.2831	0.0555	0.9709
U_6	0.0420	0.2048	0.0291	1.0000

its proportion of the total variance. The first principal component U_1 alone accounts for 47.74% of the total variance, and the first three components together already for more than 85%. If the main purpose of this principal component analysis were data reduction, it would thus be reasonable to summarize the six-dimensional data by U_1, U_2 and U_3, and to neglect the last three components. It is possible, however, that the last principal components contain information about outliers and extreme values which is lost if these variables are dropped. We shall return to this point later.

What does the principal component transformation tell us about the data? Looking at Table 10.1, a striking fact is that the first principal component (U_1) is essentially the (normalized) difference between BOTTOM and TOP, with a standard deviation of $s(U_1) = \sqrt{l_1} = 0.830$. In fact, if we simplify U_1 a little and take the normalized linear combination $U_1^* = (X_4 - X_5)/\sqrt{2}$, we get an only slightly smaller standard deviation of $s(U_1^*) = 0.825$. Hence the largest variability in the data is clearly due to the vertical position of the print image on the bank notes – a result that is interesting to compare with the specification analysis of the real notes. There is a possible explanation for this large variance: probably the bills were cut after the image had been printed on larger pieces of paper, and the mechanism which adjusts the paper for cutting was rather inaccurate – besides the insufficient adjustment noticed in Chapter 9!

In contrast to this, the direction of smallest variability is defined by the last principal component (U_6), with $s(U_6) = \sqrt{l_6} = 0.205$. This component is essentially the (normalized) difference between LEFT and RIGHT, thus indicating the slant of the cut. We have already noticed in Chapters 2 and 9 that the 'typical' real note has a positive value of RIGHT − LEFT and it turns out now that there is relatively little variability in this difference. Regarding the production process, this is again a reasonable result. If LEFT and RIGHT measured the same quantity, the variance of their difference would be due to pure error of measurement. Indeed, in applications of principal component analysis involving many similar variables it often turns out that the last components have small variances of similar magnitude. It is then assumed that these last components contain pure 'error variability'.

What about the intermediate components? U_2 has coefficients of similar absolute magnitude (around 0.4) for all six variables. A component of this type is frequently found in biometrical applications (see the examples at the end of this chapter), except that the coefficients all have the same sign. Such a component is usually labelled as 'size', since it takes a large value for an item with large measurements in all variables. Since the sign of DIAGONAL is negative in our second component, it is not a classical 'size'-variable, but in general a large value of U_2 still indicates a bill that is, overall, relatively large. For U_3 and U_4 there are no obvious interpretations, but U_5 looks somehow similar to the variable IMAGE defined in Chapter 6.

Some words of caution are in order concerning the interpretation of principal components. Since the sample covariance matrix is subject to sampling error, the same is true for its eigenvectors and eigenvalues. That is, the coefficients of the principal component transformation have themselves some variability. This variability depends, of course, on the sample size n, but even for large n the coefficients of several components may have large variability if the associated eigenvalues are close. We will come back to this problem in Section 10.7.

If the coefficient matrix (Table 10.1) is read columnwise rather than rowwise, we get the formulae for the inverse transformation, e.g.

$$X_1 = 0.06U_1 + 0.38U_2 + 0.47U_3 - 0.79U_4 + 0.11U_5 + 0.01U_6$$

In expressing the variables X_j as functions of the principal components U_h, we can interpret them as weighted sums of *uncorrelated* variables. In this way, the variables BOTTOM and TOP appear essentially as the sum and the difference of the uncorrelated variables U_1 (vertical position of the print image) and U_5 (IMAGE).

We can now apply the principal component transformation to the raw data of the genuine bills. First, we subtract from each value the mean of the respective variable, i.e. the observation $(x_{1i}, \cdots, x_{6i})$ is replaced by $(x_{1i} - \bar{x}_1, \cdots, x_{6i} - \bar{x}_6)$. To these centred data we apply the linear combinations U_1 to U_6. In this way, one obtains a new set of numbers $(u_{1i}, \cdots, u_{6i})$, $i = 1, 2, \cdots, 100$), that is, a data matrix of the principal components. Table 10.3 shows an excerpt of this data matrix.

It is often interesting to draw scattergrams of pairs of principal components. Since the U_h are pairwise uncorrelated, such scatterplots will of course not give any information about linear dependencies, but sometimes nonlinear structures in the data can be revealed. This refers especially to the first components. The last components, on the other hand, contain often valuable information about multivariate outliers. An intuitive explanation for this can easily be

Table 10.3 Data matrix after the principal component transformation

i	u_{1i}	u_{2i}	u_{3i}	u_{4i}	u_{5i}	u_{6i}
1	0.8145	1.3647	-0.2473	0.6493	-0.9892	0.1799
2	0.3213	-0.6555	-0.0754	0.0778	-0.4042	0.0965
3	0.7342	-0.5108	0.3837	0.2673	0.0669	0.0998
4	-0.6914	-0.6209	0.3834	0.0726	-0.1414	0.0364
5	3.2280	-0.4250	-0.1927	-0.1070	-0.0113	0.1722
6	0.6048	1.3316	0.4061	-0.0364	-0.2628	-0.0653
7	0.1534	-0.4149	0.2732	-0.7382	-0.3010	0.2575
8	-1.1786	-0.8554	-0.0454	0.0659	0.0151	-0.1346
9	-0.6314	-0.1839	0.3044	0.2289	0.6384	0.4060
10	0.6973	1.1389	-0.5289	-0.0210	-0.1030	0.1451
11	-1.2852	0.9312	0.7116	0.3892	0.2400	0.1077
12	-0.5856	-0.5735	0.6592	-0.0685	0.1537	0.1896
13	-0.7200	0.5954	0.1636	0.0082	-0.1175	-0.6826
14	-0.9390	-0.2501	0.1181	0.2431	0.1506	0.1649
15	-0.8308	-0.0703	0.4040	-0.0115	0.0803	0.0084

given in the two-dimensional case, if we consider the fictitious note from Fig. 8.2. This note would appear extreme in the second principal component of the variables BOTTOM and TOP, whereas in the first component it would be inconspicuous. The multidimensional equivalent of this is the situation where an observation does not appear extreme either in an univariate or bivariate sense, yet lies outside of the p-dimensional point cluster.

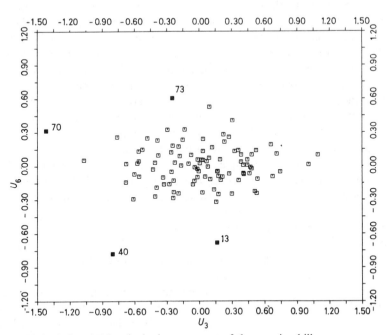

Figure 10.6 3rd and 6th principal component of the genuine bills

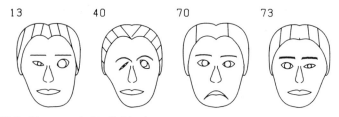

Figure 10.7   Four wanted individuals

To illustrate this, Fig. 10.6 shows a scatterplot of U_3 versus U_6. In order to stress the fact that U_3 has larger variance than U_6, the same scale was used for both axes. The scatterplot therefore appears more stretched in the horizontal direction. Four extreme points are marked by the numbers of the respective bills. Numbers 13, 40 and 73 are extreme in U_6, i.e. obliquely cut bills, according to our interpretation of U_6. No. 70 is the bill we know from Section 8.6 as one with too small an image diagonal; for this note, therefore, the scatterplot does not reveal anything new. Numbers 13 and 73, on the other hand, have not caught our attention up to now, which shows that the last principal component incorporates certain 'residual information'. Also bill no. 40, analysed in detail in Section 8.6, appears now clearly as an extremist in the last principal component. Figure 10.7 shows the faces of the four marked bills.

Let us briefly recall the geometric interpretation of the principal component transformation: the coordinate system has first been centred at the six-dimensional mean of the real notes, and has then been rotated orthogonally. So far we have considered only the genuine notes in the rotated coordinate system, but we can, of course, also look at the forged ones. In other words, we can apply the principal component transformation of the genuine notes to the data of the forged notes. In this way, the whole data set is mapped into a new coordinate system. Since the two mean vectors are not identical, however, we cannot expect the forged bills to have zero mean in the new coordinate system. The univariate descriptive statistics are as displayed in Table 10.4.

Moreover, since the two sample covariance matrices (Tables 3.3 and 3.4) are not identical, the variables U_1 to U_6 are not uncorrelated for the forged bills. The largest correlation (in absolute value) occurs between U_4 and U_5; its value is 0.65. This leads naturally to an interesting question: is it possible to find a coordinate system in which all p variables are uncorrelated in both groups? We will deal with this question in Sections 10.8 and 11.7 but, as a preview, the answer will be 'yes', if we are willing to sacrifice the condition of orthogonality; otherwise the answer will be 'maybe'.

Let us now return to the one sample situation. In Section 10.2 we already noticed that principal component analysis is a scale-dependent method: if the analysis were based on the correlation matrix rather than the covariance matrix, different linear combinations would have resulted. This raises the

Table 10.4 Univariate basic statistics of the principal components of the real bills, applied to both groups

Variable		Mean	Standard deviation	Standard distance
U_1	Genuine	0	0.8301	0.660
	Forged	0.6641	1.1565	
U_2	Genuine	0	0.5994	4.598
	Forged	2.2415	0.3405	
U_3	Genuine	0	0.4308	3.865
	Forged	−1.8519	0.5231	
U_4	Genuine	0	0.2953	0.971
	Forged	0.3759	0.4608	
U_5	Genuine	0	0.2831	2.643
	Forged	1.1631	0.5543	
U_6	Genuine	0	0.2048	1.983
	Forged	0.3717	0.1684	

question of which choice should be preferred. In general, a principal component analysis based on the covariance matrix makes sense if the unit of measurement is identical for all variables. This is the case in the bank note example, since all measurements are given in millimetres. If, on the other hand, the dimensional units are different, as is the case in many social science applications, it may be hard to interpret linear combinations and their variances. So for this reason it is more natural to use the standardized variables, i.e. to carry out the principal component analysis on the correlation matrix. The principal components are then functions of dimensionless scores. Yet another way of handling different units of measurement can be used if all scales have a uniquely defined origin, and all measurements are positive: taking logarithms before computing the covariance matrix. This is frequently done in biometrical applications. We will give an illustrative example at the end of this chapter.

10.5 THE SINGULAR CASE

We have already mentioned the singular case in Section 10.1. It is characterized by the fact that the n observations, considered as points in p-dimensional space, all lie in a linear subspace of dimension $p' < p$. An equivalent statement is that $p - p'$ variables are representable as linear combinations of the p' remaining variables.

In the bank note example we can illustrate the singular case, for example, as follows. To the six measured variables we adjoin two more variables, $X_7 =$

IMAGE and $X_8 = X_5 - X_4$ (difference of the margin widths). Together with X_1 to X_6 the $p = 8$ variables span only a subspace of dimension $p' = 6$ variables. X_7 and X_8 are linear combinations of X_2, X_3, X_4 and X_5. Likewise, we could, for example, represent X_5 as a linear combination of X_4 and X_8 ($X_5 = X_4 + X_8$) or X_2 in the form $X_2 = 2(X_7 + X_8 - 2X_5) - X_3$.

Very often, complicated linear dependencies are not known to the investigator at the beginning of a statistical study, and he carries out the principal component analysis with all p instead of p' variables. As already mentioned, the procedure then terminates after the extraction of p' principal components. Some computer programs may also refuse to print a coefficient matrix in this case. It is thus reasonable to eliminate $p - p'$ linearly dependent variables from the start and to carry out a principal component analysis with the remaining p' variables.

In practice, however, the singular case is less important than the 'nearly singular' case, which arises when relationships between the variables are not exactly linear, or when they are superimposed by small measurement errors. This manifests itself in the fact that the last principal components have very small eigenvalues l_h. If the number of variables is large, one will therefore ignore the last principal components, since they no longer contain any relevant information but merely express variability caused by imprecise methods of measurement.

The singular case also occurs when the number of observations, n, does not exceed the number of variables. The fact that the smallest eigenvalues of the covariance matrix are equal to zero then has no meaningful interpretation – it is merely caused by the insufficient number of observations. As a basic rule, therefore, principal component analysis should not be used in such a case.

10.6 PRINCIPAL COMPONENTS, STANDARD DISTANCE, AND THE MULTIVARIATE NORMAL DISTRIBUTION

In Sections 10.1 and 10.2 we sketched the derivation of the principal component transformation using maximization of the variance as a criterion. Later, we interpreted the transformation geometrically as a rotation of the coordinate system. It is interesting to know that the same rotation of the coordinate system can be found using a criterion that involves standard distance rather than variance.

We sketch this alternative derivation for the case $p = 2$. Figure 10.8 shows a scatterplot of variables BOTTOM and TOP for the genuine notes. In the same figure we construct a circle of arbitrary radius r, centred at the bivariate mean (in Fig. 10.8, $r = 3$ was chosen). This circle is characterized by the fact that all its points have the same Euclidean distance r from the mean. Now we walk around on the circle and find the point with smallest standard distance from

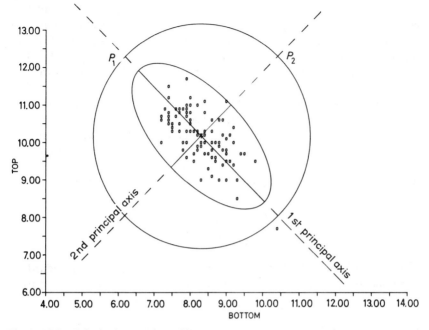

Figure 10.8   Principal axes of an ellipse

the mean. This point is called P_1. Then we put a straight line through P_1 and the mean and take this line as the first axis of the new coordinate system.

From Section 8.3 we know that sets of equal standard distance from the mean are hyperellipsoids, or, in two dimensions, ellipses. Such an ellipse is also shown in Fig. 10.8. It is intuitively clear that the straight line defined above must coincide with the longest diameter of the ellipse. We call this line, therefore, the *first principal axis* of the ellipse – and it is not very surprising that the projection onto this axis is identical with the first principal component.

The second coordinate axis of the new coordinate system is now uniquely defined by two conditions: it has to pass through the origin of the circle, and it has to be orthogonal to the first axis. This is called the *second principal axis* of the ellipse, and for $p = 2$ this completes the construction.

In higher dimensions the circle is replaced by a sphere $(p = 3)$ or hypersphere $(p > 3)$, and points P_i on the sphere are found by successive minimizations of the standard distance under orthogonality conditions. This process is very similar to the one described in Section 10.1, and yields indeed the same rotation of the coordinate system.

So far we have been looking at principal component analysis as a distribution-free, descriptive method. From the relation to the principal axes of ellipses it now becomes clear that the method is especially appropriate for elliptical distributions (cf. Section 8.3). In this case, the principal component coordinate system corresponds exactly to the principal axes of the ellipses (or ellipsoids) of constant density. In addition, if the model generating the data is multivariate normal, then uncorrelatedness even implies stochastic independence. Of course, we have to remember that the coefficients of the principal component transformation have themselves some sampling variability. Nevertheless it is sometimes possible, at least for large samples, to interpret the principal components as independent variables.

The principal component transformation offers, furthermore, an extremely simple possibility for computing standard distances between individual observations and the mean. Since the U_h are pairwise uncorrelated and have mean 0, the computation of the p-variate standard distance of the ith observation simplifies to

$$D_p = \sqrt{\left[\left(\frac{u_{1i}}{\sqrt{l_1}}\right)^2 + \cdots + \left(\frac{u_{pi}}{\sqrt{l_p}}\right)^2\right]}.$$

If instead of the actual principal components we use the standardized components $F_h = U_h/\sqrt{l_h}$, then the equation is even further simplified to

$$D_p = \sqrt{(f_{1i}^2 + f_{2i}^2 + \cdots + f_{pi}^2)}$$

i.e. the standard distance reduces to the Euclidean distance of the F_h. If we assume multivariate normality, then the principal components, as linear combinations of normally distributed variables, are themselves normally distributed. The F_h, for sufficiently large samples, are distributed as standard normal variates. From the theory of normal distribution it is known that the square of a standard normal variate is distributed as chi-square with one degree of freedom. The sum of p independent such squares is distributed as chi-square with p degrees of freedom. This gives us a simple explanation for a statement already made in Section 8.3: the square of the standard distance (or Mahalanobis distance) of a p-dimensional normal observation is approximately chi-square with p degrees of freedom.

We can now compute the standard distances for all genuine bills and study their frequency distribution. Under normality assumptions, the distribution of the 100 squared standard distances should look similar to the density curve of a chi-square distribution with 6 degrees of freedom. Figure 10.9 shows a histogram of the 100 values of D_6^2 as well as the density function of the chi-square distribution. Up to a few values, which are too large, the agreement seems to be good. The five largest values are:

no. of bill:	1	5	40	70	71
squared standard distance:	24.30	16.67	23.21	20.74	18.76

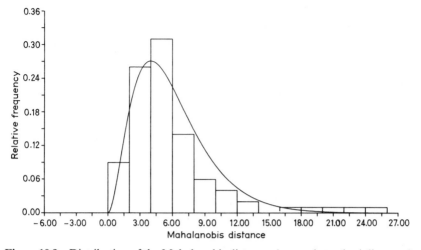

Figure 10.9 Distribution of the Mahalanobis distances (squared standard distances) in the group *Genuine* and density function of a chi-square distribution with 6 degrees of freedom

With the exception of no. 71, all the bills mentioned have already caught our attention. No. 71 is distinguished by a very small value of LENGTH.

The projection of the data of the forged bills onto the principal components of the genuine ones provides us with the possibility of computing, for these too, standard distances from the mean of the genuine bills. This gives us a simple way of comparing a new bill with the known ones: only six linear combinations need be computed. In contrast to identification analysis, however, this method gives no information about the importance of the individual variables.

10.7   STANDARD ERRORS OF THE PRINCIPAL COMPONENT COEFFICIENTS AND RELATED PROBLEMS

In Section 10.4 we already cautioned the reader to be aware of the fact that the coefficients b_{hj} of the principal component transformation as well as the eigenvalues l_h have some sampling variability. Whenever a coefficient is interpreted, one would like to be sure that the interpretation is not just based on sampling error. As with regression and discriminant analysis we will therefore indicate how to compute standard errors of the coefficients of the linear combinations considered. The problem is more complicated here, however, than it was in the preceding chapters, and it appears that no exact results are known for small samples. The formulae given in this section are approximations for large n. Furthermore, their validity depends on the assumption of multivariate normality and they hold only for principal component analysis based on the covariance matrix. For an analysis based on the correlation matrix the problem is considerably more difficult.

Despite all these limitations it is quite useful to estimate standard errors, since they give the user a reasonable feeling for the variability of the coefficients and can prevent him or her from over-interpreting the numerical results.

Before discussing this problem further, we have to consider another question, namely: are the coefficients of the principal component transformation uniquely defined? If not, then it would make no sense to talk about their standard errors! The answer to this question is as follows: all coefficients are mathematically uniquely defined, unless two or more eigenvalues of the covariance matrix are identical. This case is unlikely to occur in practical applications, but we have obviously to consider the possibility that some eigenvalues l_h differ only by sampling error.

Let us explain this in more detail for the bivariate case. Assume that two random variables X_1 and X_2 are independent and have the same variance, say σ^2. Then the principal components are not defined for this model (cf. Section 10.2), since every normalized linear combination of X_1 and X_2 has exactly variance σ^2. The covariance matrix $\begin{pmatrix} \sigma^2 & 0 \\ 0 & \sigma^2 \end{pmatrix}$ therefore has two eigenvalues that are both equal to σ^2, and the eigenvectors can be chosen arbitrarily. This is called the *spherical* case – for obvious reasons, since the ellipses of constant standard distance are circles, or spheres in higher dimensions. Sphericity in, say, r dimensions is characterized by the fact that r eigenvalues are identical.

In practice the analysis is based on a sample covariance matrix, and even if the underlying model is spherical, the two sample variances are likely to differ and the sample covariance will, in general, be different from zero. The sample principal components are thus mathematically uniquely defined; nevertheless their interpretation makes no sense if the eigenvalues differ only by sampling error.

A similar thing can occur in higher dimensions. Suppose that the distribution is spherical in the subspace spanned by two (or several) eigenvectors – then these eigenvectors are not unique, and the coefficients should not be interpreted.

Since sphericity in r dimensions is characterized by equality of r eigenvalues, it is not surprising that a test for sphericity can be constructed using the eigenvalues of the sample covariance matrix. Suppose we want to test for sphericity of the r principal components labelled $U_h, U_{h+1}, \cdots, U_{h+r-1}$. Then a test statistic (denoted by S_r for Sphericity of r components) is

$$S_r = (n-1)r \cdot \log \frac{\frac{1}{r} \sum\limits_{j=h}^{h+r-1} l_j}{\left(\prod\limits_{j=h}^{h+r-1} l_j \right)^{1/r}},$$

where log is the natural logarithm. Under this criterion the eigenvalues l_h to l_{h+r-1} appear in the form of the ratio of their arithmetic mean (numerator) and geometric mean (denominator). The statistic S_r equals zero if $l_h = l_{h+1} = \cdots = l_{h+r-1}$; otherwise S_r is positive. If the hypothesis of sphericity of the r principal components considered is true, the distribution of S_r is, for sufficiently large sample size n, approximately chi square with $r(r+1)/2 - 1$ degrees of freedom.

Since two eigenvectors are undefined whenever their associated eigenvalues are close, it is recommended to compare all $p - 1$ adjacent pairs of principal components by the sphericity criterion. That is, the statistic S_2 should be computed for the pairs (U_1, U_2), $(U_2, U_3), \ldots, (U_{p-1}, U_p)$. For the pair (U_h, U_{h+1}) the statistic S_2 is

$$S_2 = 2(n-1)\log\left[\frac{l_h + l_{h+1}}{2\sqrt{l_h l_{h+1}}}\right],$$

with 2 degrees of freedom.

A second important special case is $r = p$, i.e. sphericity in p dimensions, which means that all p variables are pairwise uncorrelated and have equal variances – clearly a case where principal component analysis makes no sense. The overall test for sphericity follows from the above definition of S_r by putting $h = 1$ and $r = p$, that is,

$$S_p = (n-1)p\log\frac{s^2_{\text{total}}/p}{\left(\prod_{j=1}^{p} l_j\right)^{1/p}},$$

the associated degrees of freedom being $p(p+1)/2 - 1$.

Let us illustrate this on the principal components of the genuine notes. From the list of eigenvalues given in Table 10.2, we compute the overall sphericity statistic as $S_6 = 99.6 \cdot \log(0.2406/0.1543) = 263.8$. For comparison, the 99% quantile of the chi square distribution with 20 degrees of freedom is 37.6, and the hypothesis of overall sphericity is clearly rejected. This result can be viewed as the justification for performing principal component analysis on the genuine notes.

Now we look at pairs of principal components, as proposed in the foregoing text. The values of S_2 for all pairs (U_h, U_{h+1}) are as follows:

	Pair of principal components				
	(U_1, U_2)	(U_2, U_3)	(U_3, U_4)	(U_4, U_5)	(U_5, U_6)
$S_2 =$	10.3	10.6	13.8	0.17	10.2

For comparison, the 95% and 99% quantiles of the chi square distribution with 2 degrees of freedom are 5.99 and 9.21, respectively. It is quite evident that U_4 and U_5, in contrast to the other four principal components, are not well defined, since we cannot reject the hypothesis of sphericity for this pair. U_4 and U_5 should therefore not be interpreted. Since all other pairs of adjacent components yield fairly large values of S_2, we can still say, however, that the two-dimensional subspace spanned by the fourth and fifth principal components is well defined.

Let us now return to the problem introduced at the beginning of this section: standard errors of the coefficients of the principal component transformation. For b_{hj}, the jth coefficient of component U_h, the formula for the standard error is

$$s(b_{hj}) = \sqrt{\left[\frac{1}{n-1} l_h \sum_{\substack{k=1 \\ k \neq h}}^{p} \frac{l_k}{(l_k - l_h)^2} b_{kj}^2\right]}.$$

The sum in this formula extends over all indexes k from 1 to p except h. The coefficients b_{kj} occurring in the formula are those associated with variable X_j, i.e. the jth column of the coefficient matrix. Although the computation of standard errors according to this formula is straightforward, it is quite laborious even for 'moderate' dimension, like $p = 6$, and there is ample opportunity for errors. It is therefore recommended to use a computer program.

For completeness, we should also discuss approximate standard errors for the eigenvalues l_h. For large n, they can be estimated as

$$s(l_h) = l_h \cdot \sqrt{\left(\frac{2}{n-1}\right)}$$

Table 10.5 gives a list of the $s(l_h)$ and $s(b_{hj})$ for all six principal components. The

Table 10.5 Standard errors of the eigenvalues and the coefficients of the principal component transformation

		$s(b_{hj})$					
Component	$s(l_h)$	X_1	X_2	X_3	X_4	X_5	X_6
U_1	0.0979	0.074	0.081	0.076	0.060	0.060	0.083
U_2	0.0511	0.088	0.042	0.053	0.113	0.114	0.129
U_3	0.0264	0.118	0.103	0.104	0.103	0.103	0.073
U_4	0.0124	0.149	0.442	0.584	0.671	0.657	0.179
U_5	0.0114	0.943	0.315	0.353	0.292	0.294	0.436
U_6	0.0060	0.112	0.067	0.085	0.094	0.093	0.074

coefficients associated with U_4 and U_5 have extremely large standard errors, which reflects the fact that these two components are poorly defined. Actually, we know this already from the comparison of l_4 and l_5, and so the computation of standard errors for these coefficients was rather superfluous. Nevertheless, the result of the sphericity test is thus again confirmed.

A closer look at the standard errors associated with the coefficients of the remaining principal components shows that it is indeed justified to be rather 'generous' in neglecting small coefficients or equating coefficients of similar magnitude. In U_1, for instance, the coefficients b_{11}, b_{12} and b_{13} have standard errors that exceed the absolute values of the coefficients (cf. Table 10.1), and b_{16} is only slightly larger than $s(b_{16})$. The coefficients b_{14} and b_{15}, on the other hand, are clearly different from zero, both with standard errors of approximately 0.06, i.e. less than one tenth of their absolute value. Similar observations can be made for the remaining components, especially for U_6, the standard errors ranging generally from 0.05 to 0.1.

Although, to our knowledge, none of the standard statistical program libraries offer the user an option for computing standard errors, we feel that they should be an integral part of any principal component analysis – mostly because they prevent the user from overinterpreting the numerical results and show her which coefficients are unstable in the sense of a relatively large standard error. Of course, one has to bear in mind that the results given in this section are asymptotic in nature and based on multivariate normality. In other words, for small samples or distinctly non-normal distributions the true standard errors may, in fact, be even larger than those given here.

10.8   PRINCIPAL COMPONENT ANALYSIS OF SEVERAL GROUPS[†]

In Section 10.4 we raised the question whether it is possible to find a coordinate system in which the p variables are uncorrelated, not only in one group but in two (or several) groups simultaneously. In Section 11.7 we will see that for two groups this is indeed always possible, but the new coordinate system will no longer be just a rotation of the original one. In the context of principal component analysis we ask a more specific question: is it possible to find a single orthogonal transformation of the coordinate system (i.e. a rotation) such that the new variables are simultaneously uncorrelated in all groups? A first answer to this question is a clear 'no': each sample has its own unique principal component transformation, and these transformations are very unlikely to be identical in several groups.

There is a second answer to this question, however. Since the coefficients of the principal component transformation have themselves some sampling

[†]This section may be omitted at the first reading

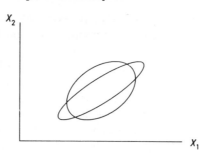

Figure 10.10   Two (fictitious) covariance matrices with identical principal axes

variability, it may occur that the transformations obtained in different groups differ only by sampling error. If the populations (or models) generating the data have one and the same principal component transformation, then it is obviously reasonable to estimate only *one* orthogonal matrix from the data.

Let us illustrate this for the bivariate case. Figure 10.10 shows two ellipses that correspond to two (fictitious) covariance matrices. Since for the moment we are not interested in mean differences, the two ellipses have been centred at a common origin. The two covariance matrices are clearly not identical, but nevertheless the directions of the two principal axes are the same: even simpler examples can be constructed by taking proportional covariance matrices, which correspond to concentric ellipses.

Let us now turn to real data, namely the variables LEFT and RIGHT in the bank note example. Figure 10.11 shows scatterplots of the two variables for both groups, with the coordinate systems corresponding to the two sets of

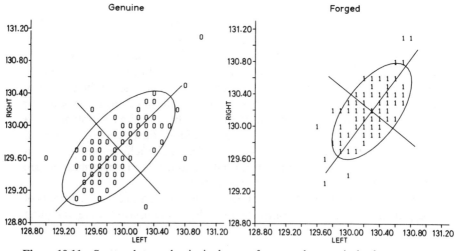

Figure 10.11   Scatterplots and principal axes of LEFT and RIGHT in both groups

principal component transformations superimposed. (In this figure we didn't superimpose the two scatterplots, for the sake of clarity.) The principal components are

$$U_1 = 0.72 \text{ LEFT} + 0.69 \text{ RIGHT}; \quad s^2(U_1) = 0.2154$$
$$U_2 = 0.69 \text{ LEFT} - 0.72 \text{ RIGHT}; \quad s^2(U_2) = 0.0435$$

for the genuine bills, and

$$U_1 = 0.61 \text{ LEFT} + 0.79 \text{ RIGHT}; \quad s^2(U_1) = 0.1253$$
$$U_2 = 0.79 \text{ LEFT} - 0.61 \text{ RIGHT}; \quad s^2(U_2) = 0.0286$$

for the forged bills. The two sets of transformations appear quite similar and it may therefore be reasonable to assume that they should actually be identical.

In order to find a common principal component transformation for both groups, we have to make some kind of compromise between the above two sets of transformations. It is beyond the scope of this book to describe in mathematical detail how such a compromise can be found, but some insight can be given. We note that the angle of rotation associated with U_1 in group *Genuine* is 44 degrees ($\cos 44° = 0.72$), while the corresponding angle in group *Forged* is 52°. The first principal axis of the compromise can be expected to correspond to an angle between 44 and 52 degrees. Numerical computations yield the following result:

$$U_1^* = 0.67 \text{ LEFT} + 0.74 \text{ RIGHT}$$
$$U_2^* = 0.74 \text{ LEFT} - 0.67 \text{ RIGHT}$$

U_1^* and U_2^* are called the *common principal components* of LEFT and RIGHT in both groups. It is easily checked that the angle of rotation corresponding to this transformation is indeed between the angles computed for each group individually. Obviously the coefficients of U_1^* and U_2^* do not differ much from the coefficients found separately in each group. The rotated coordinate system defined by U_1^* and U_2^* is shown in Fig. 10.12, where the origin was shifted to the mean of the respective group in both pictures.

As mentioned above, the variables U_1^* and U_2^* cannot be expected to be exactly uncorrelated. Indeed, the covariance matrices for U_1^* and U_2^* are

	Genuine		*Forged*	
	U_1^*	U_2^*	U_1^*	U_2^*
U_1^*	0.2147	0.0111	0.1247	-0.0076
U_2^*	0.0111	0.0442	-0.0076	0.0292

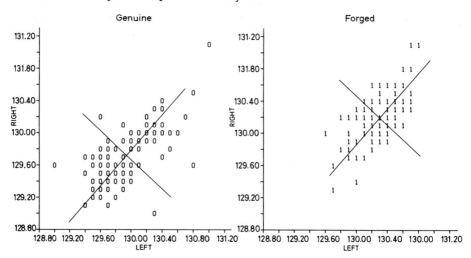

Figure 10.12 The common principal axes of LEFT and RIGHT in both groups

The correlation between U_1^* and U_2^* is thus 0.11 and -0.13 in the respective groups. We note, however, that the sum of the variances of U_1^* and U_2^* in each group equals the total variance – a property that common principal components share with ordinary principal components!

Regarding the fact that U_1^* and U_2^* are not exactly uncorrelated, the question naturally arises whether the common principal component model is appropriate for this data. To answer this question, a test statistic can be constructed as follows. Define the quantities

$$A_i = \text{product of the variances of the common principal components in group } i,$$

and

$$B_i = \text{product of the variances of the ordinary principal components in group } i.$$

The statistic, given here already for an arbitrary number of groups (k) and for p variables, is

$$X_{\text{CPC}}^2 = \sum_{i=1}^{k} (n_i - 1) \log \frac{A_i}{B_i}.$$

If the common principal component model is correct and the sample sizes n_i are sufficiently large, this statistic is distributed approximately as chi square on $(k-1)p(p-1)/2$ degrees of freedom.

In the above numerical example, we have

$$\left. \begin{aligned} A_1 &= (0.2147) \times (0.0442) = 0.00949 \\ B_1 &= (0.2154) \times (0.0435) = 0.00937 \end{aligned} \right\} Genuine$$

and

$$A_2 = (0.1247) \times (0.0292) = 0.00364 \atop B_2 = (0.1253) \times (0.0286) = 0.00358} Forged$$

The test statistic is thus

$$X^2_{\text{CPC}} = 99 \log \frac{A_1}{B_1} + 99 \log \frac{A_2}{B_2} = 2.9,$$

with one degree of freedom. (*Note*: the numerically exact value, obtained from the computer program, is 2.86.) For comparison, the 95% and 99% quantiles of the chi square distribution with one degree of freedom are 3.84 and 6.63, respectively. We conclude therefore that the common principal component model is appropriate.

The p-dimensional case can now be considered in complete analogy to the bivariate case. The common principal component model assumes that the directions of all p principal axes are identical for both (or, more generally, all k) groups. Since this will hardly ever be true for the samples, an appropriate compromise must be found between the principal component transformations found separately in each group. Again, it is well beyond the scope of this book to explain in detail how such a compromise can be found. Once a solution is obtained, the fit of the common principal component model can be tested by the above X^2_{CPC}-statistic. Since the bank note data with all six variables does not fit the common principal component model particularly well ($X^2_{\text{CPC}} = 47$; degrees of freedom = 15), we will give an example at the end of this chapter instead of illustrating common principal components using the bank note example.

The reader may have been wondering why one should want to compute common principal components instead of just performing ordinary principal component analysis in each group individually. Indeed, common components are computationally more difficult, and the model may not fit, whereas ordinary principal component analysis is always 'correct', at least as long as the structure of the multivariate data is not highly nonlinear. The answer to this question is a general *principle of parsimony*: if a simple model (that is, one with relatively few parameters) fits the data, then it should be preferred to a model that involves redundant parameters. We have actually been using this principle quite a lot in this book – all tests for redundancy of variables can be viewed as applications of the parsimony principle. More specifically, the common principal component model has the following advantages.

1. Instead of k sets of principal component transformations, only one orthogonal matrix has to be interpreted.
2. If components with relatively small variances are to be discarded, then exactly the same information is neglected in each group. Geometrically this

means that the p-dimensional data are summarized by the same subspace of dimension p' in all groups.
3. The coefficients of the common principal component transformation are more stable (in the sense of smaller standard errors) than those in ordinary principal component analysis.

This last remark seems particularly important in view of the results given in Section 10.7. For more details, the interested reader is referred to the literature listed at the end of this chapter.

DISCUSSION

Question:
I think that for the purpose of data reduction it would be equivalent, but considerably simpler, to omit individual variables, rather than first computing the principal components and then drop some of these. For example, in the case $p = 2$, and for high correlation one could, after all, simply omit a variable rather than compute the first principal component.

Answer:
This is indeed a possibility, and it has been proposed in the statistical literature under the name 'principal variables'. The basic idea is to discard variables which can (for instance in the sense of a high coefficient of determination) be well reconstructed from the set of selected variables. Discarding variables instead of principal components avoids a frequent difficulty of principal component analysis, namely the fact that the principal component transformation may be hard to interpret. On the other hand, principal component analysis has some advantages:

1. The example $p = 2$ shows, as a disadvantage of the simple method, that while the variable selected remains completely intact, the one omitted does not, i.e. the two variables are not treated equally.
   Figure 10.13 shows as an illustration a scatterplot of X_4 and X_5 in group *Forged*. We have drawn
   (a) the linear regression of X_5 on X_4:

   $$x_5 = 15.16 - 0.3825x_4$$

   (b) the linear regression of X_4 on X_5:

   $$x_4 = 24.02 - 1.212x_5$$

   (c) the first principal axis of X_4 and X_5:

   $$0.408x_4 + 0.913x_5 = 14.462$$

   The method of principal components yields a straight line which – and this is always the case – lies between the two regression lines. This

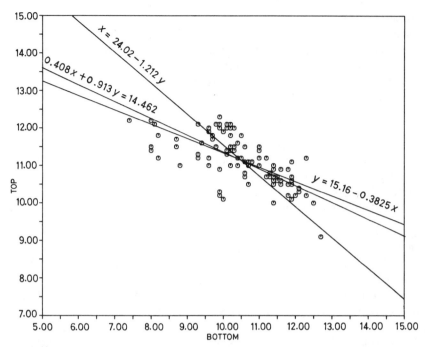

Figure 10.13   Two regression lines and the first principal component of X_4 and X_5 in group *Forged*

demonstrates the equal status of both variables in the principal component approach.

2. For $p > 2$ it is difficult to decide, without carrying out a principal component analysis, whether variables may possibly be discarded. One cannot, for example, necessarily tell from the covariance matrix

$$
\begin{array}{cccc}
1.0 \\
-0.3 & 1.0 \\
-0.3 & -0.3 & 1.0 \\
-0.3 & -0.3 & -0.3 & 1.0
\end{array}
$$

that the corresponding four-dimensional point cluster lies almost in a three-dimensional hyperplane. In this example, the first three principal components would comprise 97.5% of s_{total}^2, but any three of the four variables only 75%.

Question:
In the discussion following Chapter 5, in a multiple linear regression problem, a possibility was mentioned of using the principal components as regressors instead of the original variables. What are the advantages of this?

Answer:

Since the principal components are uncorrelated, their covariance matrix has a particularly simple form: the diagonal contains the eigenvalues, and all off-diagonal elements are zero. Matrices of this form can be numerically inverted in a particularly easy and precise way. If the solution of a multiple linear regression problem, in terms of principal components, is

$$\hat{\mu}_y = b_0 + b_1 U_1 + b_2 U_2 + \cdots + b_p U_p,$$

then the (numerically stable) solution in the original variables can be obtained by substituting the linear combinations U_1 to U_p and collecting the terms in X_1, X_2, etc. If some eigenvalues are zero or close to zero, the corresponding principal components are usually omitted from the set of regressors. For further details, see Chapter 8 in Montgomery and Peck (1982).

Question:

In the chapter on identification analysis you analysed bill no. 1 and computed its multivariate standard distance as $D_6 = 5.71$. At the end of Section 10.6 the squared standard distance of the same bill was given as $D_6^2 = 24.30$. By the usual rules of arithmetic, $\sqrt{24.30} = 4.93 \neq 5.71$. What went wrong? Is this discrepancy just a matter of numerical inaccuracy?

Answer:

Thank you for this excellent remark! No, it is not a matter of inaccuracy. The reason for the discrepancy is as follows.

   In identification analysis, the computation of standard distance is based on the means, variances and covariances obtained *without* the questionable observation. That is, identification analysis measured the distance of bill no. 1 from the mean of the remaining 99 bills, using the covariance structure of these 99 bills. In contrast to this, principal component analysis uses *all* observations to determine the mean vector and the covariance matrix. That is, principal component analysis doesn't treat the single observation *a priori* as 'suspicious'. For observations close to the mean the discrepancy is small but, as the example of bill no. 1 shows, the two results may differ considerably in the case of outliers.

   If you are not yet convinced, do the following. Perform an identification analysis of bill no. 1 against *all 100* genuine bills. (That is, you need two lines for bill no. 1 in the data matrix: it appears once as a member of the sample of 100 genuine bills, and once as the additional observation that is to be identified.) The standard distance you get from identification analysis will be exactly what we got in principal component analysis.

FURTHER STUDY

Principal component analysis is treated in almost every book on multivariate statistics. Morrison (1976) gives particularly good practical examples. From a theoretical point of view, the subject is nicely presented in Muirhead (1982) and Anderson (1984). Principal component analysis was initiated by Pearson (1901) and Hotelling (1933). The asymptotic theory leading to estimates of standard errors was developed by Anderson (1963). Common principal components have been proposed by Flury (1984). A related approach is due to Krzanowski (1979). The 'principal variables' approach to data reduction has been worked out by McCabe (1984).

Software

A good procedure for principal components is contained in SAS, while BMDP and SPSS offer principal component analysis as part of their factor analysis programs. Users who know FORTRAN may prefer a subroutine library like NAG or IMSL for computing eigenvectors or eigenvalues. No software is available, to our knowledge, for computing standard errors. A FORTRAN routine for computing common principal components has been published by Flury and Constantine (1985) and is expected to be released as a subroutine called KPRIN in the IMSL package in 1988.

EXAMPLES

Example 10.1 Decathlon

This example is based on the results of the international decathlon competition at Götzis (Austria), 1982. The data have been collected by Moser (1982), who used face plots to analyse the performance of the best athletes. Parts of Moser's analysis are reported in Flury and Riedwyl (1983).

The raw data, given in Table 10.6, consist of the scores achieved by $n = 20$ athletes in each of the ten categories. The final score assigned to each athlete is the sum of the ten scores, and the rows of Table 10.6 have been arranged in decreasing order of the final scores.

Since the number of observations is small, any multivariate analysis of the data must be exploratory. For the same reason we will analyse only four variables instead of all ten. The four selected variables are the four running disciplines: 100 m dash (DASH), 400 m run (RUN_4), 110 m hurdles (HURDLE), and 1500 m run (RUN_{15}). Table 10.7 displays univariate and bivariate basic statistics for these four variables. The correlations between the first three variables are positive and relatively high, as was to be expected. On the other hand, all correlations with RUN_{15} are small in absolute value, thus confirming the well-known fact that a good short-distance runner need not be a good long-distance runner.

Table 10.8 displays the coefficients of the principal component transformation and the associated eigenvalues. Standard errors of the principal component coefficients computed according to Section 10.7 are given in

Table 10.6 Scores achieved by 20 athletes in the international decathlon competition at Götziz (Austria) 1982. Data courtesy of Urs Moser, University of Berne.

Rank	Name	Nationality	100 m dash	Long jump	Shot put	High jump	400 m run	110 m hurdles	Discus	Pole vault	Javelin	1500 m run
1	THOMPSON	GB	935	1010	807	925	955	926	769	1028	767	585
2	HINGSEN	FRG	817	1004	844	950	905	901	781	957	738	632
3	DEGTJARJOV	USSR	768	893	759	900	825	859	868	981	732	662
4	NIKLAUS	SWITZERLAND	869	867	802	874	915	856	804	884	857	448
5	WENTZ	FRG	787	871	781	874	878	880	782	884	807	592
6	KUELVET	USSR	738	814	700	950	848	850	870	957	764	569
7	STEEN	CANADA	763	887	604	900	862	839	709	1005	753	658
8	BOREHAM	GB	795	853	701	874	890	841	680	859	772	670
9	RUEFENACHT	SWITZERLAND	903	818	700	849	877	919	718	884	716	460
10	KOLOWANOW	USSR	761	846	728	900	765	881	781	981	714	485
11	BAGINSKI	POLAND	747	796	682	849	792	800	746	932	767	564
12	MITRAKIEV	BULGARIA	771	824	668	874	802	840	704	859	710	609
13	HADFIELD	AUSTRALIA	785	911	728	680	878	805	709	884	747	527
14	GUGLER	SWITZERLAND	657	810	698	849	773	820	746	909	771	612
15	ZENIOU	GB	696	774	765	725	785	791	706	932	795	578
16	KUBISZEWSKI	POLAND	724	746	763	849	785	870	724	807	760	509
17	LYTHELL	SWEDEN	712	875	754	725	829	838	762	807	585	516
18	CLAVERIE	FRANCE	756	873	624	725	863	815	655	957	620	474
19	VLASIC	YUGOSLAVIA	622	820	673	769	759	786	698	807	695	619
20	STERRER	AUSTRIA	668	834	601	849	753	751	655	807	642	551

Table 10.7 Basic statistics in the Decathlon example

a) *Means, standard deviations, correlations*

Variable	Mean	Std. deviation	Correlation matrix			
DASH	763.70	77.86	1.00	0.85	0.78	− 0.23
RUN_4	836.95	58.54	0.85	1.00	0.61	− 0.02
HURDLE	843.40	45.38	0.78	0.61	1.00	− 0.10
RUN_{15}	566.00	68.25	− 0.23	− 0.02	− 0.10	1.00

b) *Covariance matrix*

	DASH	RUN_4	HURDLE	RUN_{15}
DASH	6062	3851	2737	− 1199
RUN_4	3851	3427	1631	− 85
HURDLE	2737	1631	2059	− 311
RUN_{15}	− 1199	− 85	− 311	4658

Table 10.8 Principal component transformation in the Decathlon example with four variables. Estimated standard errors of the principal component coefficients are given in brackets

Component	Variable				Eigenvalue
	DASH	RUN_4	HURDLE	RUN_{15}	
U_1	0.756	0.513	0.361	− 0.189	10280
	(0.034)	(0.082)	(0.069)	(0.266)	
U_2	0.052	0.224	0.082	0.970	4548
	(0.213)	(0.168)	(0.149)	(0.054)	
U_3	0.067	− 0.620	0.779	0.073	968
	(0.178)	(0.151)	(0.134)	(0.136)	
U_4	− 0.649	0.551	0.507	− 0.135	409
	(0.040)	(0.163)	(0.202)	(0.076)	

brackets. Of course, we must be very critical of these standard errors – the normality assumptions are highly questionable, and a sample size of 20 is not of a magnitude that guarantees the correctness of asymptotic approximation. Nevertheless, estimated standard errors larger than 0.1 indicate that the corresponding coefficient is very unstable. A quick glance at Table 10.8 suffices to notice that all four components have at least one unstable coefficient. This

Table 10.9 Principal component transformation in the Decathlon example with three variables (estimated standard errors are given in brackets)

Component	Variable			Eigenvalue (variance of U_h)	Std. deviation of U_h
	DASH	RUN$_4$	HURDLE		
U_1	0.762 (0.035)	0.532 (0.060)	0.369 (0.066)	10073	100.4
U_2	0.114 (0.208)	−0.671 (0.167)	0.733 (0.181)	991	31.5
U_3	−0.637 (0.054)	0.517 (0.212)	0.572 (0.230)	483	22.0

is, of course, quite unsatisfactory. We notice, however, that the second component is almost entirely defined by variable RUN$_{15}$, the corresponding coefficient being 0.97. This expresses the fact that RUN$_{15}$ is practically uncorrelated with the other three variables. Hence it may be a good idea to eliminate this variable from the analysis and consider only the remaining three.

Table 10.9 gives the results of a principal component analysis performed on the covariance matrix of DASH, RUN$_4$ and HURDLE. The picture emerging from this analysis is now fairly clear (although the warning regarding the standard errors still applies). The first component seems now sufficiently well defined and can be interpreted as a measure of 'overall performance in short distance running'. However, the three weights (0.762, 0.532 and 0.369) are not equal. The coefficient of DASH is relatively large because this variable has the largest variance among the three variables. The largest eigenvalue (variance of U_1) accounts for about 87% of the total variability, and it is therefore justified to summarize the three-dimensional data by the single principal component U_1.

Let us briefly return to the above interpretation of the first principal component as an overall measure of performance. If we are willing to accept U_1 as a good measure, then we can rank the 20 athletes along this single dimension. The total score (sum of the three or ten disciplines) serves the same purpose. Moreover, as with the first principal component, the total score is a linear combination of the single scores, all coefficients being predetermined and fixed. How do the two methods of ranking compare? In any case, if we are willing to summarize high-dimensional data meaningfully by a final score, then we would expect the final score to be closely related to the first principal component, and the first component should account for a large proportion of the total variability. In our example with three variables, the second condition

Table 10.10 Standard principal components in the Decathlon example with three variables. (*Note: SUM* = sum of scores achieved in three running disciplines. F_1, F_2 and F_3 denote the standardized principal components.)

Athlete no.	SUM	F_1	F_2	F_3	Standard distance
1	2816	2.230	0.027	-0.042	2.231
2	2623	0.977	0.084	1.553	1.837
3	2452	0.027	0.633	0.000	0.634
4	2640	1.260	-0.989	-0.890	1.832
5	2545	0.529	0.062	1.241	1.351
6	2436	-0.112	-0.175	1.176	1.194
7	2464	0.111	-0.639	0.495	0.815
8	2526	0.510	-1.073	0.277	1.220
9	2699	1.548	1.410	-1.129	2.379
10	2407	-0.264	2.399	-0.635	2.495
11	2339	-0.524	-0.113	-1.701	1.784
12	2413	-0.142	0.692	-1.121	1.325
13	2468	0.238	-1.692	-0.651	1.828
14	2250	-1.235	0.432	0.981	1.635
15	2272	-0.982	-0.358	-0.622	1.216
16	2379	-0.479	1.583	0.622	1.766
17	2379	-0.455	-0.143	1.171	1.264
18	2434	-0.025	-1.244	0.097	1.248
19	2167	-1.700	-0.188	0.782	1.881
20	2172	-1.511	-0.708	-1.603	2.314

is fulfilled. To check the first condition, standardized principal component scores were computed according to the formula

$$F_h = U_h / \sqrt{l_h}$$

of Section 10.3. Table 10.10 displays these scores, as well as the sum of the scores achieved in the three disciplines. It is left to the reader to judge how strongly the first principal component and the sum of scores are related, but it is obvious that good runners (i.e. competitors with a high value of F_1) range in general in the upper half of the table, and bad runners in the lower half.

The last column of Table 10.10 gives the standard distance of each athlete from the mean. It is interesting to notice that large standard distances occur at both ends of the list as well as for some 'intermediate' athletes. Decathlonist no. 10 (Kolowanow), for instance, has a standard distance of 2.495. This relatively large value is due to the second principal component, which contrasts the 400 m run with 110 m hurdles. Indeed, Kolowanow's results in these two disciplines do not agree well: below average in the 400 m run, above average in 110 m hurdles. A strong, balanced athlete would be expected to show a high value of the first principal component, and to have scores near 0 in the remaining components. This is indeed the case for the top-ranked athlete no. 1 (Thompson).

Finally, let us add some critical remarks. At the end of Section 10.4 we said that principal component analysis based on the covariance matrix is meaningful only if all variables are measured on the same scale. Do scores achieved in different disciplines have the same unit of measurement? This question is debatable. The same criticism applies to the final score as well – by simply adding up ten scores we implicitly assume that the ten scores are measured on the same scale! Such problems occur quite frequently in the behavioural and social sciences. For instance, measuring the social level or the intelligence of a person depends crucially on the assumption that different scores can simply be added.

Another critical remark refers to the estimation of standard errors. For a sample size of 20 it would be preferable not to use an asymptotic formula. It is indeed possible to estimate standard errors even for small samples by the bootstrap method; see Diaconis and Efron (1983). However, this method is very computer-intensive, and explaining it is beyond the scope of this book.

Example 10.2 Head dimensions of young Swiss men

The data on which this example is based were collected by a group of anthropologists on about 900 Swiss soldiers, most of them recruits. The purpose of the study was to provide sufficient data to construct a new protection mask for the members of the Swiss army. For lack of space we will report here only the data of 200 men, all of them 20 years old at the time of investigation, and only 6 of the 25 head measurements.

In order to explain why principal component analysis was a natural tool in the context of this study, let us give some more details about its purpose. It was clear from earlier investigations that, given the variability in size and shape of human faces, it would be necessary to construct several (two to five) types or sizes of masks to make sure that everybody could be provided with a sufficiently well fitting mask. The anthropologists were therefore asked to identify 'typical' individuals, on whom prototypes of masks would then be modelled.

How can such 'typical individuals' be found? Suppose for the moment that the data were univariate and, say, three types are to be defined. Then one might simply rank all individuals along the single dimension and pick out the ones, for instance, who are at the 15th, 50th and 85th percentiles of the sample distribution. In the multivariate case, an obvious generalization of this idea is to rank all individuals on the first principal component – provided that it is well defined and accounts for a substantial part of the total variance. (Actually the latter proviso is the reason why this simple procedure failed – we will return to this point later.) So the reason for performing principal component analysis on these data was to approximate high-dimensional data by a single variable – the first principal component.

In the actual study, principal component analysis was performed on ten variables that were considered to be important for the fit of protection masks.

Table 10.11 Anthropometric measurements taken on 200 young Swiss men. See text and Fig. 10.14 for descriptions of the variables. All data are in millimetres. (Data courtesy of R. Bauer, AC-Laboratorium, Spiez).

MFB	BAM	TFH	LGAN	LTN	LTG
113.2	111.7	119.6	53.9	127.4	143.6
117.6	117.3	121.2	47.7	124.7	143.9
112.3	124.7	131.6	56.7	123.4	149.3
116.2	110.5	114.2	57.9	121.6	140.9
112.9	111.3	114.3	51.5	119.9	133.5
104.2	114.3	116.5	49.9	122.9	136.7
110.7	116.9	128.5	56.8	118.1	134.7
105.0	119.2	121.1	52.2	117.3	131.4
115.9	118.5	120.4	60.2	123.0	146.8
96.8	108.4	109.5	51.9	120.1	132.2
110.7	117.5	115.4	55.2	125.0	140.6
108.4	113.7	122.2	56.2	124.5	146.3
104.1	116.0	124.3	49.8	121.8	138.1
107.9	115.2	129.4	62.2	121.6	137.9
106.4	109.0	114.9	56.8	120.1	129.5
112.7	118.0	117.4	53.0	128.3	141.6
109.9	105.2	122.2	56.6	122.2	137.8
116.6	119.5	130.6	53.0	124.0	135.3
109.9	113.5	125.7	62.8	122.7	139.5
107.1	110.7	121.7	52.1	118.6	141.6
113.3	117.8	120.7	53.5	121.6	138.6
108.1	116.3	123.9	55.5	125.4	146.1
111.5	111.1	127.1	57.9	115.8	135.1
115.7	117.3	123.0	50.8	122.2	143.1
112.2	120.6	119.6	61.3	126.7	141.1
118.7	122.9	126.7	59.8	125.7	138.3
118.9	118.4	127.7	64.6	125.6	144.3
114.2	109.4	119.3	58.7	121.1	136.2
113.8	113.6	135.8	54.3	119.5	130.9
122.4	117.2	122.2	56.4	123.3	142.9
110.4	110.8	122.1	51.2	115.6	132.7
114.9	108.6	122.9	56.3	122.7	140.3
108.4	118.7	117.8	50.0	113.7	131.0
105.3	107.2	116.0	52.5	117.4	133.2
110.5	124.9	122.4	62.2	123.1	137.0
110.3	113.2	123.9	62.9	122.3	139.8
115.1	116.4	118.1	51.9	121.5	133.8
119.6	120.2	120.0	59.7	123.9	143.7
119.7	125.2	124.5	57.8	125.3	142.7
110.2	116.8	120.6	54.3	123.6	140.1
118.9	126.6	128.2	63.8	125.7	151.1
112.3	114.7	127.7	59.4	125.2	137.5
113.7	111.4	122.6	63.3	121.6	146.8
108.1	116.4	115.5	55.2	123.5	134.1
105.6	111.4	121.8	61.4	117.7	132.6
111.1	111.9	125.2	56.1	119.9	139.5
111.3	117.6	129.3	63.7	124.3	142.8
119.4	114.6	125.0	62.5	129.5	147.7
113.4	120.5	121.1	61.5	118.1	137.2
114.7	113.8	137.7	59.8	124.5	143.3

Table 10.11 (Continued)

MFB	BAM	TFH	LGAN	LTN	LTG
115.1	113.9	118.6	59.5	119.4	141.6
114.6	112.4	122.2	54.5	121.2	126.3
115.2	117.2	122.2	60.1	123.9	135.7
115.4	119.5	132.8	60.3	127.8	140.3
119.3	120.6	116.6	55.8	121.5	143.0
112.8	119.3	129.6	61.0	121.1	139.4
116.6	109.6	125.4	54.6	120.2	122.6
106.5	116.0	123.2	52.8	121.7	134.9
112.1	117.4	128.2	59.9	120.3	131.5
112.8	113.0	125.4	64.8	119.4	136.6
114.6	119.0	116.8	57.4	123.8	140.0
110.9	116.5	125.8	53.5	124.8	142.9
109.1	117.0	123.7	60.0	120.1	137.7
111.7	117.3	121.0	51.5	119.7	135.5
106.4	111.1	124.4	59.1	122.4	138.4
121.2	122.5	117.8	54.8	121.5	143.9
115.2	121.2	117.4	54.9	121.9	144.0
123.2	124.2	120.0	57.9	119.4	138.4
113.1	114.5	118.9	56.9	121.8	135.0
110.3	108.9	115.2	55.9	119.0	138.0
115.0	114.7	123.5	66.7	120.3	133.6
111.9	111.1	122.3	63.8	117.1	131.6
117.2	117.5	120.2	60.5	119.5	129.6
113.8	112.5	123.2	62.0	113.5	132.4
112.8	113.5	114.3	53.8	128.4	143.8
113.3	118.4	123.8	51.6	122.7	141.7
123.9	120.5	118.3	54.3	122.0	133.8
119.8	119.6	126.1	57.5	124.7	130.9
110.9	113.9	123.7	62.7	124.8	143.5
111.9	125.1	121.8	58.1	112.1	134.8
114.0	120.8	131.2	61.0	124.7	152.6
113.6	110.4	130.9	60.2	118.5	132.5
118.9	126.1	121.9	56.1	127.3	145.6
119.4	127.8	128.0	61.8	120.6	141.3
121.0	121.1	116.8	56.3	124.2	140.9
109.0	105.7	126.2	59.4	121.2	143.2
117.9	125.1	122.6	58.2	128.4	151.1
124.8	123.8	128.3	60.4	129.1	147.2
120.6	124.3	120.0	59.5	123.4	144.1
115.6	115.9	117.2	54.0	119.9	135.3
116.6	119.1	131.0	58.0	123.3	136.4
118.7	118.9	129.6	68.6	123.0	141.4
114.3	117.1	127.1	55.7	119.1	139.8
110.9	113.1	124.1	60.6	115.7	132.1
119.2	120.0	136.9	55.1	129.5	142.0
117.1	123.7	108.7	53.2	125.6	136.6
109.3	110.2	129.3	58.5	121.0	136.8
108.8	119.3	118.7	58.9	118.5	132.7
109.0	127.5	124.6	61.1	117.6	131.5
101.2	110.6	124.3	62.9	124.3	138.9

Table 10.11 (Continued)

MFB	BAM	TFH	LGAN	LTN	LTG
117.8	109.0	127.1	53.9	117.9	135.8
112.4	115.6	135.3	55.8	125.0	136.1
105.3	109.8	115.4	59.6	116.6	137.4
117.7	122.4	127.1	74.2	125.5	144.5
110.9	113.7	126.8	62.7	121.4	142.7
115.6	117.5	114.2	55.0	113.2	136.6
115.4	118.1	116.6	62.5	125.4	142.1
113.6	116.7	130.1	58.5	120.8	140.3
116.1	117.6	132.3	59.6	122.0	139.1
120.5	115.4	120.2	53.5	118.6	139.4
119.0	124.1	124.3	73.6	126.3	141.6
122.7	109.0	116.3	55.8	121.8	139.4
117.8	108.2	133.9	61.3	120.6	141.3
122.3	114.2	137.4	61.7	125.8	143.2
114.4	117.8	128.1	54.9	126.5	140.6
110.6	111.8	128.4	56.7	121.7	147.5
123.3	119.1	117.0	51.7	119.9	137.9
118.0	118.0	131.5	61.2	125.0	140.5
122.0	114.6	126.2	55.5	121.2	143.4
113.4	104.1	128.3	58.7	124.1	142.8
117.0	111.3	129.8	55.6	119.5	136.1
116.6	108.3	123.7	61.0	123.4	134.0
120.1	116.7	122.8	57.4	123.2	145.2
119.8	125.0	124.1	61.8	126.9	141.2
123.5	123.0	121.6	59.2	115.3	138.4
114.9	126.7	131.3	57.3	122.7	139.2
120.6	110.8	129.6	58.1	122.7	134.7
113.0	114.8	120.7	54.1	119.7	140.9
111.8	110.2	121.0	56.4	121.4	132.1
110.8	114.9	120.5	58.7	113.4	131.6
114.8	118.8	120.9	58.4	119.7	135.9
122.5	122.3	116.7	57.4	128.1	147.3
105.9	105.6	129.3	69.5	123.6	136.6
108.0	111.3	116.9	53.8	117.8	129.6
114.4	111.7	116.3	54.3	120.2	130.1
117.9	112.9	119.1	54.2	117.9	134.8
110.7	113.9	114.5	53.0	120.1	124.5
112.3	110.4	116.8	52.0	121.0	133.4
110.9	110.0	116.7	53.4	115.4	133.0
126.6	127.0	135.2	60.6	128.6	149.6
116.2	115.2	117.8	60.8	123.1	136.8
117.2	117.8	123.1	61.8	122.1	140.8
114.5	113.2	119.8	50.3	120.6	135.1
126.2	118.7	114.6	55.1	126.3	146.7
118.7	123.1	131.6	61.8	123.9	139.7
116.2	111.5	112.9	54.0	114.7	134.2
113.9	100.6	124.0	60.3	118.7	140.7
114.4	113.7	123.3	63.2	125.5	145.5
114.5	119.3	130.6	61.7	123.6	138.5
113.3	115.9	116.1	53.5	127.2	136.5

Table 10.11 (Continued)

MFB	BAM	TFH	LGAN	LTN	LTG
120.7	114.6	124.1	53.2	127.5	139.1
119.1	115.3	116.6	53.5	128.2	142.6
113.2	107.7	122.0	60.6	119.4	124.2
113.7	110.0	131.0	63.5	117.3	134.6
116.3	119.3	116.6	57.3	122.0	141.6
117.6	117.8	122.5	59.9	119.4	136.3
114.8	115.0	115.2	58.9	122.5	135.2
127.3	123.9	130.3	59.8	128.3	138.7
130.5	125.5	127.4	62.1	130.1	153.3
110.4	105.4	122.1	56.2	114.6	122.8
108.5	105.4	119.1	59.4	120.4	134.7
121.6	112.1	126.5	60.6	122.7	142.9
117.9	115.2	139.1	59.6	125.5	141.3
112.7	111.5	114.9	53.5	113.9	132.6
121.8	119.0	116.9	56.5	120.1	139.2
118.5	120.0	129.8	59.5	127.8	150.5
118.3	120.0	127.5	56.6	122.0	139.4
117.9	114.4	116.4	56.7	123.1	136.3
114.2	110.0	121.9	57.5	116.1	126.5
122.4	122.7	128.4	58.3	131.7	148.1
114.1	109.3	124.4	62.8	120.8	133.4
114.6	118.0	112.8	55.6	118.5	135.6
113.6	114.6	127.1	60.8	123.8	143.1
111.3	116.7	117.7	51.2	125.7	141.9
111.4	120.4	112.1	56.4	120.3	137.1
119.9	114.4	128.8	69.1	124.9	144.3
116.1	118.9	128.3	55.8	123.7	139.7
119.7	118.2	113.5	59.5	127.0	146.5
105.8	106.7	131.2	61.3	123.7	144.3
116.7	118.7	128.2	55.8	121.2	143.9
106.4	107.3	122.9	57.6	122.3	132.9
112.2	121.3	130.1	65.3	120.3	137.9
114.8	117.3	130.3	60.9	125.6	137.4
110.0	117.4	114.1	54.8	124.8	135.1
121.5	121.6	125.4	59.5	128.5	144.7
119.8	119.4	119.6	53.9	122.3	143.6
107.7	108.4	125.1	62.3	122.7	137.2
118.4	115.7	121.1	57.8	124.9	140.5
119.8	113.9	132.0	60.8	122.4	137.6
114.1	112.8	119.3	52.7	114.2	136.9
117.7	121.8	120.0	59.1	122.6	138.3
111.1	117.7	117.7	60.2	124.6	139.2
111.1	117.7	117.7	59.1	124.7	141.9
128.1	118.3	129.4	61.0	134.7	148.6
120.4	118.7	126.4	59.4	133.1	147.1
112.9	112.0	123.5	57.2	121.3	133.3
118.2	114.4	114.8	55.3	126.1	149.1
119.0	112.7	129.1	62.0	127.6	146.6
111.8	116.0	117.8	60.9	114.4	128.7
116.6	111.4	115.6	60.9	117.8	137.4

We found six variables sufficient for illustration. The variables considered here are the following:

> MFB = minimal frontal breadth
> BAM = breadth of angulus mandibulae
> TFH = true facial height
> LGAN = length from glabella to apex nasi
> LTN = length from tragion to nasion
> LTG = length from tragion to gnathion.

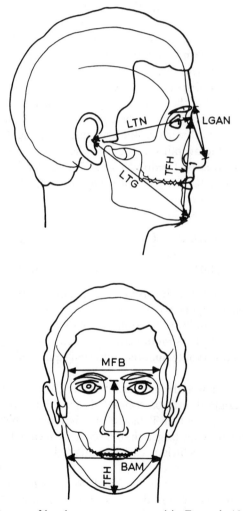

Figure 10.14   Diagram of head measurements used in Example 10.2

See Fig. 10.14 for a nontechnical description of these six variables. The data collected on 200 men, all 20 years old, are displayed in Table 10.11. All measurements were taken by the same anthropologist with a high-precision caliper and registered automatically by a portable computer. The unit of measurement is millimetres for all variables.

Table 10.12 displays basic univariate and bivariate statistics. All covariances (and therefore, correlations) between the six variables are positive. This is often the case in biometrical examples, and it implies that the first principal component has positive weights for all variables. Another frequent observation in biometrical examples is that the variability (standard deviation or variance) increases with the mean. In Table 10.12 however, no such effect can be observed: the standard deviations of LGAN and LTN, for instance, are about equal, while the means differ by a factor of 2. Does this imply that a possible effect of the kind just described is hidden by large errors of measurement is millimetres for all variables.

Table 10.13, part A, displays the coefficients of the principal component transformation. Part B of the same table gives an analysis of the eigenvalues and their relative contributions to the total variance. Before attempting an interpretation, let us check whether the principal components are well defined at all. The value of the overall statistic for sphericity (see Section 10.7) is $S_6 = 236.6$ on 20 degrees of freedom; overall sphericity is therefore clearly rejected. For all five adjacent pairs of principal components, the sphericity statistics S_2 are as follows:

Pair of components	(U_1, U_2)	(U_2, U_3)	(U_3, U_4)	(U_4, U_5)	(U_5, U_6)
Value of S_2	21.04	15.49	4.89	0.51	20.60

Hence we have a similar situation as in the bank note example: the first, second and sixth principal components seem well defined, while the tests for the pairs (U_3, U_4) and (U_4, U_5) indicate possible sphericity. It is left to the reader to compute the statistic S_3 for simultaneous sphericity of U_3, U_4 and U_5, and to compare it to an appropriate quantile of the chi square distribution with five degrees of freedom.

How stable are the 'well defined' components U_1, U_2 and U_6? To answer this question, standard errors, computed according to the formula of Section 10.7, are displayed in Table 10.14. They range between 0.024 and 0.103, most of them being larger than 0.05. This means that only the first decimal digit of each coefficient can be regarded as sufficiently stable for interpretation.

As predicted earlier, the first principal component has all coefficients positive and can roughly be considered as an overall measure of size. Hence it would seem reasonable to identify 'typical individuals' along the first principal

Table 10.12 Univariate and bivariate descriptive statistics

Variable	MFB	BAM	TFH	LGAN	LTN	LTG
Mean	114.72	115.91	123.06	57.99	122.23	138.83
Standard deviation	5.19	5.22	5.94	4.22	3.92	5.64
Covariance matrix	26.90	12.62	5.83	2.93	8.18	12.11
	12.62	27.25	2.88	2.06	7.13	11.44
	5.38	2.88	35.23	10.37	6.03	7.97
	2.93	2.06	10.37	17.85	2.92	4.99
	8.18	7.13	6.03	2.92	15.37	14.52
	12.11	11.44	7.97	4.99	14.52	31.84

Table 10.13
(a) Coefficients of the principal component transformation

Principal component	Variable					
	MFB	BAM	TFH	LGAN	LTN	LTG
U_1	0.445	0.441	0.395	0.270	0.347	0.560
U_2	−0.263	−0.375	0.799	0.345	−0.072	−0.163
U_3	0.421	0.500	0.194	0.039	−0.309	−0.662
U_4	−0.731	0.656	0.000	0.174	−0.036	0.057
U_5	0.126	−0.100	−0.404	0.896	−0.087	−0.020
U_6	−0.067	0.000	−0.063	0.056	0.878	−0.467

(b) Standard deviations of the principal components, eigenvalues, and their contribution to the total variance

Component	Standard deviation $(\sqrt{l_h})$	Variance (eigenvalue) l_h	Proportion of s^2_{total}	Cumulative proportion
U_1	8.14	66.33	0.429	0.429
U_2	5.87	34.42	0.223	0.652
U_3	4.43	19.63	0.127	0.779
U_4	3.79	14.33	0.093	0.872
U_5	3.60	12.96	0.084	0.956
U_6	2.60	6.77	0.044	1.000
		$154.44 = s^2_{total}$		

Table 10.14 Standard errors of the coefficients of the first, second and sixth principal component

Principal component	MFB	BAM	TFH	LGAN	LTN	LTG
U_1	0.048	0.056	0.087	0.051	0.029	0.042
U_2	0.091	0.092	0.056	0.068	0.064	0.103
U_6	0.075	0.072	0.056	0.097	0.024	0.045

axis of the six-dimensional distribution. However, a closer look at part B of Table 10.13 reveals that the first principal component accounts only for about 43% of the total variance ($s_{total}^2 = 154.44$). Recall that in this example the purpose of principal component analysis was to approximate the multivariate data by a single dimension. In view of this, the proportion of the total variance accounted for by the first principal component is probably too small to speak of a 'good' approximation. This result was somewhat surprising, given the fact that in many morphometrical applications of principal components (see, for instance, Example 10.3) the first component accounts for over 80% of the total variation!

We would like to discuss briefly three possible explanations for this phenomenon. The first possibility is large errors of measurement. If all variables are affected by relatively large errors, then the variances are 'inflated' and correlations tend to be relatively small. We will argue later that this cannot be the case in this example. A second explanation is that the sample of young men analysed is very homogeneous in age, so that there is no variability due to differences in age. A third (and plausible) explanation is that there are indeed many ways in which human skulls, and especially faces, can differ: it is impossible to represent them in few (one or two) dimensions without losing a lot of information. This would be even more evident if we analysed a larger number of variables.

Returning to the original purpose of this study, namely the fitting of protection masks, it is clear that with only few (say two or three) types of masks there will always be individuals for whom the fit of the mask will be relatively bad, simply because there is substantial variability in so many different directions of the space!

Let us now briefly discuss some aspects related to error of measurement. Suppose, for simplicity, that the objects measured differ only in absolute size, but not in shape. Suppose, furthermore, that we measure p variables. Then all these p variables measure essentially the same thing, namely 'size', but they may be affected by errors of measurement. If all errors of measurement are random and independent, then the $p - 1$ smallest eigenvalues are, in theory, identical, and only the first eigenvalue is distinct. Moreover, the $p - 1$ identical eigenvalues are in turn equal to the variance of the errors of measurement. In practical applications, the smallest $p - 1$ eigenvalues of the sample covariance matrix will in general not be exactly identical, but we would expect the test for sphericity, applied to principal components U_2 to U_p, to be non-significant.

Now take a slightly more complicated model, in which the p variables are actually determined by a smaller number q of dimensions, but measurements are again affected by random errors. In this case the last $p - q$ eigenvalues are identical and equal to the variance of the errors of measurement.

In general, if the last $p - q$ principal components are spherical, this may indicate that they express only error of measurement. In our example, the fifth and sixth principal components are clearly not spherical. This supports the foregoing explanation of the phenomenon that the first principal component alone is not sufficient to approximate the six-dimensional data.

Finally, let us turn to principal component scores and standard distances. For all 200 observations, the scores of the standardized principal components

$$F_h = U_h / \sqrt{l_h}$$

were computed. Scatterplots of pairs of principal components revealed

Table 10.15 Standardized principal component scores and standard distances of 20 individuals with relatively small or relatively large standard distance. (*Note:* The identification numbers (first column) refer to the relative position of an individual in the list of raw data.)

Identif. number	Standard distance	Standardized principal component scores					
		F_1	F_2	F_3	F_4	F_5	F_6
69	1.033	−0.671	−0.355	0.097	−0.035	0.210	0.660
188	1.151	0.319	−0.508	−0.197	−0.756	0.234	0.548
131	1.159	−0.254	−0.345	0.857	0.484	0.345	−0.269
142	1.159	0.459	−0.054	0.199	0.055	0.971	−0.381
173	1.233	0.500	0.713	−0.800	0.169	0.181	−0.247
21	1.236	−0.254	−0.627	0.014	0.398	−0.938	−0.175
196	1.248	−0.716	0.512	0.289	−0.437	−0.148	0.698
90	1.342	−0.681	−0.944	0.481	−0.386	−0.228	−0.119
156	1.366	−0.021	−0.108	1.055	−0.152	0.669	−0.520
61	1.415	−0.023	−1.130	−0.226	0.534	0.422	0.460
.							
.							
3	3.530	1.462	0.331	−0.520	2.080	−1.695	−1.657
147	3.715	−0.735	1.272	−1.778	−2.326	0.939	−1.480
194	3.780	2.438	−0.135	−0.482	−2.003	0.085	2.018
133	3.893	−0.502	2.629	−1.391	0.400	2.120	1.184
57	3.914	−1.392	0.916	2.104	−1.838	−0.726	2.052
99	3.940	−0.276	0.171	2.277	3.189	0.233	−0.068
80	3.988	−0.458	−0.389	2.024	2.178	0.082	−2.588
104	4.088	1.628	0.760	0.260	1.348	3.396	0.257
10	4.093	−2.718	−0.710	−2.060	1.800	−0.326	1.127
111	4.291	1.468	0.247	0.825	1.312	3.556	1.069

nothing of interest; so they are not reproduced here. What about standard distances? If we assume multivariate normality, then the 200 squared standard distances should follow approximately a chi square distribution on six degrees of freedom. From a table of quantiles of the chi square distribution we take the following values:

$V_{0.05} = 5$ percent quantile of chi square on six degrees of freedom
$= 1.64.$

$V_{0.95} = 95$ percent quantile of chi square on six degrees of freedom
$= 12.59.$

This means that, under normality assumptions, we would expect about 5% of the observations (i.e. about ten individuals) to have a standard distance larger than $\sqrt{V_{0.95}} = 3.55$. Similarly, about ten observations are expected to have a standard distance smaller than $\sqrt{V_{0.05}} = 1.28$. Table 10.15 gives a list of the ten observations with the smallest and the ten observations with the largest standard distances from the mean, as well as their standardized principal component scores. As can be seen from the table, seven observations have standard distances smaller than 1.28, and nine observations have standard distances larger than 3.55. This is quite close to the numbers predicted by normal theory, thus confirming the extraordinarily high quality of these data.

Example 10.3 Cranial morphometry of two species of voles

This application of principal component analysis is based on the data collected by Airoldi and Hoffmann (1984). In Example 7.1 we defined six variables (cf Fig. 7.18) and analysed two groups of females. We are now going to illustrate common principal component analysis, the topic of section 10.8, using samples of size $n_1 = n_2 = 55$ of male animals. The species are again (1) *Microtus californicus*, and (2) *M. ochrogaster*. In the original study, there were 173 male specimens of *M. californicus*, and 88 of *M. ochrogaster*, but we found random subsamples of 55 each to be sufficient for illustration. See Airoldi and Flury (1988) for a common principal component analysis of the full data set. The variables used here are $L_2 =$ condylo-incisive length, $B_3 =$ zygomatic width, and $H_1 =$ skull height; see Fig. 7.18. Table 10.16 displays the raw data of both groups.

In contrast to Example 7.1, there is no selection of animals according to age. Actually, one of the purposes of principal component analysis in morphometrical studies may be to study variation due to differences in age. In such cases it is customary to compute principal components on the logarithms of the variables instead of the variables themselves. One justification for this is to downweigh variables with large variances. A less pragmatic justification is provided by the allometric model of growth (Jolicoeur, 1963b), which assumes that the relative growth rates of all dimensions considered are constant. The

Table 10.16 Skull dimensions of voles. *AGE* is in days, all other variables are in 0.1 mm. See example 7.1 for a description of variables. Data courtesy of J.P. Airoldi, University of Berne.

M. californicus, males $n_1 = 55$				M. ochrogaster, males $n_2 = 55$			
AGE	L2	B3	H1	AGE	L2	B3	H1
46	257	144	104	183	265	155	104
44	251	145	111	30	234	131	97
172	299	169	112	335	283	159	104
121	285	170	113	61	259	136	97
129	285	162	106	152	274	155	107
91	275	154	105	122	264	145	99
62	282	154	109	91	266	144	97
165	285	166	111	363	274	153	102
47	218	125	96	274	279	155	103
117	289	160	113	122	246	139	99
50	261	150	106	132	266	148	104
95	279	157	110	274	271	149	108
17	214	125	97	75	251	140	99
178	304	167	110	61	253	142	100
364	292	167	113	183	272	160	103
178	288	166	114	365	286	156	104
117	280	163	110	152	282	155	106
17	210	117	94	183	258	141	102
17	217	125	96	22	211	122	95
17	216	119	90	15	191	109	93
179	298	168	114	61	248	132	92
96	297	167	111	183	247	143	101
64	286	158	110	244	274	147	102
48	249	137	101	152	259	149	103
47	216	126	96	45	256	139	102
122	267	151	104	82	260	145	103
80	272	146	102	305	276	150	109
37	250	143	107	58	245	144	102
62	277	151	108	45	247	133	100
47	264	151	103	15	205	116	93
36	262	145	104	122	273	153	106
150	291	174	118	244	267	149	104
143	312	162	110	335	283	155	107
140	296	170	112	244	267	156	101
17	201	114	95	152	253	140	101
109	292	163	111	152	267	152	108
143	278	163	116	274	272	153	105
71	256	140	100	63	242	138	100
150	312	187	126	45	242	137	100
88	267	150	104	104	256	144	99
18	209	120	95	335	274	150	106
30	251	142	102	61	261	141	99
172	304	165	111	274	261	149	103
97	292	159	106	335	275	155	103
121	288	168	113	91	238	137	93
54	259	149	107	122	241	141	95
177	286	166	108	365	278	158	112
102	285	159	113	183	273	152	102
176	286	161	112	30	238	133	96
298	289	168	109	30	216	119	95
68	276	151	105	30	235	130	95
62	280	155	109	183	270	151	100
17	225	129	98	213	268	152	100
110	272	158	110	305	283	153	105
17	217	125	97	30	237	133	95

coefficients of the first principal component, based on the covariance matrix of log-variables, can then be used to estimate these relative growth rates or constants of allometry. In addition, if the growth rates are identical for all p variables, we speak of isometric growth. Hence, if growth is isometric, we would expect all coefficients of the first principal component to be approximately $1/\sqrt{p}$. By the way, it does not matter whether we use common or natural logarithms, since the two functions are proportional to each other. We will always use natural logarithms in this example.

In mathematical language, using log-variables means that we are actually studying multiplicative functions of the original variables. Let

$$Y = a_1 \log X_1 + a_2 \log X_2 + \cdots + a_p \log X_p$$

denote a linear combination of $\log X_1$ to $\log X_p$, then we can equivalently write

$$Y^*: = e^Y = \exp\left[a_1 \log X_1 + \cdots + a_p \log X_p\right]$$
$$= X_1^{a_1} \times X_2^{a_2} \times \cdots \times X_p^{a_p}.$$

Here, 'exp' denotes the exponential function.

In the voles example we transformed the data according to

$$LL_2 = 100 \cdot \log(L_2)$$
$$LB_3 = 100 \cdot \log(B_3)$$
$$LH_1 = 100 \cdot \log(H_1).$$

The factor 100 was introduced merely for numerical convenience; multiplying all variables by the same constant doesn't affect the principal component transformation.

The sample covariance matrices of both groups are displayed in Table 10.17. It is left to the reader to perform a principal component analysis individually on each group, and to compare the resulting principal component transformations. See Exercise 20 in Chapter 12.

Table 10.18 shows the coefficients of the common principal component transformation, and the associated variances. Evidently, in both groups the first component (U_1) accounts for a very large proportion of the total variance: 96.8% for *M. californicus*, and 93.6% for *M. ochrogaster*.

Table 10.17 Covariance matrices of log-variables

M. californicus ($n_1 = 55$)			*M. ochrogaster* ($n_2 = 55$)		
LL_2	138.15	133.17	69.42	70.61	65.25	29.22
LB_3	133.17	136.29	72.88	65.25	66.52	28.99
LH_1	69.42	72.88	44.16	29.22	28.99	19.87
	LL_2	LB_3	LH_1	LL_2	LB_3	LH_1

Table 10.18 Common principal components and their variances

	Coefficients of common principal components			Variances of common principal components	
	LL_2	LB_3	LH_1	*M. californicus*	*M. ochrogaster*
U_1	0.670	0.660	0.339	308.56	146.99
U_2	−0.566	0.158	0.810	7.81	6.27
U_3	−0.481	0.734	−0.479	2.24	3.74

Table 10.19 Correlation matrices of common principal components in both groups

M. californicus				*M. ochrogaster*		
1.00	0.11	−0.03	U_1	1.00	−0.15	0.07
0.11	1.00	0.10	U_2	−0.15	1.00	−0.26
−0.03	0.10	1.00	U_3	0.07	−0.26	1.00
U_1	U_2	U_3		U_1	U_2	U_3

Before attempting an interpretation, we have to check whether the common principal component model is appropriate. The variances of the ordinary principal components (eigenvalues of the two covariance matrices) are as follows:

$$M.\ californicus: 308.66, 7.74, 2.20$$
$$M.\ ochrogaster: 147.15, 6.63, 3.22$$

(see Exercise 20 in Chapter 12).

Hence, using the formula given in Section 10.8, we get $X^2_{\text{CPC}} = 6.4$. The critical value of the chi square distribution on three degrees of freedom at a significance level of 5% is 7.81, and so we conclude that the common principal component model fits sufficiently well.

We can now apply the common principal component transformation to the data. Recall that, if the model is correct, we would expect U_1 to U_3 to be 'almost uncorrelated' in both groups. Indeed, as Table 10.19 shows, all correlations are very small, except for a correlation coefficient of −0.26 between U_2 and U_3 in group *M. ochrogaster*. A scatterplot of U_2 vs U_3 in this group is shown in Fig. 10.15. The negative correlation is visible, but certainly not very strong. Notice that both axes in Fig. 10.15 were drawn to the same scale, thus illustrating the difference in variability between U_2 and U_3.

Let us study the first component, U_1, in more detail. Its variance is

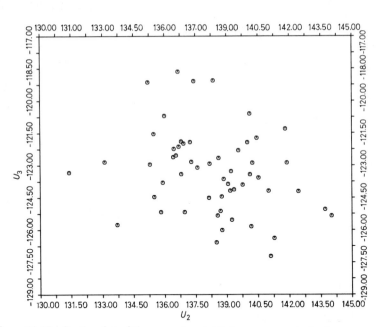

Figure 10.15 Scatterplot of the second and third common principal components in group *M. ochrogaster*

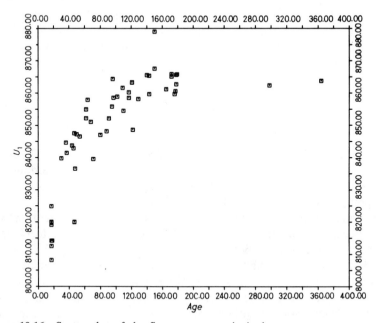

Figure 10.16 Scatterplot of the first common principal component versus age in group *M. californicus*

considerably larger in *M. californicus* than in *M. ochrogaster*, but in both groups it accounts for over 90% of the total variance. As the exact age of the animals is known, we can analyse the relationship between U_1 and *Age* by drawing a scatterplot; this has been done in Fig. 10.16 for *M. californicus*. A strong nonlinear dependency is obvious. On the other hand, scatterplots of U_2 and U_3 vs *Age* revealed no dependencies, and hence it is reasonable to assume that U_1 does contain all variability due to age. This could be used to construct a growth-invariant discriminant function between the two groups (see also Example 7.1): simply use the common components U_2 and U_3 (or, in general, U_2 to U_p) for discrimination, but not U_1! It is left to the reader to actually compute such a discriminant function; see Exercise 20 in Chapter 12.

The first component has a remarkable property: its coefficients are almost exactly $\frac{2}{3}$, $\frac{2}{3}$ and $\frac{1}{3}$. Hence we can write, approximately,

$$U_1 = \tfrac{1}{3}[2\log(L_2) + 2\log(B_3) + \log(H_1)]$$

or

$$3U_1 = \log(L_2)^2 + \log(B_3)^3 + \log(H_1),$$

where the factor 100 has been omitted for simplicity. Transforming back to the original variables, we get

$$\exp(3U_1) = (L_2)^2 \cdot (B_3)^2 \cdot H_1.$$

The exponents of the three variables in this formula can be considered as constants of allometry, indicating that the relative growth in the direction of L_2 and B_3 is twice the relative growth in the direction of H_1. Even without a formal test it seems clear that this result is not in accordance with the isometric model of growth, which would predict all exponents to be equal (that is, all coefficients of U_1 would be approximately $1/\sqrt{3} = 0.577$).

The second and third common components can also be ascribed a meaning: U_2 contrasts LH_1 with LL_2, that is, animals with a relatively large value of H_1/L_2 score high on the second component. Similarly, the third component contrasts the width (B_3) with length and height. In biometrical studies it is customary to label such principal components as 'shape'-variables, while U_1 would be called a 'size'-variable.

This example has many similarities with the classical applications of principal component analysis to morphometrical data published by Jolicoeur (1963a) and by Jolicoeur and Mosimann (1960). A wealth of morphometrical applications can be found in Reyment *et al.* (1984). For discussions of 'size' and 'shape' variables, see also the articles by Mosimann and Malley (1979) and Bookstein (1986).

11

Comparing the covariance structures of two groups

11.1 INTRODUCTION

In Tables 3.1 to 3.4 we noticed some differences between the correlation and covariance matrices of the genuine and forged bills, respectively. The correlation between BOTTOM and DIAGONAL, for instance, is stronger in group *Forged* than in group *Genuine*. For the variables LENGTH, LEFT, RIGHT and TOP, the standard deviation is larger in group *Genuine* than in group *Forged*, while the opposite is true for BOTTOM and DIAGONAL.

If we want to interpret differences between variances or between correlations, we should make sure, however, that the differences are not merely due to sampling variability. More formally, we can postulate a null hypothesis of *equality of the covariance matrices* of both populations. (Recall that we actually assumed this in the chapter on discriminant analysis.) Unless this null hypothesis can be rejected, we should not interpret any differences between the sample covariance matrices.

From univariate statistics we know the following test for equality of variances. Let s_1 and s_2 denote the standard deviations of a variable in two independent samples of size n_1 and n_2, respectively. If the null hypothesis of equality of the two population variances holds, the ratio

$$F = s_1^2/s_2^2$$

deviates from unity only by sampling error. Under normality assumptions, the distribution of the F-ratio is F with $(n_1 - 1)$ and $(n_2 - 1)$ degrees of freedom. The hypothesis of equality is rejected if $F < f_l$ or $F > f_u$, where f_l and f_u are the lower and upper $\alpha/2$-quantiles of the null distribution.

We are now going to indicate how this univariate F-ratio can be generalized to the multivariate case. If the p variables were all mutually independent in both groups, we could form p independent ratios of variances and compare each of them individually with critical values of the F-distribution. For correlated variables, however, the p variance ratios would not be independent. Even worse, differences between correlations or covariances would be neglected in this approach.

Yet there is a simple argument that allows us to define F-ratios also in the multivariate case: if the null hypothesis of equality of the two covariance matrices holds true, then the variance of every linear combination must be identical in both groups; conversely, if for every linear combination the variances are identical in both groups, then the covariance matrices must be the same. Our null hypothesis is therefore equivalent to the condition that for every linear combination the same standard deviation results in both groups, or, in other words, that the ratio of variances of every linear combination equals unity. This condition can be checked by determining linear combinations for which the empirical ratio of variances deviates as strongly as possible from one.

Formally, we look at linear combinations

$$Y = a_1 X_1 + a_2 X_2 + \cdots + a_p X_p,$$

compute their variances s_1^2 and s_2^2 in both groups and form the ratio

$$F = F(a_1, \ldots, a_p) = s_1^2 / s_2^2.$$

The particular linear combination for which F becomes maximal is called Y_{max}; analogously, Y_{min} will be the linear combination with minimal ratio of variances. It should be noted here that equivalent linear combinations in the sense of Section 6.4 have the same variance ratio. We can therefore limit ourselves to normalized linear combinations.

If, instead of F, we form the reciprocal ratio

$$F' = 1/F = s_2^2 / s_1^2$$

then we obtain only the linear combinations

$$Y'_{max} = Y_{min} \qquad \text{and} \qquad Y'_{min} = Y_{max}.$$

The respective maximal and minimal ratios of variances are

$$F'_{max} = 1/F_{min} \qquad \text{and} \qquad F'_{min} = 1/F_{max}.$$

From this we see that the choice of group identification, i.e. which group is labelled first and which second, leads only to unessential changes in the results.

11.2   THE BIVARIATE CASE

In the bank note example we will take for illustration the variables $X_4 = $ BOTTOM and $X_5 = $ TOP. Figure 11.1 shows a scatterplot of these two variables in the groups *Genuine* and *Forged*, as well as projections in various directions. Table 11.1 shows the angles corresponding to the projections, the associated linear combinations and their ratios of variances.

Since the variance ratio of a linear combination does not depend on the means, we need not pay any attention to the differences in location in Fig. 11.1.

Table 11.1 Linear combinations of Fig. 11.1

| | | | Variance in group | | Variance ratio |
No.	Angle (degrees)	Normalized linear combination	Genuine	Forged	(F/G)
1	0	X_4	0.4132	1.2813	3.10
2	90	X_5	0.4212	0.4045	0.96
3	202.14	$-0.926X_4 - 0.377X_5$	0.2304	0.8145	3.54
4	253.25	$-0.288X_4 - 0.958X_5$	0.2754	0.2070	0.75

Projections 1 and 2 illustrate only the univariate comparison of the variances of BOTTOM and TOP between *Genuine* and *Forged*. For linear combination 3 the ratio of variances attains its maximum, for no. 4 its minimum. Since multiplication of a linear combination by -1 does not affect its variance, we get from Table 11.1.

$$Y_{max} = 0.926X_4 + 0.377X_5$$

and

$$Y_{min} = 0.288X_4 + 0.958X_5.$$

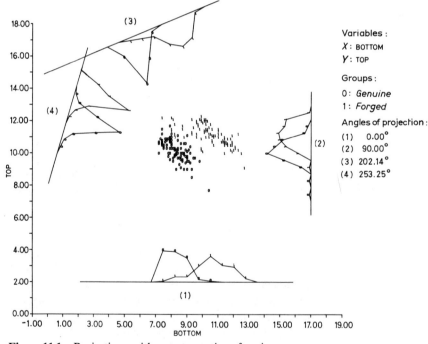

Figure 11.1 Projections with extreme ratios of variances

As was to be expected from a comparison of the univariate variance ratios of BOTTOM and TOP, variable X_4 plays the dominant role in Y_{max}, and likewise variable X_5 in Y_{min}. Yet the coefficients of X_5 in Y_{max} and X_4 in Y_{min} do not vanish completely. This is due to the correlatedness of X_4 and X_5: if the two variables were uncorrelated in both groups, then Y_{max} and Y_{min} would be identical with X_4 and X_5, respectively.

While the minimum F-ratio $F_{min} = 0.75$ does not deviate strongly from 1, the maximum ratio $F_{max} = 3.54$ seems to indicate a real difference between the covariance structures of the two groups. In terms of standard deviations, the forged bills vary $\sqrt{3.54} = 1.88$ times as much as the genuine ones with respect to the projection Y_{max}.

11.3   THE MULTIVARIATE CASE

In order to determine Y_{max} and Y_{min} in the case of $p \geqslant 2$ variables, one has to compute the p eigenvectors and associated eigenvalues of the so-called multivariate F-matrix. The mathematically interested reader is referred to Section 13.7 in the Appendix.

Each of the p eigenvectors contains the coefficients of a particular linear combination, and the associated eigenvalue gives just the corresponding value of the ratio of variances. As in the chapter on principal components, we denote the eigenvalues by $l_1, l_2, \ldots, l_p$ and order them decreasingly, that is

$$l_1 \geqslant l_2 \geqslant \cdots \geqslant l_p.$$

With this notation we have $F_{max} = l_1$ and $F_{min} = l_p$. From now on we will devote our attention mainly to l_1 and l_p and to the corresponding linear combinations.

The extreme eigenvalues F_{max} and F_{min} can be used to test the hypothesis of equality of the two covariance matrices as follows. Under the null hypothesis, these two extremes differ from 1 only by sampling error, and so l_1 and l_p would be expected close to 1. On the other hand, if F_{max} is much larger than 1 or F_{min} much smaller than 1, this indicates that the covariance structures of the two groups are not identical. The test statistic is thus actually a pair of statistics (l_1, l_p) or (F_{max}, F_{min}), and it is most often referred to as Roy's largest and smallest roots criterion.

Since F_{max} and F_{min} are the maximum and minimum respectively over all linear combinations of p variables, they cannot be compared with critical values of the familiar F-distribution. What we need instead are quantiles of the so-called multivariate F-distribution; see Table 11.3. This table gives selected critical values c_{min} and c_{max} such that, under the null hypothesis of equality of both covariance matrices,

$$P(F_{min} \leqslant c_{min}) = 0.025$$

and

$$P(F_{\max} \geqslant c_{\max}) = 0.025.$$

At a significance level of approximately $\alpha = 5\%$, the null hypothesis is rejected if $F_{\min}$ is smaller than $c_{\min}$, or if $F_{\max}$ is larger than $c_{\max}$. It should be noted, however, that the actual significance level of this test may differ from α if the data are not normal. As a general rule, the range $(c_{\min}, c_{\max})$ is too narrow in the case of heavy-tailed distributions. That is, the probability of erroneously rejecting the null hypothesis will be larger than α in such a case.

If the decision is to reject the hypothesis of equality, we proceed to a more detailed analysis of the linear combination – $Y_{\min}$ or $Y_{\max}$ or both–which is responsible for the rejection. We can distinguish between the following three cases:

$$Case\ 1:\ F_{\max} \geqslant c_{\max}\ \text{and}\ F_{\min} > c_{\min}$$
$$Case\ 2:\ F_{\min} \leqslant c_{\min}\ \text{and}\ F_{\max} < c_{\max}$$
$$Case\ 3:\ F_{\max} \geqslant c_{\max}\ \text{and}\ F_{\min} \leqslant c_{\min}.$$

In Case 1, $F_{\max}$ alone is responsible for the rejection, and we will have to analyse more closely the maximum ratio of variances. In Case 2, $F_{\min}$ is of interest, whereas in Case 3 both $(F_{\max}$ and $F_{\min})$ will be considered. Before discussing this further, however, we shall illustrate the preceding theory using the bank note data.

11.4 COMPARISON OF THE COVARIANCE MATRICES OF THE GENUINE AND FORGED BANK NOTES

In the bank note example, maximization and minimization of the ratio s_F^2/s_G^2 yields the eigenvalues and eigenvectors listed in Table 11.2. Each row in this table contains the coefficients of a linear combination, but not in the normalized form. The form given here is the one usually used by computer routines for computing eigenvectors of this type. It is distinguished by the fact

Table 11.2 Eigenvalues and eigenvectors of the multivariate F-matrix

	X_1	X_2	X_3	X_4	X_5	X_6	Eigenvalue (l_h)
Y_1	0.975	0.705	0.419	− 2.256	− 1.553	− 1.067	$6.223 = F_{\max}$
Y_2	− 0.072	0.043	1.419	− 0.476	0.490	1.927	1.675
Y_3	− 1.413	1.012	1.921	− 0.350	− 1.309	0.120	1.052
Y_4	1.984	1.353	− 1.616	− 0.045	− 0.754	− 0.580	0.900
Y_5	− 1.342	3.363	− 2.554	− 0.247	0.032	0.635	0.546
Y_6	− 0.396	− 1.174	− 0.374	− 0.512	− 0.842	0.587	$0.284 = F_{\min}$

that the variance in the denominator of the F-ratio is unity for all six linear combinations. In other words, the eigenvalues l_h are exactly the variances of the linear combinations Y_h in the group of *forged* bills, while the standard deviation of Y_h is unity in the *genuine* group. The two linear combinations of interest to us are those in the first and last row of Table 11.2. The largest ratio of variances $F_{max} = 6.223$ is realized by the first linear combination $Y_1 = Y_{max} = 0.975X_1 + 0.705X_2 + \cdots - 1.067X_6$, while $Y_6 = Y_{min}$ has the smallest ratio of variances $F_{min} = 0.284$.

From the tables of the multivariate F-distribution (cf. Section 11.8), we obtain the critical values $c_{min} = 0.43$ and $c_{max} = 2.32$. Since $F_{min} < c_{min}$ as well as $F_{max} > c_{max}$, we conclude (at a significance level of approximately 5%) that the two covariance matrices are different. It is interesting to notice that the null hypothesis can be rejected by both F_{min} and F_{max} – that is, we are dealing with Case 3 of the preceding section. In other words, the forged bills have too much variability, compared with the genuine ones (Y_{max}), but at the same time they have too little variability, as expressed by Y_{min} and its associated variance ratio F_{min}! This last fact speaks for the quality of the forger's production: in terms of variability and with respect to the projection Y_{min}, his production is even more accurate than the official manufacturer's production! We should not forget, however, that some of the variability of the genuine bills might also be due to their different wear and tear.

Figures 11.2 and 11.3 show frequency polygons of the variables Y_{max} and Y_{min} in both groups. Once again, we are interested in differences in variability,

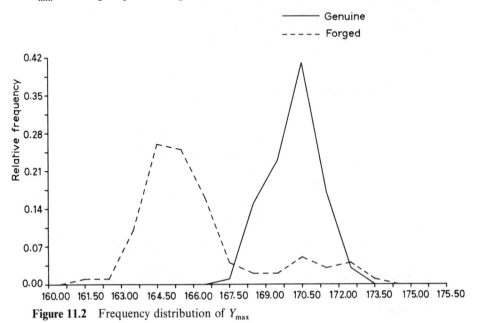

Figure 11.2   Frequency distribution of Y_{max}

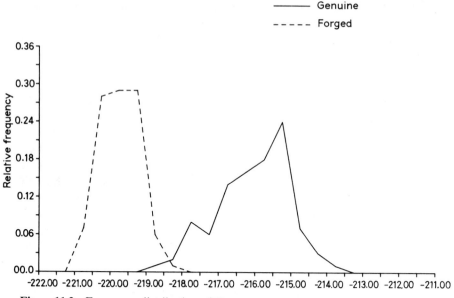

Figure 11.3   Frequency distribution of Y_{min}

rather than differences in location. Because of the special normalization of Y_{max} and Y_{min}, the standard deviation of both linear combinations is 1 in group *Genuine*, whereas in group *Forged* it is $\sqrt{6.223} = 2.49$ for Y_{max} and $\sqrt{0.284} = 0.533$ for Y_{min}. The shape of the histogram of Y_{max} in the forged group leads us to suspect that the excessive variability could be the result of an inhomogeneity of this group, that is, a mixture of two or several subgroups.

11.5   PARTIAL STATISTICS FOR THE ANALYSIS OF Y_{max} AND Y_{min}

Once it has been established that the two covariance matrices are different, the question arises which variables are mainly responsible for the rejection of the null hypothesis. The situation is in fact quite similar to the one encountered in multiple regression and discriminant analysis. In those two methods, we used the coefficient of determination (R^2) and the standard distance (D) as overall measures of dependency and difference in location, respectively, and we asked for simplified linear combinations with only 'slightly' smaller R^2 or D. In contrast to those methods, however, we may now have to analyse Y_{min} or Y_{max} or even both of them, depending on the situation as described in Section 11.3.

We are now going to define some statistics that are useful for analysing Y_{max}. Later we will define analogous statistics for the analysis of Y_{min}.

If a variable does not contribute much to the maximization of the F-ratio, we expect its coefficient in Y_{max} to be close to zero. In analogy to the regression situation, we will call such a variable *redundant* for Y_{max}. How can we assess the importance of variable X_j (say) for Y_{max}? A simple way of doing this is to compute the maximum ratio of variances that can be obtained using all variables except X_j. This quantity is called $F_{max}^{(p-1)}(j)$. The ratio

$$PCF(j) = F_{max}^{(p-1)}(j)/F_{max}^{(p)},$$

where the index p indicates the number of variables involved, is called the *Partial Change* of the F-ratio due to elimination of X_j. Since $F_{max}^{(p-1)}(j)$ cannot exceed $F_{max}^{(p)}$, this statistic is always less than or equal to 1. $PCF(j)$ tells us to what fraction of its original value the largest variance ratio drops upon elimination of X_j. In addition, we will compute

$$LPCF(j) = \log PCF(j),$$

where 'log' is the natural logarithm. The LPCF-statistics take negative values, and if variable X_j is redundant for Y_{max}, we can expect $LPCF(j)$ to be close to zero.

We will illustrate the use of the PCF- and LPCF-statistics in a stepwise elimination procedure. This procedure starts in step 1 with a table containing the coefficients of $Y_{max}^{(p)}$ (that is, Y_{max} based on p variables), as well as the partial PCF and LPCF-statistics. In the second step we find the variable whose elimination has the least influence on Y_{max}. That is, we determine the variable with the largest PCF-value, or equivalently, with the smallest absolute LPCF-value. After having eliminated this variable, we set up again a table of coefficients and partial statistics, this time, however, based on $p-1$ variables.

This procedure can be continued analogously until some stopping criterion is satisfied, or until only one variable is left after p steps.

A different way of assessing the importance of variable X_j in Y_{max} is to estimate the standard error of its coefficient. Let us denote the coefficients of linear combination Y_h (cf. Table 11.2) as $b_{h1}, b_{h2}, \ldots, b_{hp}$. The coefficients of $Y_{max} = Y_1$ are thus denoted by $b_{11}, b_{12}, \ldots, b_{1p}$. Moreover, put $k_1 = (n_1 + n_2 - 2)/(n_1 - 1)$ and $k_2 = (n_1 + n_2 - 2)/(n_2 - 1)$, where n_i are the sample sizes and n_1 refers to the sample whose variance is in the numerator of the F-ratio. If n_1 and n_2 are sufficiently large, the standard error of b_{1j} can be estimated as

$$s(b_{1j}) = \sqrt{\left[\frac{1}{n_1 + n_2 - 2} \sum_{h=2}^{p} \frac{k_2 l_1^2 + k_1 l_1 l_h}{(l_1 - l_h)^2} b_{hj}^2 \right]}.$$

Using this estimate of the standard error, it is possible to construct a formal test for redundancy of variable X_j in Y_{max}: for large samples and multivariate normal distributions, the statistic

$$R_1(X_j) = b_{1j}/s(b_{1j})$$

is distributed approximately as standard normal, if the hypothesis of redundancy of X_j holds. Large absolute values of R_1 will thus indicate that the corresponding variable cannot be eliminated.

Computing the standard errors $s(b_{1j})$ is, unfortunately, rather laborious, and the user is well advised to do it with a computer program rather than by hand. It should also be noted that the standard errors depend on all p eigenvalues and eigenvectors, so that at each stage of the stepwise procedure all eigenvectors must be computed.

The reader who is familiar with principal component analysis may have noticed a similarity between the above formula for $s(b_{1j})$ and the formula given in Section 10.7. Indeed, most of the remarks on standard errors in principal component analysis apply as well to the method of this chapter. In particular, we note that the standard errors will tend to be large if l_2, the second eigenvalue, is close to l_1. This indicates that the coefficients b_{1j} are poorly defined if $F_{\max}$ is not well separated from the other $p-1$ eigenvalues.

The concepts introduced for the analysis of $Y_{\max}$ can now be carried over to $Y_{\min}$ as follows. Let $F_{\min}^{(p-1)}(j)$ denote the smallest ratio of variances that can be obtained without variable X_j. Again, we put

$$PCF(j) = F_{\min}^{(p-1)}(j)/F_{\min}^{(p)},$$

which tells us to what proportion of its original value the smallest ratio of variances rises upon elimination of X_j. Similarly, we compute again

$$LPCF(j) = \log PCF(j),$$

which takes now only positive values. Values close to zero indicate again that a variable can be eliminated without much loss of information.

The reasons for computing the LPCF-statistics can now be summarized as follows:

1. The elimination rule can be formulated identically for $Y_{\max}$ and $Y_{\min}$ in terms of $|LPCF|$: eliminate the variable with the smallest absolute value of LPCF.
2. The values of $|LPCF|$ are in the 'familiar' range from zero to infinity, with a value close to zero indicating that the corresponding variable can be eliminated without much loss of information.
3. The values of $|LPCF|$ do not depend on the numbering of the two groups and are therefore directly comparable in the analyses of $Y_{\max}$ and $Y_{\min}$. It is convenient to use the same stopping criterion for the analyses of both $Y_{\max}$ and $Y_{\min}$: stop eliminating as soon as the smallest of the $|LPCF(j)|$-values is larger than some fixed constant c.

Standard errors of the coefficients of $Y_{\min}$ can be computed as

$$s(b_{pj}) = \sqrt{\left[\frac{1}{n_1 + n_2 - 2}\sum_{h=1}^{p-1}\frac{k_2 l_p^2 - k_1 l_p l_h}{(l_p - l_h)^2} b_{hj}^2\right]}.$$

11.6 STEPWISE ANALYSIS OF Y_{max} AND Y_{min}

The stepwise analysis of Y_{min} begins with a table of coefficients, standard errors and partial statistics as follows:

Step 1: All six variables ($F_{min}^{(6)} = 0.284$)

Variable	Coefficient	Std. error	PCF	LPCF
LENGTH	0.396	0.334	1.034	0.033
LEFT	1.174	0.645	1.092	0.088
RIGHT	0.374	0.529	1.014	0.014
BOTTOM	0.512	0.079	1.515	0.416
TOP	0.842	0.135	1.539	0.431
DIAGONAL	− 0.587	0.169	1.216	0.195

LENGTH, LEFT and RIGHT have rather small values of LPCF, and the elimination of each of them wouldn't affect F_{min} much. The coefficients of the same three variables have relatively large standard errors. On the other hand, elimination of BOTTOM or TOP would increase F_{min} by more than 50% (see the PCF-values of these two variables). The first candidate for exclusion is RIGHT, whose elimination increases F_{min} by mere 1.4% (PCF (RIGHT) = 1.014).

Step 2: Elimination of RIGHT ($F_{min}^{(5)} = 0.288$)

Variable	Coefficient	Std. error	PCF	LPCF
LENGTH	0.347	0.319	1.026	0.026
LEFT	1.522	0.295	1.423	0.353
BOTTOM	0.498	0.078	1.519	0.418
TOP	0.849	0.137	1.536	0.429
DIAGONAL	− 0.525	0.137	1.214	0.194

Compared with step 1, variable LEFT has now more weight (LPCF (LEFT) = 0.353 instead of 0.088), and the coefficient of LEFT has changed more than all other coefficients, which remain essentially constant. A similar effect occurs if we eliminate LEFT instead of RIGHT. This means that we can remove either LEFT or RIGHT without much loss of information, but not both of them. The next variable to be eliminated is now LENGTH.

Step 3: Elimination of LENGTH ($F_{min}^{(4)} = 0.295$)

Variable	Coefficient	Std. error	PCF	LPCF
LEFT	1.734	0.209	1.826	0.602
BOTTOM	0.462	0.072	1.500	0.406
TOP	0.845	0.141	1.512	0.413
DIAGONAL	− 0.491	0.137	1.188	0.172

This table is very similar to the one of step 2, except perhaps for the fact that LEFT has again gained some weight. All LPCF-values are now rather large (the minimum increase of F_{min} by eliminating one more variable is 18.8%), which might be taken as a criterion for stopping the procedure. At the same time, the coefficients of the remaining four variables seem now rather stable in the sense of relatively small standard errors. What happens if we proceed nevertheless? Well, let's see.

Step 4: Elimination of DIAGONAL ($F_{min}^{(3)} = 0.351$)

Variable	Coefficient	Std. error	PCF	LPCF
LEFT	2.097	0.182	2.143	0.762
BOTTOM	0.359	0.074	1.283	0.249
TOP	0.794	0.172	1.348	0.299

Step 5: Elimination of BOTTOM ($F_{min}^{(2)} = 0.450$)

Variable	Coefficient	Std. error	PCF	LPCF
LEFT	2.511	0.165	2.134	0.758
TOP	0.397	0.200	1.090	0.086

Finally, in step 6, we are left with variable LEFT and its univariate ratio of variances.

In step 4 we can see that BOTTOM and TOP have lost some of their importance. This can again be taken as a hint that the elimination of DIAGONAL was not justified. The same effect occurs even more distinctly in step 5, after the elimination of BOTTOM: variable TOP, which is highly correlated with BOTTOM in both groups, loses its importance almost entirely. The importance of BOTTOM and TOP for Y_{min} lies therefore in their joint contribution – which shows another advantage of the elimination procedure, since a forward selection algorithm would not discover the joint importance of two variables.

If we decide (arbitrarily) that eliminating a single variable should not increase F_{min} by more than 10%, we have to stop after step 3, thus getting

$$Y_{min}^{(4)} = 1.73 \text{ LEFT} + 0.46 \text{ BOTTOM} + 0.84 \text{ TOP} - 0.49 \text{ DIAGONAL}$$

as a reduced solution. The associated $F_{min}^{(4)}$ is 0.295, which is not much larger than $F_{min}^{(6)}$ and still well below the critical value of $c_{min} = 0.43$. Since the second smallest eigenvalue in Table 11.2 is much closer to 1, it is reasonable to summarize the 'too small variability' of the forged notes, compared with the real ones, in the single linear combination $Y_{min}^{(4)}$.

What is the interpretation of $Y_{min}^{(4)}$? Since we do not know exactly how the bank notes were produced, it is not obvious. However, the importance of LEFT in step 3 (and even more so in step 4) suggests that the forger's mechanism for cutting the notes horizontally is very precise. After all, it is rather surprising (and speaks for the quality of the forger's work) that there *is* a linear combination with smaller variability in the forged notes than in the real notes!

It is interesting to compare the results of the analysis of Y_{min} with the univariate ratios of variances of the six variables. These are as follows:

Variance	LENGTH	LEFT	RIGHT	BOTTOM	TOP	DIAGONAL
ratio of variances (F/G)	0.826	0.490	0.704	3.101	0.960	1.558

We see that variables with a univariate F-ratio smaller than 1 may be redundant for Y_{min} (e.g. LENGTH, RIGHT). On the other hand, there are variables playing an important role in Y_{min}, but having a univariate F-ratio larger than 1 (BOTTOM, DIAGONAL). This shows that a previous selection of variables based on univariate F-ratios might be badly misleading, and that the multivariate approach indeed furnishes much more information than a univariate analysis.

The stepwise analysis of Y_{max} proceeds as follows:

Step 1: All six variables ($F_{max}^{(6)} = 6.223$)

Variable	Coefficient	Std. error	PCF	LPCF
LENGTH	0.975	0.349	0.907	− 0.097
LEFT	0.705	0.460	0.972	− 0.028
RIGHT	0.419	0.490	0.990	− 0.010
BOTTOM	− 2.256	0.107	0.312	− 1.164
TOP	− 1.553	0.229	0.638	− 0.450
DIAGONAL	− 1.007	0.323	0.854	− 0.158

Variable BOTTOM appears clearly as very important, both by its large value of |LPCF| and by the relatively small standard error of its coefficient.

Step 2: Elimination of RIGHT ($F_{max}^{(5)} = 6.161$)

Variable	Coefficient	Std. error	PCF	LPCF
LENGTH	1.046	0.333	0.888	− 0.119
LEFT	0.917	0.407	0.938	− 0.064
BOTTOM	− 2.225	0.105	0.295	− 1.222
TOP	− 1.534	0.229	0.643	− 0.442
DIAGONAL	− 1.082	0.319	0.849	− 0.164

Step 3: Elimination of LEFT ($F_{max}^{(4)} = 5.778$)

Variable	Coefficient	Std. error	PCF	LPCF
LENGTH	1.340	0.303	0.799	− 0.224
BOTTOM	− 2.055	0.098	0.301	− 1.201
TOP	− 1.347	0.223	0.685	− 0.379
DIAGONAL	− 1.276	0.298	0.784	− 0.243

All coefficients seem now stable in the sense of relatively small standard errors. Eliminating the next variable (LENGTH) would reduce F_{max} to about 80% of its current value. Using the same rule as for Y_{min}, we decide to stop at this point, thus getting the linear combination

$$Y_{max}^{(4)} = 1.34 \text{ LENGTH} - 2.06 \text{ BOTTOM} - 1.35 \text{ TOP} - 1.28 \text{ DIAGONAL}$$

as a reduced solution. The standard deviation of the forged bills in this linear combination is $\sqrt{5.778} = 2.4$ times as large as the standard deviation of the genuine bills.

From the forger's point of view, the fact that F_{max} is relatively large should be a reason for concern, and since BOTTOM, TOP and DIAGONAL are strongly related to the print image, he may be well advised to check his printing device. We will come back to a possible explanation for the excessive variability of the forged bills in the next paragraph.

11.7   RELATIONSHIPS TO STANDARD DISTANCE AND PRINCIPAL COMPONENT ANALYSIS

In Section 10.6 we indicated how principal components can be defined using maximization of the standard distance as a criterion. Similarly, the variance ratios F_{max} and F_{min} can be derived using a criterion based on standard distance. The construction is as follows. First, we shift the data of both groups over the origin of the coordinate system, that is we subtract from each variable the mean of the respective sample. By doing this, the two covariance matrices remain unchanged, but both groups are now centered at $(0,\ldots,0)$. Then we compute for each point in the p-dimensional space its standard distance from $(0,\ldots,0)$ with respect to the two groups. We denote these distances by $D_p(G)$

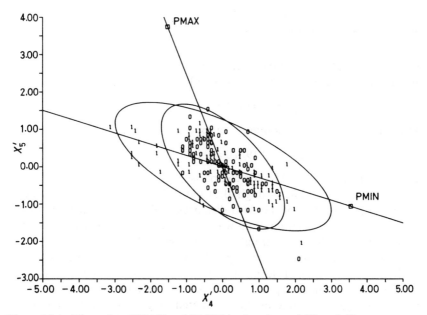

Figure 11.4   The points PMAX and PMIN in the plane of X'_4 and X'_5

and $D_p(F)$ for the genuine and forged bills, respectively. The most interesting points are now certainly those for which $D_p(G)$ and $D_p(F)$ differ as much as possible, i.e. for which the ratio

$$q = D_p(F)/D_p(G)$$

takes its minimum or its maximum. It turns out that q takes the maximum value $q_{max} = 1/\sqrt{F_{min}}$, and the minimum value $q_{min} = 1/\sqrt{F_{max}}$. This means, of course, that this approach is equivalent to the maximization and minimization of the ratio of variances.

To illustrate this relationship Fig. 11.4 shows a scatterplot of BOTTOM and TOP for all 200 bills. The two groups have been shifted to a common mean, through which a new coordinate system (X'_4, X'_5) has been placed. Two ellipses indicate the sets of all points with a standard distance of $\sqrt{5.0}$ with respect to the two groups. The smaller ellipse refers to the group *Genuine*, the larger to the group *Forged*. Points of intersection of the two ellipses have the same standard distance from the origin with respect to both groups. The two points PMAX and PMIN have the following standard distances from the origin:

Point	Coordinates	D_2 (*Genuine*)	D_2 (*Forged*)
PMAX	$(-1.524, \quad 3.745)$	6.0	6.92
PMIN	$(3.543, -1.066)$	6.0	3.19

The points PMAX and PMIN are precisely those with the maximum and minimum ratio of the two distances. For PMAX, the ratio is

$$q_{max} = 6.92/6.0 = 1.15 = 1/\sqrt{F_{min}}.$$

At PMIN we obtain the minimum ratio

$$q_{min} = 3.19/6.0 = 0.53 = 1/\sqrt{F_{max}}$$

(See Fig. 11.1 and Table 11.1 for comparison).

If we put a straight line through $(0,0)$ and PMAX, then every point on this line has the same ratio of standard distances as PMAX – an analogy to the equivalence of linear combinations with the same ratio of variances. The same, of course, holds also for a straight line through PMIN.

There are also some interesting relationships to principal component analysis. Already on purely formal grounds, the comparison of two covariance matrices is quite similar to principal component analysis, since, for p variables, p eigenvalues and eigenvectors are computed. In general, these eigenvectors are displayed in the form of a matrix:

	X_1	X_2	$\cdots$	X_p
Y_1	b_{11}	b_{12}	$\cdots$	b_{1p}
Y_2	b_{21}	b_{22}	$\cdots$	b_{2p}
.	.	.		.
.	.	.		.
.	.	.		.
Y_p	b_{p1}	b_{p2}	$\cdots$	b_{pp}

Each row of this matrix contains the coefficients of an eigenvector, and each eigenvector defines a linear combination Y_i according to

$$Y_i = b_{i1} X_1 + b_{i2} X_2 + \cdots + b_{ip} X_p \quad (i = 1, \ldots, p).$$

Up to this point, the similarity is purely formal. Let us recall, however, an important property of principal components: the linear combinations U_1, $U_2, \ldots, U_p$ are all pairwise uncorrelated. Indeed, the variables $Y_1, \ldots, Y_p$ are also pairwise uncorrelated, and this in both groups! Hence the method of this chapter can be regarded as a generalization of principal component analysis to two groups.

In contrast to principal component analysis it turns out, however, that the p eigenvectors are not generally perpendicular to each other. That is, the transformation from the variables X_j to the p linear combinations Y_h is, in general, *not* just a rotation of the coordinate system. Loss of orthogonality is, as it were, the price paid for the generalization to two groups. To illustrate this non-orthogonality, Fig. 11.1 can serve once again, the angle between directions of projection of $Y_{\min}$ and $Y_{\max}$ being 51.11°.

Even though, in general, the eigenvectors resulting from the comparison of two covariance matrices are not orthogonal, one can, of course, think of special cases in which orthogonality is preserved. What are these special cases?

The answer to this question shows again an interesting relationship to principal component analysis: the eigenvectors are orthogonal precisely when the principal axes in both groups are identical. In this case, comparison of the two covariance matrices yields exactly the same eigenvectors as those obtained from the principal component analyses of the two groups. Of course, this is exactly what we called the 'common principal component model' in Section 10.8! For an example of two covariance matrices with identical principal axes, the reader is referred to Fig. 10.10. In the example depicted in this figure, the directions of projection for the minimum and maximum ratio of variances coincide with the principal axes, and also the points PMIN and PMAX defined at the beginning of this section lie precisely on the principal axes.

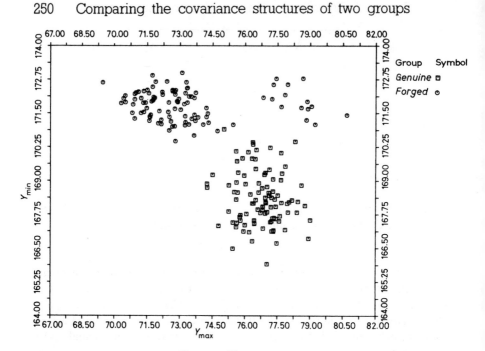

Figure 11.5   Scatterplot of $Y_{max}^{(4)}$ and $Y_{min}^{(4)}$. Real notes are marked as squares, forged notes as circles

To conclude, let us again consider the linear combinations analysed in Section 11.6:

$$Y_{max}^{(4)} = 1.3X_1 - 2.05X_4 - 1.35X_5 - 1.28X_6$$

and

$$Y_{min}^{(4)} = 1.73X_2 + 0.46X_4 + 0.84X_5 - 0.49X_6.$$

Since $Y_{max}^{(4)}$ and $Y_{min}^{(4)}$ are based only in part on the same variables, we cannot expect that they are exactly uncorrelated. Nevertheless, the correlation should not differ much from zero, provided the reduction to four variables is justified. Fig. 11.5 shows a scatterplot of $Y_{max}^{(4)}$ and $Y_{min}^{(4)}$ for both groups. The correlation is -0.13 for the genuine bills and 0.05 for the forged ones. Because of the special normalization of the eigenvectors, the genuine bills appear spherical with standard deviation 1 in both dimensions, whereas the scatterplot of the forged bills appears on one hand too narrow (Y_{min}), on the other hand too wide (Y_{max}).

The most striking result of this graph consists of the fact that the group *Forged* appears clearly as a mixture of two subgroups. Although this result may look surprising, it is nevertheless explainable. If group *Forged* is indeed composed of two subgroups that differ in location, the variance in direction of the mean difference is inflated by the variability between subgroups. It is then plausible that this direction yields a relatively large variance for the forged bills, compared with the genuine ones.

We have thus repeatedly found indications suggesting that group *Forged* is inhomogeneous. In the next chapter we will address this problem in more detail.

11.8 CRITICAL VALUES OF THE DISTRIBUTION OF F_{max} AND F_{min}

The distributions of the test statistics appearing in Chapters 1 to 10 of this book are of four types: standard normal, t, F, or chi square. Since tables of these four classes of distributions appear in almost any textbook on applied statistics, we did not include such tables in this book. In contrast to this, tables of critical values c_{min} and c_{max} as described in Section 11.3 are not readily available. We give here selected 2.5% quantiles for dimensions p from 2 to 10, that is, critical values c_{max} such that

$$P(F_{max} \geqslant c_{max}) = 0.025.$$

From this, critical values c_{min} satisfying

$$P(F_{min} \leqslant c_{min}) = 0.025$$

can easily be obtained. The joint inequality

$$c_{min} \leqslant F_{min} \leqslant F_{max} \leqslant c_{max}$$

is then satisfied with probability approximately 5%. The critical values tabulated here can thus be used for an overall test of equality of two covariance matrices at a significance level of approximately $\alpha = 0.05$. For other significance levels and dimensions p up to 20 see the articles by Pillai and Flury (1984 and 1985).

The critical values are listed in Table 11.3. One subtable is given for each dimension p (= number of variables) between 2 and 10. Let the sample sizes be denoted by n_1 (for the sample whose variance is in the numerator of the F-ratio) and n_2 (denominator). Put $v_1 = n_1 - 1$ and $v_2 = n_2 - 1$. Enter the table for dimension p in the column labelled v_1 and the row labelled v_2 to get the critical value c_{max} as described above. For values of v_1 and v_2 falling between two columns or two rows, respectively, linear interpolation gives sufficiently accurate results.

In the bank note example, we have $v_1 = 99$ (forged bills) and $v_2 = 99$ (genuine bills). We enter Table 11.3 with $p = 6$ and read off the following values:

Table 11.3 Upper 2.5% quantiles of the largest characteristic root of the multivariate F-matrix

P = 2

v_2/v_1	43	53	63	73	83	103	123	143	173	203	243	283	343	403	603
43	2.245	2.188	2.147	2.117	2.094	2.060	2.036	2.019	2.001	1.988	1.975	1.966	1.956	1.949	1.936
53	2.124	2.065	2.023	1.992	1.968	1.933	1.908	1.891	1.871	1.857	1.844	1.834	1.824	1.817	1.803
63	2.043	1.983	1.940	1.908	1.884	1.847	1.822	1.804	1.784	1.769	1.755	1.745	1.734	1.727	1.712
73	1.985	1.924	1.881	1.848	1.823	1.786	1.760	1.741	1.720	1.705	1.691	1.680	1.669	1.661	1.645
83	1.942	1.880	1.836	1.803	1.777	1.739	1.713	1.693	1.672	1.656	1.642	1.631	1.619	1.611	1.594
103	1.881	1.818	1.773	1.739	1.713	1.673	1.646	1.626	1.603	1.587	1.571	1.560	1.547	1.538	1.521
123	1.841	1.777	1.731	1.696	1.669	1.629	1.601	1.579	1.556	1.539	1.523	1.511	1.498	1.488	1.470
143	1.812	1.747	1.701	1.666	1.638	1.597	1.568	1.546	1.522	1.505	1.488	1.475	1.461	1.452	1.433
173	1.781	1.716	1.669	1.633	1.604	1.562	1.532	1.510	1.485	1.467	1.449	1.436	1.422	1.412	1.391
203	1.759	1.694	1.646	1.609	1.581	1.538	1.507	1.484	1.459	1.440	1.422	1.408	1.393	1.383	1.361
243	1.739	1.673	1.624	1.587	1.558	1.515	1.483	1.460	1.434	1.414	1.395	1.381	1.366	1.354	1.332
283	1.724	1.657	1.609	1.572	1.542	1.498	1.468	1.442	1.415	1.396	1.376	1.361	1.345	1.334	1.310
343	1.709	1.642	1.592	1.555	1.525	1.480	1.448	1.423	1.396	1.375	1.355	1.340	1.323	1.311	1.287
403	1.698	1.630	1.581	1.543	1.513	1.467	1.434	1.410	1.382	1.361	1.340	1.325	1.307	1.295	1.269
603	1.677	1.609	1.559	1.520	1.489	1.443	1.409	1.384	1.355	1.333	1.311	1.295	1.276	1.263	1.235

P = 3

v_2/v_1	44	54	64	74	84	104	124	144	174	204	244	284	344	404	604
44	2.588	2.516	2.465	2.427	2.398	2.356	2.326	2.305	2.281	2.265	2.248	2.237	2.224	2.216	2.199
54	2.418	2.345	2.293	2.255	2.225	2.181	2.151	2.128	2.104	2.087	2.070	2.058	2.045	2.036	2.018
64	2.306	2.232	2.180	2.140	2.110	2.065	2.034	2.011	1.986	1.968	1.950	1.938	1.924	1.915	1.896
74	2.226	2.152	2.099	2.059	2.028	1.982	1.950	1.927	1.901	1.882	1.864	1.851	1.837	1.827	1.808
84	2.167	2.092	2.038	1.998	1.966	1.920	1.887	1.863	1.837	1.818	1.799	1.786	1.771	1.761	1.741
104	2.084	2.008	1.954	1.912	1.880	1.832	1.798	1.773	1.746	1.726	1.707	1.692	1.677	1.661	1.645
124	2.030	1.953	1.897	1.855	1.822	1.773	1.739	1.713	1.684	1.664	1.644	1.629	1.613	1.601	1.579
144	1.990	1.913	1.857	1.814	1.781	1.731	1.696	1.669	1.640	1.619	1.598	1.583	1.566	1.554	1.531
174	1.949	1.871	1.814	1.771	1.737	1.686	1.650	1.622	1.592	1.570	1.549	1.533	1.515	1.503	1.478
204	1.920	1.841	1.784	1.740	1.706	1.654	1.617	1.589	1.558	1.536	1.514	1.497	1.479	1.466	1.440
244	1.893	1.814	1.756	1.711	1.676	1.624	1.586	1.558	1.526	1.503	1.480	1.462	1.444	1.430	1.403
284	1.873	1.794	1.735	1.691	1.655	1.602	1.564	1.535	1.503	1.479	1.455	1.437	1.418	1.404	1.376
344	1.853	1.773	1.714	1.669	1.633	1.579	1.540	1.510	1.477	1.453	1.428	1.410	1.390	1.375	1.346
404	1.838	1.758	1.699	1.653	1.617	1.563	1.523	1.493	1.459	1.434	1.410	1.391	1.370	1.355	1.324
604	1.811	1.730	1.670	1.624	1.587	1.531	1.491	1.460	1.425	1.399	1.373	1.353	1.331	1.315	1.282

P=4

v_2/v_1	45	55	65	75	85	105	125	145	175	205	245	285	345	405	605
45	2.908	2.825	2.765	2.721	2.686	2.636	2.601	2.575	2.547	2.527	2.508	2.494	2.479	2.468	2.448
55	2.689	2.605	2.545	2.499	2.464	2.413	2.377	2.351	2.322	2.301	2.281	2.267	2.251	2.240	2.219
65	2.545	2.460	2.400	2.354	2.318	2.266	2.229	2.202	2.173	2.152	2.131	2.116	2.100	2.089	2.067
75	2.444	2.359	2.297	2.251	2.215	2.162	2.124	2.097	2.067	2.045	2.024	2.008	1.992	1.980	1.957
85	2.369	2.283	2.221	2.174	2.138	2.084	2.046	2.018	1.987	1.965	1.943	1.927	1.910	1.898	1.875
105	2.264	2.178	2.115	2.067	2.030	1.974	1.935	1.906	1.875	1.851	1.829	1.812	1.795	1.782	1.757
125	2.195	2.108	2.044	1.996	1.958	1.902	1.862	1.832	1.799	1.775	1.752	1.735	1.716	1.703	1.677
145	2.146	2.058	1.994	1.945	1.907	1.850	1.809	1.779	1.745	1.720	1.696	1.679	1.659	1.646	1.619
175	2.094	2.006	1.941	1.892	1.852	1.794	1.753	1.721	1.687	1.661	1.637	1.618	1.598	1.584	1.555
205	2.058	1.969	1.904	1.854	1.814	1.755	1.718	1.681	1.646	1.620	1.594	1.575	1.554	1.539	1.510
245	2.024	1.935	1.869	1.818	1.778	1.718	1.675	1.643	1.606	1.580	1.553	1.534	1.512	1.496	1.465
285	2.000	1.910	1.844	1.793	1.753	1.692	1.648	1.615	1.578	1.551	1.524	1.504	1.481	1.465	1.433
345	1.974	1.884	1.817	1.766	1.725	1.664	1.619	1.586	1.548	1.520	1.492	1.471	1.448	1.431	1.398
405	1.957	1.866	1.799	1.747	1.706	1.644	1.599	1.565	1.526	1.498	1.469	1.448	1.424	1.407	1.372
605	1.923	1.831	1.764	1.711	1.669	1.606	1.560	1.525	1.485	1.456	1.426	1.403	1.378	1.359	1.322

P=5

v_2/v_2	46	56	66	76	86	106	126	146	176	206	246	286	346	406	606
46	3.220	3.125	3.058	3.007	2.967	2.909	2.869	2.839	2.807	2.784	2.762	2.746	2.728	2.716	2.693
56	2.949	2.854	2.786	2.735	2.695	2.636	2.596	2.565	2.533	2.509	2.486	2.470	2.452	2.439	2.415
66	2.772	2.678	2.609	2.558	2.517	2.458	2.417	2.386	2.352	2.323	2.305	2.288	2.269	2.256	2.231
76	2.649	2.554	2.485	2.433	2.392	2.332	2.290	2.259	2.224	2.200	2.176	2.158	2.139	2.126	2.100
86	2.557	2.462	2.393	2.340	2.299	2.238	2.196	2.164	2.129	2.104	2.079	2.061	2.042	2.028	2.002
106	2.430	2.334	2.265	2.213	2.170	2.108	2.064	2.031	1.995	1.969	1.944	1.925	1.905	1.891	1.863
126	2.347	2.250	2.180	2.126	2.084	2.021	1.976	1.943	1.906	1.879	1.853	1.834	1.813	1.798	1.768
146	2.288	2.191	2.120	2.066	2.023	1.959	1.914	1.880	1.842	1.815	1.788	1.763	1.746	1.731	1.700
176	2.226	2.128	2.057	2.002	1.959	1.894	1.847	1.813	1.774	1.745	1.718	1.697	1.674	1.658	1.626
206	2.182	2.084	2.013	1.957	1.913	1.848	1.801	1.765	1.726	1.697	1.668	1.647	1.624	1.607	1.574
246	2.142	2.043	1.971	1.915	1.871	1.804	1.756	1.720	1.680	1.650	1.621	1.599	1.575	1.557	1.522
286	2.113	2.014	1.941	1.885	1.840	1.773	1.725	1.688	1.647	1.617	1.586	1.564	1.539	1.521	1.485
346	2.082	1.983	1.910	1.853	1.808	1.740	1.692	1.654	1.612	1.581	1.550	1.526	1.501	1.482	1.444
406	2.061	1.961	1.888	1.831	1.786	1.717	1.667	1.629	1.587	1.555	1.524	1.500	1.473	1.454	1.415
606	2.021	1.921	1.846	1.789	1.743	1.673	1.622	1.583	1.539	1.506	1.473	1.448	1.420	1.400	1.358

Table 11.3 (Continued)

P = 6

v_2/v_1	47	57	67	77	87	107	127	147	177	207	247	287	347	407	607
47	3.527	3.422	3.347	3.290	3.246	3.181	3.136	3.102	3.066	3.040	3.015	2.996	2.977	2.963	2.936
57	3.202	3.098	3.023	2.966	2.922	2.856	2.811	2.777	2.740	2.714	2.688	2.669	2.649	2.635	2.607
67	2.992	2.888	2.813	2.756	2.711	2.646	2.599	2.565	2.528	2.501	2.474	2.455	2.435	2.418	2.392
77	2.845	2.741	2.666	2.609	2.564	2.497	2.451	2.416	2.378	2.350	2.324	2.304	2.283	2.268	2.239
87	2.737	2.633	2.557	2.500	2.455	2.388	2.340	2.305	2.266	2.238	2.211	2.191	2.170	2.154	2.125
107	2.587	2.483	2.407	2.349	2.303	2.235	2.187	2.151	2.111	2.082	2.054	2.034	2.011	1.995	1.964
127	2.489	2.385	2.308	2.250	2.204	2.134	2.085	2.049	2.008	1.978	1.949	1.928	1.905	1.888	1.856
147	2.420	2.315	2.238	2.179	2.133	2.063	2.013	1.976	1.934	1.904	1.874	1.852	1.829	1.811	1.778
177	2.347	2.242	2.165	2.105	2.058	1.987	1.937	1.898	1.856	1.825	1.794	1.772	1.747	1.729	1.694
207	2.297	2.191	2.114	2.054	2.006	1.934	1.883	1.844	1.801	1.769	1.738	1.714	1.689	1.670	1.634
247	2.249	2.144	2.065	2.005	1.957	1.884	1.832	1.793	1.749	1.716	1.684	1.660	1.633	1.614	1.576
287	2.216	2.110	2.031	1.970	1.922	1.849	1.796	1.756	1.711	1.678	1.645	1.620	1.593	1.573	1.534
347	2.180	2.074	1.995	1.934	1.885	1.811	1.757	1.717	1.671	1.637	1.603	1.578	1.550	1.529	1.488
407	2.155	2.049	1.969	1.908	1.859	1.784	1.730	1.689	1.643	1.608	1.574	1.548	1.519	1.498	1.455
607	2.109	2.002	1.922	1.860	1.810	1.734	1.679	1.637	1.589	1.553	1.517	1.490	1.459	1.437	1.391

P = 7

v_2/v_1	48	58	68	78	88	108	128	148	178	208	248	288	348	408	608
48	3.833	3.719	3.636	3.574	3.525	3.453	3.407	3.366	3.326	3.297	3.268	3.248	3.226	3.210	3.180
58	3.451	3.339	3.257	3.195	3.147	3.075	3.025	2.987	2.946	2.917	2.889	2.868	2.845	2.830	2.799
68	3.206	3.095	3.013	2.951	2.902	2.830	2.780	2.742	2.701	2.671	2.642	2.621	2.598	2.582	2.551
78	3.036	2.924	2.843	2.781	2.732	2.659	2.608	2.570	2.529	2.493	2.469	2.447	2.424	2.408	2.376
88	2.910	2.799	2.717	2.655	2.606	2.533	2.482	2.443	2.401	2.370	2.340	2.318	2.295	2.278	2.245
108	2.738	2.626	2.545	2.482	2.432	2.359	2.306	2.267	2.224	2.192	2.162	2.139	2.114	2.097	2.063
128	2.625	2.513	2.431	2.368	2.318	2.244	2.191	2.151	2.107	2.074	2.043	2.020	1.994	1.976	1.941
148	2.545	2.434	2.351	2.288	2.238	2.162	2.108	2.068	2.023	1.990	1.958	1.934	1.908	1.889	1.853
178	2.462	2.350	2.267	2.203	2.153	2.076	2.022	1.981	1.935	1.901	1.868	1.843	1.816	1.797	1.758
208	2.404	2.292	2.209	2.145	2.094	2.017	1.961	1.919	1.873	1.838	1.804	1.779	1.751	1.731	1.691
248	2.350	2.237	2.154	2.090	2.038	1.960	1.904	1.861	1.814	1.779	1.744	1.718	1.689	1.668	1.627
288	2.311	2.199	2.115	2.050	1.998	1.920	1.863	1.820	1.772	1.736	1.700	1.674	1.644	1.623	1.589
348	2.271	2.158	2.074	2.009	1.956	1.877	1.820	1.776	1.727	1.690	1.654	1.626	1.596	1.574	1.529
408	2.243	2.129	2.045	1.980	1.927	1.847	1.790	1.745	1.695	1.658	1.621	1.593	1.562	1.539	1.493
608	2.190	2.076	1.991	1.925	1.872	1.791	1.732	1.687	1.635	1.597	1.558	1.529	1.496	1.472	1.422

P = 8

ν_2/ν_1	609	409	349	289	249	209	179	149	129	109	89	79	69	59	49
49	3.427	3.460	3.477	3.502	3.524	3.555	3.588	3.632	3.673	3.728	3.806	3.859	3.927	4.016	4.139
59	2.991	3.025	3.042	3.067	3.090	3.121	3.153	3.193	3.238	3.293	3.371	3.424	3.491	3.579	3.699
69	2.709	2.743	2.761	2.786	2.809	2.841	2.873	2.918	2.959	3.014	3.092	3.145	3.211	3.298	3.418
79	2.511	2.546	2.564	2.590	2.613	2.645	2.678	2.723	2.764	2.820	2.898	2.950	3.017	3.104	3.223
89	2.364	2.400	2.418	2.444	2.468	2.500	2.533	2.579	2.621	2.676	2.755	2.808	2.874	2.961	3.079
109	2.160	2.197	2.216	2.242	2.267	2.300	2.334	2.381	2.423	2.479	2.558	2.611	2.678	2.765	2.883
129	2.023	2.062	2.081	2.109	2.134	2.168	2.203	2.250	2.293	2.350	2.430	2.483	2.550	2.637	2.755
149	1.926	1.965	1.985	2.013	2.039	2.074	2.109	2.157	2.201	2.258	2.339	2.393	2.460	2.547	2.665
179	1.821	1.862	1.883	1.912	1.939	1.974	2.011	2.060	2.104	2.162	2.244	2.298	2.365	2.453	2.571
209	1.747	1.790	1.811	1.841	1.868	1.905	1.942	1.992	2.036	2.095	2.177	2.232	2.300	2.387	2.505
249	1.676	1.720	1.743	1.773	1.801	1.839	1.876	1.927	1.973	2.033	2.115	2.170	2.238	2.326	2.444
289	1.625	1.670	1.693	1.725	1.753	1.791	1.830	1.881	1.927	1.988	2.071	2.126	2.195	2.283	2.401
349	1.569	1.617	1.640	1.673	1.702	1.741	1.780	1.833	1.879	1.940	2.024	2.080	2.149	2.237	2.355
409	1.529	1.578	1.603	1.636	1.666	1.706	1.745	1.799	1.846	1.907	1.992	2.047	2.117	2.205	2.324
609	1.452	1.505	1.531	1.566	1.597	1.638	1.679	1.734	1.782	1.845	1.930	1.987	2.056	2.145	2.264

P = 9

ν_2/ν_1	610	410	350	290	250	210	180	150	130	110	90	80	70	60	50
50	3.676	3.713	3.732	3.759	3.784	3.817	3.852	3.901	3.945	4.005	4.090	4.147	4.220	4.316	4.447
60	3.184	3.221	3.240	3.267	3.292	3.326	3.361	3.409	3.453	3.512	3.596	3.653	3.724	3.818	3.946
70	2.867	2.905	2.924	2.951	2.976	3.010	3.045	3.094	3.138	3.197	3.281	3.337	3.408	3.501	3.628
80	2.646	2.684	2.704	2.731	2.756	2.791	2.826	2.875	2.919	2.979	3.062	3.118	3.189	3.282	3.407
90	2.482	2.521	2.541	2.568	2.594	2.629	2.665	2.714	2.759	2.818	2.902	2.958	3.029	3.121	3.245
110	2.255	2.295	2.316	2.344	2.371	2.406	2.443	2.493	2.538	2.598	2.682	2.738	2.809	2.901	3.025
130	2.105	2.146	2.167	2.196	2.223	2.260	2.297	2.347	2.393	2.454	2.539	2.595	2.666	2.757	2.881
150	1.997	2.039	2.061	2.091	2.119	2.156	2.193	2.245	2.291	2.352	2.437	2.494	2.565	2.657	2.780
180	1.882	1.926	1.949	1.980	2.008	2.046	2.085	2.137	2.184	2.246	2.332	2.389	2.460	2.552	2.675
210	1.801	1.847	1.870	1.902	1.930	1.969	2.009	2.062	2.109	2.172	2.258	2.318	2.387	2.479	2.692
250	1.724	1.771	1.795	1.827	1.857	1.897	1.937	1.991	2.039	2.102	2.189	2.247	2.319	2.411	2.534
290	1.668	1.716	1.741	1.774	1.804	1.845	1.886	1.940	1.989	2.053	2.141	2.199	2.271	2.363	2.486
350	1.607	1.658	1.683	1.717	1.748	1.790	1.831	1.887	1.936	2.001	2.089	2.147	2.220	2.312	2.435
410	1.564	1.616	1.642	1.677	1.709	1.751	1.793	1.850	1.899	1.964	2.053	2.112	2.184	2.277	2.400
610	1.480	1.536	1.564	1.601	1.634	1.678	1.721	1.779	1.830	1.896	1.936	2.045	2.118	2.211	2.334

Table 11.3 (Continued)

P=10

v_2/v_1	51	61	71	81	91	111	131	151	181	211	251	291	351	411	611
51	4.758	4.619	4.517	4.439	4.377	4.286	4.222	4.174	4.121	4.083	4.046	4.020	3.990	3.970	3.930
61	4.194	4.058	3.959	3.883	3.822	3.733	3.639	3.622	3.570	3.532	3.495	3.468	3.439	3.419	3.379
71	3.836	3.703	3.605	3.529	3.470	3.381	3.317	3.270	3.218	3.180	3.144	3.117	3.087	3.067	3.026
81	3.589	3.458	3.360	3.285	3.226	3.137	3.074	3.027	2.974	2.936	2.899	2.872	2.843	2.822	2.781
91	3.409	3.278	3.182	3.107	3.048	2.959	2.895	2.848	2.796	2.757	2.720	2.692	2.663	2.641	2.600
111	3.163	3.034	2.938	2.863	2.804	2.715	2.651	2.603	2.550	2.511	2.473	2.445	2.415	2.393	2.350
131	3.004	2.875	2.779	2.705	2.645	2.556	2.492	2.443	2.390	2.350	2.311	2.283	2.251	2.229	2.185
151	2.892	2.764	2.668	2.593	2.534	2.444	2.379	2.331	2.276	2.236	2.197	2.167	2.135	2.112	2.067
181	2.775	2.647	2.552	2.477	2.417	2.327	2.263	2.212	2.157	2.116	2.076	2.046	2.013	1.989	1.942
211	2.695	2.567	2.471	2.397	2.337	2.246	2.180	2.130	2.074	2.032	1.991	1.961	1.927	1.903	1.854
251	2.620	2.492	2.396	2.322	2.261	2.170	2.103	2.053	1.996	1.953	1.911	1.880	1.845	1.820	1.770
291	2.567	2.439	2.343	2.268	2.208	2.116	2.049	1.997	1.940	1.897	1.854	1.822	1.787	1.761	1.710
351	2.511	2.383	2.287	2.212	2.151	2.059	1.991	1.939	1.881	1.837	1.793	1.761	1.724	1.698	1.644
411	2.472	2.345	2.249	2.173	2.112	2.019	1.951	1.899	1.839	1.795	1.751	1.717	1.680	1.653	1.598
611	2.400	2.272	2.176	2.100	2.038	1.944	1.875	1.822	1.761	1.715	1.669	1.635	1.596	1.567	1.508

		v_1	
		87	107
v_2	87	2.455	2.388
	107	2.303	2.235

For $v_2 = 87$, linear interpolation between $v_1 = 87$ and $v_1 = 107$ gives

$$c_{max}(v_1 = 99, v_2 = 87) = 2.455 + \tfrac{12}{20}(2.388 - 2.455)$$
$$= 2.415.$$

Similarly for $v_2 = 107$, linear interpolation yields

$$c_{max}(v_1 = 99, v_2 = 107) = 2.303 + \tfrac{12}{20}(2.235 - 2.303)$$
$$= 2.262.$$

Finally, by interpolating linearly between $v_2 = 87$ and $v_2 = 107$, we get

$$c_{max}(v_1 = 99, v_2 = 99) = 2.415 + \tfrac{12}{20}(2.262 - 2.415)$$
$$= 2.323.$$

This is the desired critical value for F_{max}. The same value is obtained if we interpolate first for v_2 and then for v_1.

To determine c_{min}, interchange the roles of n_2 and n_1 and find from Table 11.3 the critical value $c_{max}(n_2 - 1, n_1 - 1)$. The desired value is then

$$c_{min} = 1/c_{max}(n_2 - 1, n_1 - 1).$$

This relationship is easily explained by the fact that interchanging the two groups transforms F_{min} into $F_{max}^* = 1/F_{min}$, and F_{max} into $F_{min}^* = 1/F_{max}$.

For the bank notes, we again have $v_1 = v_2 = 99$ and therefore

$$c_{min} = 1/2.323 = 0.430.$$

Table 11.3 gives critical values c_{max} for v_1 and v_2 roughly between 40 and 600. No tables are currently available for larger sample sizes, and to the authors' knowledge no good large sample approximation is known. For v_2 smaller than 40, critical values can be obtained from two articles by Pillai and Flury (1984 and 1985). For v_1 and v_2 both smaller than 40, see the references given in these two articles.

DISCUSSION

Question:
Although the comparison of two covariance matrices yields p linear combinations and associated variance ratios, we have been looking at only two of

them. Is there no additional information in the remaining $p-2$ linear combinations?

Answer:

It may indeed be possible to get additional information about differences in variability from the intermediate eigenvalues l_2 to l_{p-1}. Let us recall, from Section 11.7, that the p eigenvectors define p linear combinations $Y_1, \ldots, Y_p$, where Y_h has variance ratio l_h. Since the Y_h are uncorrelated in both groups, they provide (under normality assumptions) a set of independent variance ratios. All information about differences in variability is therefore contained in the p ratios $l_1, \ldots, l_p$. In practical applications it is often the case that l_1 and/or l_p differ markedly from 1, while l_2 to l_{p-1} are rather close to 1. In this case, no information (or very little) is lost if we restrict our attention to Y_{max} and/or Y_{min}. If several eigenvalues are simultaneously much larger or much smaller than 1, we may have to consider several linear combinations simultaneously. As a particular example, assume that the two covariance matrices are exactly proportional, the proportionality factor being c. Then all p eigenvalues will be identical and equal to c. In real data examples this will of course hardly ever occur, since the eigenvalues l_h are always affected by sampling variability. Yet proportionality may sometimes be a reasonable model for the data.

FURTHER STUDY

The overall test for equality of two covariance matrices using the criterion (l_1, l_p) is due to Roy (1957). Roy's test as well as other criteria are treated in most multivariate textbooks. The sampling distribution of l_1 and l_p, on which Table 11.3 is based, was developed in a series of papers by Pillai (see Pillai (1965); Pillai and Flury (1984, 1985)). The analysis of Y_{max} and Y_{min} described in Section 11.5 has been proposed by Flury (1985). The formula for standard errors of the coefficients of Y_{max} and Y_{min} is based on the work of Tyler (1981) and Flury (1986).

EXAMPLES

Example 11.1: Electrodes produced by two machines

This is the continuation of Example 7.2, where linear discriminant analysis was applied to two samples of 50 electrodes produced by two different machines. We noticed in Table 7.8 that there seem to be substantial differences in variability between the two groups. Indeed, the univariate ratios of variance (ratio of machine 2 to machine 1) are 0.30, 0.51, 2.27, 1.34 and 0.25, respectively, for variables X_1 to X_5. We are now going to compare the covariance structures in more detail. Table 11.4 displays the two covariance matrices. The eigenvalues and eigenvectors of the multivariate F-matrix are given in

Table 11.4 Sample covariance matrices for electrodes produced by two machines

Machine 1 ($n_1 = 50$)

	x_1	x_2	x_3	x_4	x_5
x_1	2.480	0.720	3.278	− 1.875	1.047
x_2	0.720	2.417	3.702	− 4.119	0.723
x_3	3.278	3.702	20.000	− 2.682	1.049
x_4	− 1.875	− 4.119	− 2.682	27.617	− 0.588
x_5	1.047	0.723	1.049	− 0.588	3.274

Machine 2 ($n_2 = 50$)

	x_1	x_2	x_3	x_4	x_5
x_1	0.753	0.294	− 0.580	− 1.349	0.145
x_2	0.294	1.224	− 0.820	− 1.518	0.318
x_3	− 0.580	− 0.820	15.372	17.389	− 1.828
x_4	− 1.349	− 1.518	17.389	36.924	− 1.468
x_5	0.145	0.318	− 1.828	− 1.468	0.834

Table 11.5 Eigenvalues and eigenvectors of the multivariate F-matrix

	x_1	x_2	x_3	x_4	x_5	Eigenvalue
$Y_{max} = Y_1$	0.342	0.489	− 0.293	0.021	− 0.074	4.370 $\doteq F_{max}$
Y_2	0.130	0.573	− 0.056	0.228	− 0.136	1.684
Y_3	− 0.320	0.523	0.042	− 0.038	0.095	0.424
Y_4	0.558	0.110	0.016	− 0.016	− 0.403	0.361
$Y_{min} = Y_5$	0.273	− 0.107	0.019	0.014	0.432	$0.190 = F_{min}$

Table 11.5. The extreme variance ratios are $F_{max} = 4.370$ and $F_{min} = 0.190$, respectively. From Table 11.3, the critical values (at an overall significance level of approximately 5%) are $C_{max} = 3.110$ and $C_{min} = 3.22$, obtained by linear interpolation for $p = 5$ and $v_1 = v_2 = 49$. Since $F_{max} > c_{max}$ as well as $F_{min} < c_{min}$, we will analyse both extreme variance ratios in more detail. In any case, the hypothesis of equality of the two covariance matrices is clearly rejected, and could be rejected even at a significance level of 1%.

Table 11.6 gives a more detailed analysis of Y_{max}, the linear combination associated with the largest variance ratio F_{max}. Part A of the table is based on all five variables. Two variables, namely X_4 and X_5, seem redundant. In a stepwise elimination procedure, first X_4 and then X_5 were removed, leading to

Table 11.6 Analysis of Y_{max}

(a) All five variables included ($F_{max}^{(5)} = 4.370$)

Variable	Coefficient	Std. error	PCF	LPCF
x_1	0.3418	0.118	0.831	-0.186
x_2	0.4892	0.181	0.802	-0.221
x_3	-0.2929	0.017	0.408	-0.897
x_4	0.0214	0.063	0.995	-0.005
x_5	-0.0744	0.101	0.987	-0.013

(b) Reduced solution based on X_1, X_2, X_3 ($F_{max}^{(3)} = 4.302$)

Variable	Coefficient	Std. error	PCF	LPCF
x_1	0.2991	0.104	0.839	-0.176
x_2	0.4257	0.106	0.721	-0.327
x_3	-0.2833	0.006	0.199	-2.131

the simplified solution displayed in part B of Table 11.6. Any further elimination would now affect F_{max} considerably. As was to be expected, variable X_3 plays an important role in Y_{max}. Surprisingly, also variables X_1 and X_2, both having variance ratios smaller than 1, are not redundant. The reason for this is that for both X_1 and X_2 the correlation to X_3 differs considerably between the two groups. The variance ratio associated with the linear combination $Y_{max}^{(3)} = 0.299X_1 + 0.428X_2 - 0.283X_3$ is $F_{max}^{(3)} = 4.302$. For comparison, the largest univariate variance ratio is 2.27.

The stepwise analysis of Y_{min} is left to the reader as an exercise; see Exercise 14 in Chapter 12. It turns out that a solution with either two or three variables is appropriate. The solution based on two variables is

$$Y_{min}^{(2)} = 0.0272X_3 + 0.5399X_5,$$

with an associated variance ratio of $F_{min}^{(2)} = 0.223$. It is again interesting to notice that variable X_3 appears to contribute substantially to Y_{min}, despite the fact that its univariate variance ratio is larger than 1.

Figure 11.6 shows scatterplots of $Y_{max}^{(3)}$ versus $Y_{min}^{(2)}$ for both machines. Since the two groups overlap considerably, a separate graph was drawn for each group, but the scales are identical for both scatterplots. The differences in variability between the two machines are clearly visible, but in contrast to the bank note example no subgroups are revealed. This confirms the homogeneity of the production within each machine. Lacking a detailed knowledge of the production process, no further interpretation is attempted.

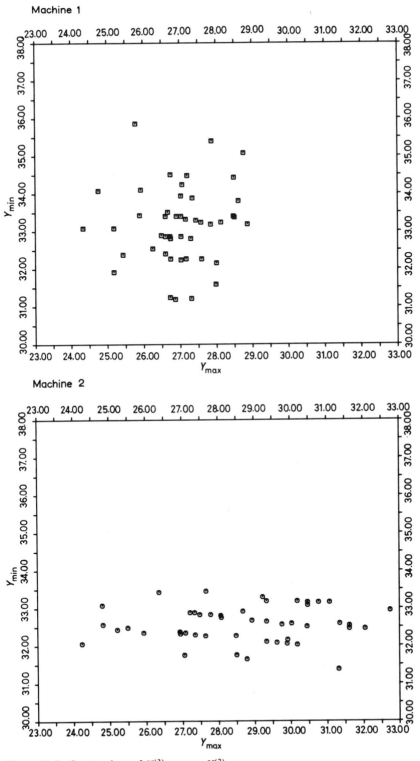

Figure 11.6 Scatterplots of $Y_{\max}^{(3)}$ versus $Y_{\min}^{(2)}$

Since this was originally a problem of discriminant analysis (see Example 7.2), the question arises how strongly the linear discriminant function is affected by the differences in variability. From a purely theoretical point of view, linear discrimination is clearly not optimal. Nevertheless, we can give heuristic arguments why the linear discriminant function is not 'terribly wrong' in this case. First, variable X_4 is the single most important variable in the discriminant function, but it is redundant in both Y_{max} and Y_{min}. Second, the scatterplots of Y_{max} vs Y_{min} show only relatively small differences in location between the two groups. Hence we can argue that the direction of a a large difference in location (discriminant function) is not the same as any of the two directions of extreme difference in variability (Y_{max}, Y_{min}). However, some more careful arguments would be needed to support the validity of the linear discrimination method, and we shall therefore return to this problem in Exercise 14 of Chapter 12.

12
Exercises

12.1 EXERCISES BASED ON THE BANK NOTE DATA

We would like to invite our reader to put the data presented in this book on the computer and to solve some of the exercises given in this chapter. For most exercises one of the standard statistical software packages may be used. These programs most often produce more numerical results than those discussed in the respective chapters of this book. The reader will thus have to distinguish between the important and the not-so-important aspects of the computer output. Another possibility, which readers with sufficiently good programming knowledge may prefer, is to use a subroutine library like NAG or IMSL, and to produce custom made output. This may have considerable advantages: for instance, with SPSS or BMDP it is not possible to apply a linear combination obtained from a subset of the data to the whole data set without exiting and re-entering the program. The same thing could be done relatively easily within a FORTRAN program that uses NAG or IMSL. An attractive compromise between these two possibilities is offered by the procedure MATRIX of SAS, which requires some knowledge of matrix algebra.

For the exercises based on the bank note data we have to give some preliminaries. As has been noticed a number of times (cf. Figs 4.4, 7.16 and 11.5), the group of forged bills seems to be inhomogeneous. We attempted therefore to define homogeneous subgroups of the forged notes. Methods for dividing a data set into *a priori* unknown subgroups are usually called *cluster analysis*, and there is a vast amount of literature on this topic. See, for instance, Chapter 7 in Seber (1984), and the references therein.

Since we have not dealt with cluster analysis in this book, we used a simple visual method: we asked the 22 participants of a course on applied multivariate statistics to use the faces of the 100 forged bills (Fig. 4.4) to find subgroups of similar faces. They were instructed to go more by the overall impression than by details. The participants agreed on considering the following 13 bank notes as a homogeneous subgroup: nos. 111, 116, 138, 148, 160, 161, 168, 171, 180, 182, 187, 192 and 194. Bills nos. 103, 162 and 167 were judged to be conspicuous, but could not unequivocally be assigned to either the above group of 13 bills or to the remaining 84 bills.

Table 12.1 Identification functions for bills nos. 103, 162 and 167 vs $Forged_{84}$ and $Forged_{13}$. In brackets standard errors

	no. 103 vs $Forged_{84}$	no. 103 vs $Forged_{13}$	no. 162 vs $Forged_{84}$	no. 162 vs $Forged_{13}$	no. 167 vs $Forged_{84}$	no. 167 vs $Forged_{13}$
intercept	−18.10	−5067.04	143.67	18667.99	−1920.92	1770.11
LENGTH	−1.26	−9.92	4.65	−19.46	15.76	15.58
	(4.95)	(15.03)	(3.67)	(12.72)	(3.04)	(22.40)
LEFT	5.97	−23.52	10.58	−15.01	4.47	36.54
	(6.40)	(34.10)	(4.67)	(32.95)	(4.55)	(50.87)
RIGHT	−5.67	30.78	2.88	−64.96	2.22	−37.61
	(5.14)	(31.45)	(3.87)	(20.23)	(1.70)	(48.10)
BOTTOM	−6.62	25.96	−10.03	−19.87	−7.95	−22.30
	(2.60)	(10.17)	(1.68)	(11.10)	(1.70)	(19.38)
TOP	−5.07	49.25	−10.90	−71.82	−10.24	−59.14
	(3.22)	(26.73)	(2.12)	(14.78)	(2.02)	(43.29)
DIAGONAL	2.70	39.54	−19.09	−22.16	−15.29	−29.72
	(4.62)	(7.41)	(2.72)	(13.43)	(2.81)	(22.27)
R^2	0.1337	0.8354	0.5132	0.8518	0.5606	0.6316
D_6	3.60	8.09	9.41	8.62	10.35	4.71

For the moment, we denote the group of 13 bills defined above as $Forged_{13}$ and the remaining 84 bills as $Forged_{84}$. How should the three questionable bills be handled? One possibility would be to compute a discriminant function between $Forged_{84}$ and $Forged_{13}$, and to classify nos. 103, 162 and 167 according to their value in this discriminant function. We should consider the possibility, however, that a bill belongs to neither of the two groups. Therefore we prefer to analyse each of the three bills separately.

Exercise 1 For each of the three bills, nos. 103, 162 and 167, perform an identification analysis versus $Forged_{84}$ and $Forged_{13}$, respectively. Make a decision upon allocation or rejection based on the overall F-statistic or on the multivariate standard distance. In case of rejection, identify the variables that are mainly responsible for the large standard distance.

As a check for correctness of the computations, Table 12.1 gives some numerical results. We obtained the identification function using a regression program and the group codes $c_1 = 0$ (for the sample) and $c_2 = 100$ (for the additional bill).

Exercise 2 Consider the identification functions (possibly after elimination of redundant variables) of bill no. 162 vs $Forged_{84}$ and $Forged_{13}$. Call these two linear combinations Y_1 and Y_2, respectively, and apply them to all 100 forged bills. Draw a scatterplot of Y_1 vs Y_2. What does this scatterplot tell you about the position of bill no. 162 relative to the two subgroups?

Based on the overall F-statistics associated with the above identification functions we decided to allocate no. 103 to group $Forged_{84}$ and no. 167 to group $Forged_{13}$. Since the multivariate standard distance of no. 162 to both subgroups is quite large, we will consider this bill as an outlier from now on. The subgroups of the forged notes are now defined as follows:

$Forged_{14}$: nos. 111, 116, 138, 148, 160, 161, 167, 168, 171, 180, 182, 187, 192, 194

Outlier: no. 162

$Forged_{85}$: remaining forged bills (not including nos. 201–205).

Since the definition of subgroups based on face plots is affected by subjective decisions, it is reasonable to confirm the clustering by some other method. First, it is recommended to compute means and standard deviations for all six variables in both subgroups and to replace the frequency polygons of group *Forged* in Figs. 2.1 to 2.6 by frequency polygons for the subgroups. Another useful method is to mark the members of group $Forged_{14}$ and no. 162 by a

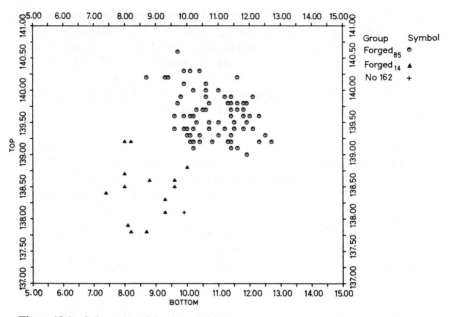

Figure 12.1 Subgroups of the forged bills

special symbol in the scatterplots of all pairs of variables. Figure 12.1 shows a scatterplot of BOTTOM VS DIAGONAL. Bill no. 162 appears in this scatterplot close to $Forged_{14}$ – but recall Exercise 2! Another way of checking whether the subgroups are reasonable is to compute a discriminant function between them.

Exercise 3 Compute a discriminant function between $Forged_{85}$ and $Forged_{14}$ and eliminate redundant variables. Apply the discriminant function to both groups and plot a histogram of the discriminant variable. Estimate the probabilities of misclassification as illustrated in Section 7.7. Use the discriminant function to classify bills no. 201 to 205.

As a check for correctness of the results, we give our solution, obtained with a regression program and group codes $c_1 = 0$ (for $Forged_{85}$) and $c_2 = 100$ (for $Forged_{14}$):

$$DF = -649.73 + 13.72 \text{ LENGTH} + 19.43 \text{ LEFT} + 4.79 \text{ RIGHT}$$
$$(3.77) \qquad\qquad (6.31) \qquad\quad (5.28)$$

$$-20.45 \text{ BOTTOM} - 19.56 \text{ TOP} - 35.89 \text{ DIAGONAL}.$$
$$(1.72) \qquad\qquad (2.76) \qquad\quad (2.60)$$

The multivariate standard distance between $Forged_{85}$ and $Forged_{14}$ was $D_6 = 8.30$.

Exercise 4 Compute the discriminant functions of the group of 100 genuine bills vs $Forged_{85}$ and $Forged_{14}$, respectively. Call the two linear combinations DF_{85} and DF_{14}, respectively. Eliminate redundant variables, and compare the two discriminant functions with respect to the importance of individual variables.

For comparison, here are our numerical results, obtained with a regression program and using $c_1 = 0$ (genuine bills), $c_2 = 100$ (respective group of forged bills):

$$DF_{85} = 2825.50 - 5.71 \text{ LENGTH} - 12.24 \text{ LEFT} + 10.06 \text{ RIGHT}$$
$$(3.29) \qquad\qquad (4.28) \qquad\qquad (3.93)$$
$$+ 19.82 \text{ BOTTOM} + 19.95 \text{ TOP} - 11.85 \text{ DIAGONAL}$$
$$(1.56) \qquad\qquad (1.99) \qquad\qquad (2.57)$$
standard distance: $D_6 = 7.31$

$$DF_{14} = 3138.72 + 5.00 \text{ LENGTH} - 7.74 \text{ LEFT} + 4.17 \text{ RIGHT}$$
$$(3.36) \qquad\qquad (5.20) \qquad\qquad (4.94)$$
$$+ 2.52 \text{ BOTTOM} + 2.39 \text{ TOP} - 26.79 \text{ DIAGONAL}$$
$$(3.06) \qquad\qquad (1.79)$$
standard distance: $D_6 = 7.03$

Exercise 5 Apply the linear combinations DF_{85} and DF_{14} to all 200 bills, and draw a scatterplot of DF_{85} vs DF_{14}. What would you expect this scatterplot to look like? Based on the scatterplot, try to answer the following questions.
1. For the purpose of discriminating between genuine and forged bills, did we make a bad mistake in Chapter 7 by assuming homogeneity of the forged group?
2. Can you imagine a situation where ignoring subgroups would be fatal?

Exercise 6 Compute a discriminant function between *Genuine* and $Forged_{85}$, using the four variables LENGTH, DIAGONAL, HEIGHT $= (X_2 + X_3)/2$ and IMAGE $= (X_2 + X_3)/2 - (X_4 + X_5)$. Compare the discriminant function with DF_{85} from Exercise 4. Using the same technique as in section 7.5, test the hypothesis that the variables LEFT, RIGHT, BOTTOM and TOP can be replaced by HEIGHT and IMAGE without loss of information.

Here is our solution, the group codes again being 0 and 100:

$$DF = 2776.47 - 6.52 \text{ LENGTH} - 11.40 \text{ DIAGONAL}$$
$$(3.33) \qquad\qquad (2.61)$$
$$- 20.25 \text{ IMAGE} + 19.31 \text{ HEIGHT}$$
$$(1.57) \qquad\qquad (3.66)$$
standard distance: $D_4 = 7.11$

We will now turn our attention to the covariance structure of group $Forged_{85}$.

Exercise 7 Compute the covariance and correlation matrices for group $Forged_{85}$. Compared with the group of all 100 forged bills (cf Table 3.4), would you expect the variances to become rather smaller or rather larger? Why? Can you explain the differences between the new correlation matrix and the one given in Table 3.2?

As a check for correctness of the computations, the covariance matrix of group $Forged_{85}$ is given in Table 12.2

Table 12.2 Covariance matrix of group $Forged_{85}$

	LENGTH	LEFT	RIGHT	BOTTOM	TOP	DIAGONAL
LENGTH	0.0764					
LEFT	0.0296	0.0641				
RIGHT	0.0304	0.0489	0.0940			
BOTTOM	−0.0512	0.0289	−0.0109	0.7242		
TOP	0.0413	−0.0130	0.0071	−0.4330	0.4039	
DIAGONAL	0.0389	0.0353	0.0531	0.0959	0.0259	0.1166

Exercise 8 Compute the principal components in group $Forged_{85}$. What proportion of the total variance is contained in the first component? In the first three components? Can you give some meaningful interpretation to the first three components?

The numerical results we obtained are given in Table 12.3. (Note that your computer program may give the matrix of coefficients of the principal component transformation in transposed form).

Table 12.3 Coefficients of the principal component transformation in group $Forged_{85}$, and eigenvalues (variances) of the components

	LENGTH	LEFT	RIGHT	BOTTOM	TOP	DIAGONAL	Eigenvalue
U_1	0.071	−0.025	0.020	−0.816	0.564	0.104	1.041
U_2	0.352	0.422	0.550	0.015	−0.179	0.603	0.207
U_3	0.222	0.242	0.213	0.491	0.733	0.263	0.115
U_4	−0.833	0.072	0.543	−0.019	0.069	−0.030	0.051
U_5	0.262	0.243	0.347	−0.297	0.328	−0.745	0.040
U_6	0.245	−0.836	0.487	0.070	0.016	0.005	0.025

Exercise 9 Apply the principal component transformation from Exercise 8 to the bills in group $Forged_{85}$. Draw a scatterplot of the first versus the last principal component, using the same scale for both axes. Does this scatterplot reveal anything interesting? Using the standardized or unstandardized principal components, compute the standard distance for each bill in group $Forged_{85}$, and plot a histogram of the squared standard distances. Are there any 'suspiciously' large standard distances?

Exercise 10 Using your numerical results or Table 12.3, decide whether the principal components are well-defined at all in group $Forged_{85}$. Compute the criterion for overall sphericity, for sphericity of the last three components, and for sphericity of all pairs of adjacent principal components. Finally, compute standard errors of the coefficients and decide whether or not it was justified to interpret the first three principal components.

As a last exercise involving the bank note data, we turn now to a comparison of the covariance structures of $Forged_{85}$ and *Genuine*.

Exercise 11 Compare the covariance matrices of *Genuine* and $Forged_{85}$ by computing the linear combinations Y_{max} and Y_{min}. Compare the extreme variance ratios, F_{max} and F_{min}, with appropriate quantiles from Table 11.3. Can the two covariance matrices be assumed to be equal? Apply Y_{max} and Y_{min} to all 185 bank notes in the two groups, and draw a scatterplot of Y_{max} vs Y_{min}. Does this scatterplot reveal any inhomogeneity such as that in Fig. 11.5?

For comparison, the numerical results we obtained are listed in Table 12.4. The table gives the coefficients of the intermediate eigenvectors as well, since they will be needed in Exercise 12.

Since $F_{max} = 2.489$ exceeds the corresponding critical value c_{max} by only a small amount, we will not analyse Y_{max} in detail. On the other hand, F_{min} is well below c_{min}, and so it may be worth looking at Y_{min} more closely.

Table 12.4 Eigenvectors and eigenvalues in the comparison of the covariance matrices of *Genuine* and $Forged_{85}$

	LENGTH	LEFT	RIGHT	BOTTOM	TOP	DIAGONAL	Eigenvalue
Y_1	0.634	0.465	1.211	− 1.883	− 0.647	0.683	$2.489 = F_{max}$
Y_2	1.019	− 1.129	− 1.703	− 0.038	0.884	− 0.927	1.097
Y_3	− 0.920	− 2.830	2.854	0.845	1.297	0.139	0.728
Y_4	0.354	1.296	− 1.335	1.194	1.633	1.512	0.592
Y_5	2.530	− 1.807	0.759	0.162	− 0.307	− 0.347	0.399
Y_6	0.203	1.265	0.523	− 0.234	− 0.026	− 1.483	$0.197 = F_{min}$

Exercise 12 Using the numerical results from Exercise 11, compute the standard errors and partial statistics for the analysis of Y_{min} as proposed in Section 11.6. Try to simplify Y_{min} by eliminating redundant variables. Remembering the fact that Y_{min} is a variable with respect to which the forged notes have relatively small variability, can you ascribe a meaning to Y_{min}?

12.2 ADDITIONAL EXERCISES

The following exercises are based on the examples given at the end of Chapters 7 to 11. Some of them may require considerable computational efforts, and may even introduce some ideas and techniques not mentioned in the text. No solutions to the exercises are provided here.

Exercise 13 This exercise is based on the female vole data analysed in Example 7.1.
1. Compute the covariance matrices for all variables except *Age*, and for both groups. Compare them using the method of Chapter 11. (*Note*: the table of quantiles of the largest characteristic root given in Section 11.8 starts with degrees of freedom $v_1 = v_2 = 47$, which is larger than the degrees of freedom associated with the two covariance matrices given in this example. Use the references given in Section 11.8 to obtain the correct quantiles, or use the value for $v_1 = v_2 = 47$ as a rough approximation. This approximate quantile is slightly too small. Why?)
2. Apply the linear discriminant function DF based on L_2, L_7 and B_4 to the data, and compute means and variances of DF in both groups. Does the variance of DF appear to differ between groups? Compute also the pooled variance of DF and verify your results using the formulae given in Section 7.6. In conclusion, do you think that the differences in variability between the two groups affect linear discrimination?
3. Compute a linear discriminant function based on the 'redundant' variables L_9, B_3 and H_1. Apply it to the data and plot it against the discriminant function based on the sufficient variables L_2, L_7 and B_4. In this plot, draw (by eye) a straight line that separates the two groups as well as possible. If L_9, B_3 and H_1 are redundant, what should the direction of this straight line be?
4. Compute a discriminant function based on variables L_7 and B_4 only. Determine a classification boundary as proposed in Section 7.7. Supplement the scatterplot by a straight line that indicates the two classification regions according to the chosen boundary. Estimate the probability of misclassification using the normal theory approach.

Exercise 14 This exercise is based on the electrode data used in Examples

7.2 and 11.1. (*Note*: Part 3 of this exercise may be rather difficult and should be attempted only by advanced readers.)

1. Compute the discriminant function DF based on all five variables and verify the numerical results given in Example 7.2. Using the backward elimination procedure, discard redundant variables. Apply the discriminant function to all 100 observations and draw frequency polygons of its distribution in both groups. Compute the variance of DF in both groups as well as the pooled variance.

2. Using the linear combinations Y_{max} and Y_{min} from Example 11.1, draw scatterplots of DF vs Y_{max} and DF vs Y_{min}. Check whether the heuristic arguments for the validity of the linear discriminant function given in the last paragraph of Example 11.1 are valid or not.

3. In Example 11.1 we said that the direction of large difference in location (i.e. the discriminant function) does not seem to be heavily affected by the differences in variability. Use the following procedure to verify this statement:

   (i) Compute a discriminant function of the data of machine 1 versus the mean values of machine 2, as explained in Section 9.4. That is, compute this discriminant function as if no data, but only the mean vector, were available for machine 2. Call this discriminant function DF_1. (ii) Switch the roles of the two groups, that is, compute a discriminant function DF_2 for the data of machine 2 versus the mean values of machine 1. (iii) Apply the linear combinations DF_1 and DF_2 to all 100 observations and draw a scatterplot of DF_1 vs DF_2.

   If the two covariance matrices were identical, what could you predict for this scatterplot? Compute the standard distances between the two groups based on DF_1 and DF_2, respectively. Try to find a situation where these two distances differ considerably. Find also a situation where the two measures of distance are equal although the two covariance matrices are not identical.

4. Perform stepwise analyses of Y_{max} and Y_{min} as outlined in Example 11.1, thus confirming the numerical results given there.

5. In Fig. 7.21 we noticed that some of the items produced by machine 1 appear as outliers. Perform a full identification analysis of the ninth electrode of machine 1 versus the 49 remaining items.

6. Compute the principal components of all five variables, using only the data from machine 1. Using standardized principal component scores, compute standard distances of all 50 items. Why is the standard distance of item no. 9 not the same as the one obtained from identification analysis? Draw a histogram of the frequency distribution of all 50 squared standard distances. Under normality assumptions, and if no outliers are present, this histogram should resemble a chi square distribution on five degrees of freedom. From a table of the chi square

Table 12.5 Data of 20 additional electrodes

X_1	X_2	X_3	X_4	X_5
39	58	40	44	59
44	59	19	19	60
41	61	42	44	62
44	60	36	43	61
41	59	30	42	61
40	62	38	45	60
40	59	38	44	60
40	59	35	51	57
42	59	33	39	59
42	62	36	45	60
40	60	37	42	59
41	59	39	39	60
42	62	30	38	58
40	58	31	50	55
40	61	32	36	63
43	61	29	43	62
42	58	33	30	60
42	58	26	19	58
42	62	36	44	60
38	60	37	46	60

distribution, read selected quantiles (e.g., the 10%, 20%, 80% and 90% quantiles) and compare them to the empirical distribution of the 50 squared standard distances. Do you think some of the electrodes must be considered as outliers?

7. Table 12.5 gives the data of 20 additional electrodes that are known to have been produced by one of the two machines. Apply the discriminant function of Example 7.2 to these observations and classify them.

Exercise 15 This exercise is based on the medical data of Example 7.3.
1. Compute univariate and bivariate descriptive statistics, such as means, standard deviations, standard distances, and correlations. In case of the binary variables B_1 to B_3, what is the interpretation of their means? Do you think the concept of standard distance is meaningful for binary variables? If you consider only the univariate results, would you think that discriminant analysis is reasonable at all in this example?
2. The discriminant function DF given in Example 7.3 has several unstable coefficients. Use the stepwise elimination procedure to find a reasonable subset of variables. (*Note:* The result of this analysis is somewhat puzzling, showing a need to collect more data).
3. The values of the three continuous variables (see Table 7.9) are all integers, except for two cases in group 1. The first exception is a value of 1.5 in variable C_1. This value seems plausible, given the fact that C_1 can take only positive values. The second exception is a value of 15.6 for variable C_2 in the third observation. There is some suspicion that this

measurement should actually be 156.0 and was incorrectly recorded. Repeat the discriminant analysis with the 'corrected' data and try to answer the question whether the 'error' was influential.

4. Apply the 'holdout' procedure (Lachenbruch, 1975) to estimate error rates. (*Note*: this is a highly laborious task unless appropriate software is available). The procedure works as follows:

    (i) Start with group 1. Omit one observation from this group and compute a discriminant function based on the remaining $n_1 - 1$ and n_2 observations.

    (ii) Classify the 'holdout' observation using the discriminant function constructed in step (i).

    (iii) Repeat steps (i) and (ii) for all observations of group 1. Let f_1 be the number of 'holdout observations' misclassified in this group.

    (iv) Repeat steps (i) through (iii) for the n_2 observations from group 2. Let f_2 be the number of 'holdout observations' misclassified in this group.

Estimate the misclassification probabilities as f_1/n_1 and f_2/n_2, and the true error rate as $(f_1 + f_2)/(n_1 + n_2)$. (See also Johnson and Wichern 1982, Section 10.6, for an illustration of this procedure.)

Exercise 16 This exercise is based on the switch-drum data of Example 8.1.

1. Compute the identification functions IDF_{51} and IDF_{52} of Example 8.1 and confirm the results given there. Apply the identification function IDF_{52} to the reference sample and to observation no. 52. Compute the mean and variance of IDF_{52} in the reference sample, and verify your result using the formulae given at the end of Section 8.2.

2. Perform a backward elimination procedure on IDF_{52} to verify the statements made in Example 8.1.

3. Draw a scatterplot of X_2 vs X_4 and mark item no. 52 by a special symbol. Can you see why no. 52 has a relatively large bivariate standard distance, although its values in X_2 and X_4 are close to average?

Exercise 17 In this exercise we use the cork data analysed in Example 9.1.

1. Verify the results of Example 9.1 by computing the specification function. Apply the necessary corrections to F-statistics and standard errors. Construct an appropriate F-test to compare the specification function based on $DIFF_1$, $DIFF_2$ and $DIFF_3$ with the one based on $DIFF_4$.

2. Use the three contrasts $N - S$, $E - W$ and $N - W$ to compute a specification function and a standard distance. Is the standard distance different from the one given in Example 9.1? Write the specification function in terms of the original variables N, E, S and W. Do the same with the specification function given in Example 9.1, and compare.

3. Compute a specification function based on the contrasts $E - W$, $N - S$ and $E + W - N - S$. Eliminate redundant variables and compare your results with those of Example 9.1.

4. Draw a scatterplot of $DIFF_1$ vs $DIFF_3$ and mark the 'hypothetical mean' (0, 0) by a special symbol.

Exercise 18 This exercise is based on the decathlon data used in Example 10.1.

1. Verify the numerical result given in Example 10.1 by performing a principal component analysis on the variables DASH, RUN4, HURDLE and RUN15. Repeat the analysis after omitting RUN15.

2. Draw a scatterplot of the first principal component of DASH, RUN4 and HURDLE vs SUM, the sum of scores achieved in the three running disciplines. How well do the two measures of performance agree?

3. Perform a similar analysis for the throwing disciplines or for the jumping disciplines.

Exercise 19 In this exercise, the 'head dimension' data of Example 10.2 are used.

1. Use a computer program for principal component analysis to verify the results of Example 10.2.

2. Perform a test for sphericity of all six components and a test for sphericity of the third to fifth components.

3. As an alternative to asymptotic standard errors and tests for sphericity, use the following method. Divide the data in four groups of 50 individuals each. Compute the principal component transformation and the eigenvalues individually in each group. Compare the four analyses and check whether, for some components, similar pictures emerge in all four subgroups.

4. Perform identification analyses of individuals no. 104 and no. 111 vs the remaining observations. Which variables are mostly responsible for the large standard distances? Why are the standard distances obtained from these two analyses not identical with those given in Table 10.15? How could you guess from Table 10.15 which variables contribute most to the large standard distances? Apply the two identification functions to the data of all 200 observation and draw a scatterplot.

Exercise 20 This exercise is based on the male vole data used in Example 10.3.

1. Use the log-variables to compute principal components individually in each group, and check the correctness of the eigenvalues given in Example 10.3. Check for sphericity of the second and third components in both groups, using the sphericity criterion proposed in Section 10.7.

Compute standard errors of the coefficients of the first principal components of both groups. Comparing the first principal components across groups, do you think the first component can be assumed to be common to both species?

2. Based on the second and third common components, i.e.

$$U_2 = -0.566LL_2 + 0.158LB_3 + 0.810LH_1$$

$$U_3 = -0.481LL_2 + 0.734LB_3 - 0.479LH_1,$$

compute a 'growth-invariant' discriminant function between *M. californicus* and *M. ochrogaster* (*Note*: do not centre the data at a common mean before applying U_2 and U_3 to them.) Plot the discriminant function vs *Age* to confirm growth-invariance.

13
Mathematical appendix

13.1 INTRODUCTION AND PRELIMINARIES

In this appendix some results from Chapters 2, 3 and 5 through 11 are given in concise matrix notation. Only a few selected proofs are given, and the more difficult aspects – multivariate distribution theory – are omitted altogether. The appendix is merely an aid to the reader who is familiar with linear algebra to recognize how the mostly verbal statements of the respective chapters translate into mathematical language. The reader who is not familiar with matrix theory but would like to understand the mathematical basis of multivariate statistics should first read an introductory text on matrix algebra. Some books on matrix methods have been written especially with regard to applications in statistics; see, for instance, Basilevsky (1983) or Searle (1982). Bronson (1970) is particularly easy to read. Good introductions to the basic concepts of matrix theory are also provided by special chapters in the books of Morrison (1976), Johnson and Wichern (1982), and in the regression texts of Draper and Smith (1981) and Younger (1979). Almost every book on multivariate statistics contains an appendix that summarizes the most important matrix techniques, but these appendices are most often too difficult for the beginner.

This appendix may also be used, at least in principle, as a basis for writing appropriate computer programs, using a subroutine library like NAG or IMSL, or using the MATRIX procedure of SAS. The computational aspects of matrix methods are themselves far from trivial; see, for example, the recent book by Golub and Van Loan (1983). A text by Parlett (1980) is devoted exclusively to the computation of eigenvalues and eigenvectors.

Here are some remarks concerning the notation: bold print is used to mark matrices and vectors, Capital letters are used for matrices, small letters for vectors. The transpose of a matrix $\mathbf{A} = (a_{ij})$ is denoted by $\mathbf{A}'$, the inverse (provided that it exists) by $\mathbf{A}^{-1}$. The dimensions of matrices and vectors are either clear from the context, or given in brackets when the symbol is introduced. The $(k \times k)$-unit matrix is denoted by $\mathbf{I}_k$. All vectors are to be understood as column vectors, their transposes as row vectors. A square matrix **A** is called diagonal if all its off-diagonal elements (i.e. those a_{ij} with $i \neq j$) are zero.

13.2   DATA MATRIX, MEAN VECTOR, COVARIANCE AND CORRELATION

It is convenient to represent the data of n observations, taken on p variables, by an $(n \times p)$-matrix **X**. The ith row of **X** contains the measurements taken on the ith individual, while the jth column refers to the jth variable. Let **1** denote a vector of length n containing 1 in every position, then the vector of means can be written in matrix notation as

$$\bar{\mathbf{x}} = \begin{bmatrix} \bar{x}_1 \\ \bar{x}_2 \\ \vdots \\ \bar{x}_p \end{bmatrix} = \frac{1}{n} \mathbf{X}' \mathbf{1}. \tag{1}$$

For the sample covariance matrix **S**, we define the so-called centering matrix of dimension $(n \times n)$,

$$\mathbf{H} = \mathbf{I}_n - \frac{1}{n} \mathbf{1} \mathbf{1}'. \tag{2}$$

It is left to the reader to verify that the typical element s_{ij} of the matrix

$$\mathbf{S} = \mathbf{X}' \mathbf{H} \mathbf{X}/(n-1) \tag{3}$$

is indeed the sample covariance between the ith and the jth variable.

The correlation matrix can be written as

$$\mathbf{R} = (\text{diag } \mathbf{S})^{-1/2} \mathbf{S} (\text{diag } \mathbf{S})^{-1/2}, \tag{4}$$

where

$$(\text{diag } \mathbf{S})^{-1/2} = \begin{bmatrix} \frac{1}{\sqrt{s_{11}}} & 0 & \cdots & 0 \\ 0 & \frac{1}{\sqrt{s_{22}}} & \cdots & 0 \\ \vdots & \vdots & & \vdots \\ 0 & 0 & \cdots & \frac{1}{\sqrt{s_{pp}}} \end{bmatrix}. \tag{5}$$

See also Mardia, Kent and Bibby (1979, Section 1.4).

13.3   MULTIPLE LINEAR REGRESSION

In the multiple linear regression model it is assumed that the mean μ_y of the random variable Y has the functional form

$$\mu_y = \beta_0 + \beta_1 x_1 + \cdots + \beta_p x_p, \tag{6}$$

where the parameters β_j are unknown. For the ith measurement y_i, taken at the values $(x_{1i}, x_{2i}, \ldots, x_{pi})$ of the regressors, this equation can be written as

$$y_i = \beta_0 + \beta_1 x_{1i} + \cdots + \beta_p x_{pi} + e_i \quad (i = 1, \ldots, n) \tag{7}$$

where e_i is the random component. In matrix notation, the n equations (7) can be written as

$$\mathbf{y} = (1{:}\mathbf{X})\boldsymbol{\beta} + \mathbf{e}, \tag{8}$$

where

$$\mathbf{y} = \begin{bmatrix} y_1 \\ \vdots \\ y_n \end{bmatrix} \tag{9}$$

is the vector of observed values y_i, $\mathbf{X}$ is the data matrix of the regressors,

$$\boldsymbol{\beta} = \begin{bmatrix} \beta_0 \\ \beta_1 \\ \vdots \\ \beta_p \end{bmatrix} \tag{10}$$

is the vector of unknown parameters, and

$$\mathbf{e} = \begin{bmatrix} e_1 \\ \vdots \\ e_n \end{bmatrix} \tag{11}$$

is the vector of deviations. Writing $\mathbf{Z} = (1{:}\mathbf{X})$, the sum of squares for given $\boldsymbol{\beta}$ is

$$S(\boldsymbol{\beta}) = \sum_{i=1}^{n} e_i^2 = \mathbf{e}'\mathbf{e} = (\mathbf{y} - \mathbf{Z}\boldsymbol{\beta})'(\mathbf{y} - \mathbf{Z}\boldsymbol{\beta})$$
$$= \mathbf{y}'\mathbf{y} - 2\boldsymbol{\beta}'\mathbf{Z}'\mathbf{y} + \boldsymbol{\beta}'\mathbf{Z}'\mathbf{Z}\boldsymbol{\beta}, \tag{12}$$

where we have used the fact that $\boldsymbol{\beta}'\mathbf{Z}'\mathbf{y}$ is scalar.

According to the principle of least squares, $\boldsymbol{\beta}$ is to be chosen such that $S(\boldsymbol{\beta})$ is a minimum. By taking partial derivatives with respect to the β_j and setting them equal to zero, the least squares estimates are obtained as

$$\hat{\boldsymbol{\beta}} = (\mathbf{Z}'\mathbf{Z})^{-1}\mathbf{Z}'\mathbf{y}, \tag{13}$$

provided that $\mathbf{Z}'\mathbf{Z}$ is not singular. For a nice proof of this result that does not involve derivatives see Johnson and Wichern (1982, p. 295–296).

Using (13), the minimum sum of squares turns out to be

$$S_{\min} = S(\hat{\boldsymbol{\beta}}) = \mathbf{y}'\mathbf{y} - \mathbf{y}'\mathbf{Z}\hat{\boldsymbol{\beta}} = \mathbf{y}'(\mathbf{y} - \hat{\mathbf{y}}) \tag{14}$$

where

$$\hat{\mathbf{y}} = \mathbf{Z}\hat{\boldsymbol{\beta}} \tag{15}$$

is the vector of predicted values $\hat{y}_i$. Defining the vector of residuals as

$$\hat{\mathbf{e}} = \mathbf{y} - \hat{\mathbf{y}}, \tag{16}$$

the minimum sum of squares can also be written as $S_{min} = \mathbf{y}'\hat{\mathbf{e}}$.

According to (13), computing the least squares estimates involves mainly the inversion of the $[(p+1) \times (p+1)]$-matrix $\mathbf{Z}'\mathbf{Z}$. This matrix has the form

$$\mathbf{Z}'\mathbf{Z} = n \begin{bmatrix} 1 & \bar{\mathbf{x}}' \\ \bar{\mathbf{x}} & \dfrac{1}{n}\mathbf{X}'\mathbf{X} \end{bmatrix}. \tag{17}$$

If the regressors are centred, that is, all x-variables have mean zero, the lower right $(p \times p)$-submatrix of (17) is exactly $(n-1)$ times the covariance matrix of the regressors. If the correlations between the regressors are high, the least squares estimates may be unstable both in a statistical sense and from the point of view of numerical accuracy.

13.4   LINEAR COMBINATIONS

The coefficients of a linear combination of p variables can conveniently be arranged in the form of a p-vector $\mathbf{a}$. Applying the linear combination to the data means transforming the data matrix $\mathbf{X}$ into an n-vector $\mathbf{y}$ according to

$$\mathbf{y} = \mathbf{X}\mathbf{a}. \tag{18}$$

If several, say k, linear combinations are considered simultaneously, their coefficients are arranged as a $(p \times k)$-matrix

$$\mathbf{A} = (\mathbf{a}_1, \mathbf{a}_2, \ldots, \mathbf{a}_k), \tag{19}$$

each column containing the coefficients of one linear combination. Applying these k linear combinations simultaneously to the data matrix $\mathbf{X}$, we get a new data matrix $\mathbf{Y}$ of dimension $(n \times k)$:

$$\mathbf{Y} = \mathbf{X}\mathbf{A}. \tag{20}$$

The ith row of $\mathbf{Y}$ contains the data of the ith observation in the k linear combinations.

Using formulae (1) and (3), the mean vector $\bar{\mathbf{y}}$ and the covariance matrix $\mathbf{S}_y$ of the k linear combinations are

$$\bar{\mathbf{y}} = \frac{1}{n}\mathbf{Y}'\mathbf{1} = \frac{1}{n}\mathbf{A}'\mathbf{X}'\mathbf{1} = \mathbf{A}'\bar{\mathbf{x}} \tag{21}$$

and

$$S_y = \frac{1}{n-1} Y'HY = \frac{1}{n-1} A'X'HXA = A'S_x A, \tag{22}$$

where S_x is the $(p \times p)$-covariance matrix of the original variables. The formulae given in Section 6.5 follow from (21) and (22) as special cases for $k = 1$.

13.5 MULTIVARIATE STANDARD DISTANCE AND THE LINEAR DISCRIMINANT FUNCTION

Let $\bar{x}_1, \bar{x}_2, S_1, S_2, n_1$ and n_2 denote the mean vectors, covariance matrices and sample sizes of two p-variate samples. If we apply a linear combination Y with coefficients $a \in \mathbb{R}^p$ to the data of the two groups, we get, according to Section 13.4, the following means and variances of Y in the two samples:

$$\bar{y}_1 = a'\bar{x}_1; \qquad \bar{y}_2 = a'\bar{x}_2 \tag{23}$$

and

$$s_{y_1}^2 = a'S_1 a; \qquad s_{y_2}^2 = a'S_2 a. \tag{24}$$

The pooled variance of Y is

$$\begin{aligned}
s_y^2 &= \frac{(n_1 - 1)s_{y_1}^2 + (n_2 - 1)s_{y_2}^2}{n_1 + n_2 - 2} \\
&= a' \left[\frac{(n_1 - 1)S_1 + (n_2 - 1)S_2}{n_1 + n_2 - 2} \right] a \\
&= a'Sa, \tag{25}
\end{aligned}$$

where S is the pooled covariance matrix of both groups.

The multivariate standard distance between the two samples is defined as the maximum of function

$$D(a) = \frac{|a'\bar{x}_1 - a'\bar{x}_2|}{(a'Sa)^{1/2}} = \frac{|a'd|}{(a'Sa)^{1/2}} \tag{26}$$

over all vectors $a \in \mathbb{R}^p$, where

$$d = \bar{x}_1 - \bar{x}_2 \tag{27}$$

is the vector of mean differences. Instead of maximizing $D(a)$, we can also maximize its square

$$D^2(a) = \frac{(a'd)^2}{a'Sa} = \frac{a'(dd')a}{a'Sa}, \tag{28}$$

where the second equality holds because $a'd$ is scalar. Since $D^2(a) = D^2(ka)$ for every non-zero $k \in \mathbb{R}$, the maximization can be restricted by some suitable constraint, for instance, $\mathbf{a}'\mathbf{a} = 1$. That is, in the terminology of Chapter 6, we can restrict ourselves to normalized linear combinations. A more convenient constraint is to restrict $\mathbf{a}$ such that $\mathbf{a}'\mathbf{S}\mathbf{a} = 1$. That is, the pooled variance is required to be 1, which can always be achieved, provided that $\mathbf{S}$ is not singular.

Introducing a Lagrange-multiplier λ for the constraint, we wish thus to maximize the function

$$F(\mathbf{a}) = \mathbf{a}'(\mathbf{d}\mathbf{d}')\mathbf{a} - \lambda(\mathbf{a}'\mathbf{S}\mathbf{a} - 1) \tag{29}$$

over $\mathbf{a} \in \mathbb{R}^p$. Taking partial derivatives with respect to the elements of $\mathbf{a}$, setting them equal to zero and writing the resulting equations in matrix form, we get

$$\mathbf{d}\mathbf{d}'\mathbf{a} - \lambda\mathbf{S}\mathbf{a} = 0 \tag{30}$$

Multiplying from the left by $\mathbf{S}^{-1}$ and noticing that $\mathbf{d}'\mathbf{a}$ is scalar, we get

$$\mathbf{a} = \frac{\mathbf{d}'\mathbf{a}}{\lambda} \cdot \mathbf{S}^{-1}\mathbf{d}, \tag{31}$$

that is, $\mathbf{a}$ is proportional to $\mathbf{S}^{-1}\mathbf{d}$. Since proportional linear combinations are equivalent, we can simply take

$$\mathbf{a}_0 = \mathbf{S}^{-1}\mathbf{d} \tag{32}$$

as the solution of the maximization problem. Formula (32) is the usual definition of the coefficients of the linear discriminant function.

The multivariate standard distance is thus

$$D(\mathbf{a}_0) = \frac{|\mathbf{a}_0'\mathbf{d}|}{(\mathbf{a}_0'\mathbf{S}\mathbf{a}_0)^{1/2}} = \frac{\mathbf{d}'\mathbf{S}^{-1}\mathbf{d}}{(\mathbf{d}'\mathbf{S}^{-1}\mathbf{S}\mathbf{S}^{-1}\mathbf{d})^{1/2}}$$
$$= (\mathbf{d}'\mathbf{S}^{-1}\mathbf{d})^{1/2}. \tag{33}$$

(Note that $\mathbf{d}'\mathbf{S}^{-1}\mathbf{d}$ is always positive, provided that $\mathbf{d} \neq 0$ and that $\mathbf{S}$ is positive definite – see Section 13.6).

For proofs of the relationship between linear regression and the discriminant function (32), see Healy (1965), Cramer (1967), Kendall (1957, p. 159), Lachenbruch (1975, p. 17), Anderson (1984, p. 212), or Flury and Riedwyl (1985).

Essentially the same formulae hold for identification and specification analysis. In identification analysis, we start with a single sample and denote its mean vector and covariance matrix by $\bar{\mathbf{x}}$ and $\mathbf{S}$, respectively. Writing $\mathbf{x}$ for the additional observation, we put

$$\mathbf{d} = \mathbf{x} - \bar{\mathbf{x}} \tag{34}$$

instead of (27), and continue analogously. In specification analysis, let $\bar{\mathbf{x}}$ and $\mathbf{S}$

again be the mean vector and covariance matrix of the sample, and denote by $\boldsymbol{\mu}_0$ the vector of p hypothetical means (specifications). Then put

$$\mathbf{d} = \bar{\mathbf{x}} - \boldsymbol{\mu}_0 \tag{35}$$

and proceed as in the text following (27).

13.6   PRINCIPAL COMPONENT ANALYSIS

Principal component analysis is based on a very useful theorem from matrix theory, called the spectral decomposition theorem. We state this theorem without proof.

Spectral decomposition theorem for symmetric matrices: Let $\mathbf{A}$ denote a symmetric $(p \times p)$-matrix. Then $\mathbf{A}$ can be written as

$$\mathbf{A} = l_1 \mathbf{b}_1 \mathbf{b}_1' + l_2 \mathbf{b}_2 \mathbf{b}_2' + \cdots + l_p \mathbf{b}_p \mathbf{b}_p', \tag{36}$$

where the l_i are real numbers, and the $\mathbf{b}_i$ are p-vectors of unit length ($\mathbf{b}_i \mathbf{b}_i = 1$), and mutually orthogonal (i.e. $\mathbf{b}_i' \mathbf{b}_j = 0$ for $i \neq j$). For a proof, see Basilevsky (1983, Section 5.3), Searle (1982, p. 308), Mardia, Kent and Bibby (1979, p. 469), or Muirhead (1982, appendix A7). The l_i and $\mathbf{b}_i$ are eigenvalues and eigenvectors (characteristic values, characteristic vectors) of the matrix $\mathbf{A}$, since

$$\mathbf{A}\mathbf{b}_i = \left(\sum_{j=1}^{p} l_j \mathbf{b}_j \mathbf{b}_j' \right) \mathbf{b}_i = l_i \mathbf{b}_i \tag{37}$$

by the orthogonality of the $\mathbf{b}_i$. Furthermore, we state without proof that the representation (36) of $\mathbf{A}$ is unique up to multiplication of the characteristic vectors by -1, provided that the characteristic values l_i are all different from each other. In case some l_i are identical, the associated $\mathbf{b}_i$ can still be chosen such that the spectral decomposition theorem holds.

Arranging the p orthogonal vectors $\mathbf{b}_i$ in form of a $(p \times p)$-matrix

$$\mathbf{B} = (\mathbf{b}_1, \mathbf{b}_2, \ldots, \mathbf{b}_p), \tag{38}$$

we get, from the orthogonality of the characteristic vectors,

$$\mathbf{B}'\mathbf{B} = \mathbf{B}\mathbf{B}' = \mathbf{I}_p. \tag{39}$$

This implies

$$\mathbf{B}' = \mathbf{B}^{-1} \tag{40}$$

that is, $\mathbf{B}$ is an orthogonal matrix.

Furthermore, arranging the eigenvalues l_i on the diagonal of a $(p \times p)$-

matrix

$$L = \mathrm{diag}\,(l_1, l_2, \ldots, l_p)$$

$$= \begin{bmatrix} l_1 & 0 & \cdots & 0 \\ 0 & l_2 & \cdots & 0 \\ \vdots & \vdots & & \vdots \\ 0 & 0 & & l_p \end{bmatrix}, \tag{41}$$

the spectral decomposition (36) of $\mathbf{A}$ can be written as

$$\mathbf{A} = \mathbf{BLB'}. \tag{42}$$

From the orthogonality of $\mathbf{B}$ (40) it follows then that

$$\mathbf{B'AB} = \mathbf{L}. \tag{43}$$

The symmetric matrix $\mathbf{A}$ is called positive definite, if all its eigenvalues l_i are strictly positive, and positive semidefinite, if the l_i are non-negative. If $\mathbf{A}$ is positive definite, the quadratic function (or quadratic form)

$$q(\mathbf{y}) = \mathbf{y'Ay}; \quad \mathbf{y} \in \mathbb{R}^p \tag{44}$$

is always positive. This follows from

$$q(\mathbf{y}) = \sum_{j=1}^{p} l_j \mathbf{y'b}_j \mathbf{b}_j' \mathbf{y}$$

$$= \sum_{j=1}^{p} l_j (\mathbf{y'b}_j)^2. \tag{45}$$

In principal component analysis, $\mathbf{A}$ is a sample covariance matrix (denoted by $\mathbf{S}$), and we notice without proof that $\mathbf{S}$ is positive definite exactly if the data matrix $\mathbf{X}$ has at least $p + 1$ linearly independent rows.

We are now going to sketch a derivation of principal components based on the spectral decomposition

$$\mathbf{S} = \mathbf{BLB'} = \sum_{j=1}^{p} l_j \mathbf{b}_j \mathbf{b}_j' \tag{46}$$

of a sample covariance matrix $\mathbf{S}$. This proof follows Johnson and Wichern (1982, p. 67). For simplicity, we assume that the eigenvalues l_i (which form the diagonal of $\mathbf{L}$) are arranged in decreasing order, that is,

$$l_1 > l_2 > \cdots l_p > 0 \tag{47}$$

and that no two eigenvalues are identical.

The first principal component is defined as the normalized linear combination with largest variance. To find its coefficients, we consider the function

$$v(\mathbf{y}) = \mathbf{y'Sy} \tag{48}$$

for vectors $y \in \mathbb{R}^p$, $y'y = 1$. By (22), $v(y)$ is the variance of a linear combination whose coefficients are the elements of y. Since the characteristic vectors b_j of S form a basis of $\mathbb{R}^p$, y can be written as

$$y = \alpha_1 b_1 + \alpha_2 b_2 + \cdots + \alpha_p b_p = B\alpha \qquad (49)$$

for some vector $\alpha \in \mathbb{R}^p$. Since $y'y = 1$, it follows that $\alpha'B'B\alpha = \alpha'\alpha = 1$, that is, α is a normalized vector. Now

$$v(y) = \alpha'B'SB\alpha$$
$$= \alpha'L\alpha$$
$$= \sum_{j=1}^{p} l_j \alpha_j^2$$
$$\leqslant \sum_{j=1}^{p} l_1 \alpha_j^2$$
$$= l_1 \sum_{j=1}^{p} \alpha_j^2 = l_1, \qquad (50)$$

and so $v(y)$ cannot exceed l_1. This maximum can be attained, however, since

$$v(b_1) = b_1' S b_1$$
$$= b_1' \left(\sum_{j=1}^{p} l_j b_j b_j' \right) b_1$$
$$= \sum_{j=1}^{p} l_j b_1' b_j b_j' b_1$$
$$= l_1 (b_1' b_1)^2 = l_1, \qquad (51)$$

by the pairwise orthogonality of all b_j. Therefore the coefficients of the first principal component are given by b_1, the characteristic vector associated with the largest root l_1, and l_1 itself is its variance.

Suppose now that the first $h-1$ principal components have been found to be defined by $b_1, \ldots, b_{h-1}$, the associated variances being $l_1, \ldots, l_{h-1}$. In the hth step we consider again the function $v(y)$ for normalized vectors $y \in \mathbb{R}^p$, but now under the additional restriction of uncorrelatedness with the first $h-1$ components. By (22), zero correlation implies, for $j = 1, \ldots, h-1$:

$$0 = y'Sb_j$$
$$= y' l_j b_j, \qquad (52)$$

that is, $y'b_j = 0$ for $j = 1, \ldots, h-1$. In the representation (49) of y this implies that $\alpha_1 = \cdots = \alpha_{h-1} = 0$, since

$$y'b_j = \sum_{i=1}^{p} \alpha_i b_i' b_j = \alpha_j. \qquad (53)$$

The restriction of uncorrelatedness implies therefore that y is orthogonal to

$\mathbf{b}_1, \ldots, \mathbf{b}_{h-1}$. Proceeding as in (50), we get now

$$v(\mathbf{y}) = \sum_{j=h}^{p} l_j \alpha_j^2 \leqslant l_h \sum_{j=h}^{p} \alpha_j^2 = l_h, \tag{54}$$

and the maximum is attained for $\mathbf{y} = \mathbf{b}_h$. Thus the hth principal component is defined by the coefficients of $\mathbf{b}_h$, and its variance is l_h.

The trace of a $(p \times p)$-matrix $\mathbf{D} = (d_{ij})$ is defined as the sum of its diagonal elements:

$$\operatorname{tr}(\mathbf{D}) = \sum_{j=1}^{p} d_{jj}. \tag{55}$$

As is easily shown, the equality

$$\operatorname{tr}(\mathbf{DC}) = \operatorname{tr}(\mathbf{CD}) \tag{56}$$

holds for arbitrary $(p \times p)$-matrices $\mathbf{C}$ and $\mathbf{D}$. Using this, we get

$$s_{\text{total}}^2 = \operatorname{tr}(\mathbf{S}) = \operatorname{tr}(\mathbf{BLB'})$$

$$= \operatorname{tr}(\mathbf{LB'B}) = \operatorname{tr}(\mathbf{L}) = \sum_{j=1}^{p} l_j, \tag{57}$$

that is, the total variance is not affected by the principal component transformation.

Consider next the p-variate standard distance of an arbitrary point $\mathbf{c} \in \mathbb{R}^p$ from the mean vector $\bar{\mathbf{x}}$. By (33), the squared standard distance is

$$D_p^2 = (\mathbf{c} - \bar{\mathbf{x}})'\mathbf{S}^{-1}(\mathbf{c} - \bar{\mathbf{x}}) = (\mathbf{c} - \bar{\mathbf{x}})'\mathbf{BL}^{-1}\mathbf{B}'(\mathbf{c} - \bar{\mathbf{x}}), \tag{58}$$

where we have used the spectral representation (46) of $\mathbf{S}$. But

$$\mathbf{u} = \mathbf{B}'(\mathbf{c} - \bar{\mathbf{x}}) = (u_1, \ldots, u_p) \tag{59}$$

is the vector of coordinates of $\mathbf{c}$ in the coordinate system defined by the principal component transformation, and therefore

$$D_p^2 = \mathbf{u}'\mathbf{L}^{-1}\mathbf{u} = \sum_{j=1}^{p} u_j^2 / l_j. \tag{60}$$

Finally, let us look at the transformation of the data to principal component scores. Shifting the data to the origin of the coordinate system means subtracting the transposed mean vector $\bar{\mathbf{x}}'$ from each row of the data matrix:

$$\mathbf{Y} = \mathbf{X} - \begin{bmatrix} \bar{\mathbf{x}}' \\ \vdots \\ \bar{\mathbf{x}}' \end{bmatrix} \tag{61}$$

$\mathbf{Y}$ is called the matrix of centred data. Defining an n-vector $\mathbf{1}$ as in Section 13.2

and using (1), we can write

$$
\begin{bmatrix} \bar{\mathbf{x}}' \\ \vdots \\ \bar{\mathbf{x}}' \end{bmatrix} = \frac{1}{n} \begin{bmatrix} \mathbf{1}' \\ \vdots \\ \mathbf{1}' \end{bmatrix} \mathbf{X} = \frac{1}{n} \mathbf{1}\mathbf{1}'\mathbf{X}. \tag{62}
$$

Using the centering matrix $\mathbf{H}$ defined in (2) we get furthermore

$$
\mathbf{Y} = \mathbf{H}\mathbf{X}. \tag{63}
$$

Applying the principal component transformation to the centred data yields then the $(n \times p)$-matrix of principal component scores:

$$
\mathbf{U} = \mathbf{Y}\mathbf{B} = \mathbf{H}\mathbf{X}\mathbf{B}. \tag{64}
$$

It is easily verified that the principal components have mean zero and covariance matrix $\mathbf{L}$:

$$
\bar{\mathbf{u}} = \frac{1}{n}\mathbf{U}'\mathbf{1} = \frac{1}{n}\mathbf{B}'\mathbf{X}'\mathbf{H}'\mathbf{1} = \mathbf{0}, \tag{65}
$$

since $\mathbf{H}'\mathbf{1} = \mathbf{0}$, and

$$
\frac{1}{n-1}\mathbf{U}'\mathbf{H}\mathbf{U} = \frac{1}{n-1}\mathbf{B}'\mathbf{X}'\mathbf{H}'\mathbf{H}^2\mathbf{X}\mathbf{B}
$$

$$
= \mathbf{B}' \cdot \frac{1}{n-1}\mathbf{X}'\mathbf{H}\mathbf{X}\mathbf{B}
$$

$$
= \mathbf{B}'\mathbf{S}\mathbf{B} = \mathbf{L}, \tag{66}
$$

since $\mathbf{H}$ is symmetric and $\mathbf{H}^2 = \mathbf{H}$.

13.7   COMPARISON OF TWO COVARIANCE MATRICES

The method described in Chapter 11 is based on the simultaneous decomposition of two covariance matrices. We state the underlying theorem from matrix algebra again without proof.

Simultaneous decomposition of two positive definite matrices

Let the $(p \times p)$-matrices $\mathbf{U}$ and $\mathbf{V}$ be positive definite and symmetric. Then there exists a nonsingular $(p \times p)$-matrix $\mathbf{C} = (\mathbf{c}_1,\ldots,\mathbf{c}_p)$ such that

$$
\mathbf{U} = \mathbf{C}\mathbf{C}' = \sum_{j=1}^{p} \mathbf{c}_j\mathbf{c}_j',
$$

$$
\mathbf{V} = \mathbf{C}\mathbf{L}\mathbf{C}' = \sum_{j=1}^{p} l_j\mathbf{c}_j\mathbf{c}_j', \tag{67}
$$

where $L = \text{diag}(l_1, \ldots, l_p)$, all l_j being positive. For a proof, see, for instance, Basilevsky (1983, Section 5.5).

In the notation of the theorem, we put $\mathbf{B} = (\mathbf{b}_1, \ldots, \mathbf{b}_p) = (\mathbf{C}')^{-1}$ and get

$$\mathbf{U}^{-1}\mathbf{V} = \mathbf{B}\mathbf{B}'(\mathbf{B}')^{-1}\mathbf{L}\mathbf{B}^{-1} = \mathbf{B}\mathbf{L}\mathbf{B}^{-1}. \tag{68}$$

Multiplying (68) from the right by $\mathbf{B}$ yields then

$$\mathbf{U}^{-1}\mathbf{V}\mathbf{B} = \mathbf{B}\mathbf{L}. \tag{69}$$

From (69) we see that the l_j and $\mathbf{b}_j$ are the characteristic values and characteristic vectors of $\mathbf{U}^{-1}\mathbf{V}$:

$$\mathbf{U}^{-1}\mathbf{V}\mathbf{b}_j = l_j\mathbf{b}_j. \tag{70}$$

Let now $\mathbf{S}_1$ and $\mathbf{S}_2$ denote the $(p \times p)$ covariance matrices of two samples. To find the linear combinations with extreme variance ratios, we form the ratio

$$q(\mathbf{z}) = \frac{\mathbf{z}'\mathbf{S}_2\mathbf{z}}{\mathbf{z}'\mathbf{S}_1\mathbf{z}} \tag{71}$$

for vectors $\mathbf{z} \in \mathbb{R}^p$. Since $q(\mathbf{z}) = q(k\mathbf{z})$ for arbitrary scalars $k \neq 0$, we can restrict the maximization or minimization of q to vectors $\mathbf{z}$ such that $\mathbf{z}'\mathbf{S}_1\mathbf{z} = 1$. Writing $\mathbf{S}_1 = \mathbf{CC}'$, $\mathbf{S}_2 = \mathbf{CLC}'$ as in (67), we thus have

$$q(\mathbf{z}) = \frac{\mathbf{z}'\mathbf{CLC}'\mathbf{z}}{\mathbf{z}'\mathbf{CC}'\mathbf{z}} = \frac{\mathbf{y}'\mathbf{Ly}}{\mathbf{y}'\mathbf{y}}, \tag{72}$$

where $\mathbf{y} = \mathbf{C}'\mathbf{z}$, and $\mathbf{y}'\mathbf{y} = 1$. Assuming that the eigenvalues l_j that form the diagonal of $\mathbf{L}$ are arranged in decreasing order, we get

$$\mathbf{y}'\mathbf{Ly} = \sum_{j=1}^{p} l_j y_j^2 \leqslant l_1 \sum_{j=1}^{p} y_j^2 = l_1, \tag{73}$$

that is, the variance ratio cannot exceed the largest characteristic value. This bound can be attained, however, by taking $\mathbf{y} = (1, 0, \ldots, 0)'$ and

$$\mathbf{z} = (\mathbf{C}')^{-1}\mathbf{y} = \mathbf{By} = \mathbf{b}_1. \tag{74}$$

That is, the linear combination $Y_{\max}$ is defined by the characteristic vector $\mathbf{b}_1$ associated with the largest root l_1. Similarly, $Y_{\min}$ is defined by $\mathbf{b}_p$, and the corresponding ratio of variances is $q(\mathbf{b}_p) = l_p$.

Since $\mathbf{B} = (\mathbf{b}_1, \ldots, \mathbf{b}_p) = (\mathbf{C}')^{-1}$, it follows immediately that

$$\mathbf{B}'\mathbf{S}_1\mathbf{B} = \mathbf{B}'(\mathbf{CC}')\mathbf{B} = \mathbf{I}_p$$
$$\mathbf{B}'\mathbf{S}_2\mathbf{B} = \mathbf{B}'(\mathbf{CLC}')\mathbf{B} = \mathbf{L}. \tag{75}$$

The p linear combinations defined by $\mathbf{b}_1, \ldots, \mathbf{b}_p$ are therefore uncorrelated in both groups.

References

Afifi, A.A. and Clark, V. (1984) *Computer-Aided Multivariate Analysis*, Lifetime Learning Publications, Belmont, California.

Airoldi, J.P. and Flury, B. (1987) *An application of common principal component analysis to cranial morphometry of Microtus californicus and M. ochrogaster* (Mammalia, Rodentia), (in press).

Airoldi, J.P. and Hoffmann, R.S. (1984) Age variation in voles (*Microtus californicus, M. ochrogaster*) and its significance for systematic studies. *Occasional Papers of the Museum of Natural History*, No. 111, The University of Kansas, Lawrence, pp. 1–45.

Anderson, T.W. (1963) Asymptotic theory for principal component analysis. *Annals of Mathematical Statistics*, **34**, 122–48.

Anderson, T.W. (1984, 2nd edn) *An Introduction to Multivariate Statistical Analysis*. Wiley, New York.

Andrews, D.F. (1972) Plots of high dimensional data. *Biometrika*, **28**, 125–36.

Barnett, V., ed. (1981) *Interpreting Multivariate Data*. Wiley, New York.

Basilevsky, A. (1983) *Applied Matrix Algebra in the Statistical Sciences*. North Holland, New York.

Bekman, R.J. and Cook, R.D. (1983) Outlier..........s. *Technometrics*, **25**, 119–49.

Belsley, D.A., Kuh, E. and Welsch, R.E. (1980) *Regression Diagnostics*. Wiley, New York.

Bookstein, F.L. (1986) Size and shape spaces for landmark data in two dimensions. *Statistical Science*, **1**, 181–242.

Bronson, R. (1970) *Matrix Methods*. Academic Press, New York.

Chernoff, H. (1973) Using faces to represent points in k-dimensional space graphically. *Journal of the American Statistical Association*, **68**, 361–68.

Cook, R.D. and Weisberg, S. (1982) *Residuals and Influence in Regression*. Chapman and Hall, London.

Cramer, E.M. (1967) Equivalence of two methods of computing discriminant function coefficients. *Biometrics*, **23**, 153.

Daniel, C. and Wood, F.S. (1980, 2nd edn) *Fitting Equations to Data*. Wiley, New York.

Diaconis, P. and Efron, B. (1983) Computer-intensive methods in statistics. *Scientific American*, **248** (May 1983), 116–30.

Draper, N.R. and Smith, H. (1981, 2nd edn) *Applied Regression Analysis*. Wiley, New York.

Efron, B. and Gong, G. (1983) A leisurely look at the bootstrap, the jackknife, and cross-validation. *The American Statistician*, **37**, 36–48.

Everitt, B.S. (1978) *Graphical Techniques for Representing Multivariate Data*. Heinemann Educational Books, London.

Fisher, R.A. (1936) The use of multiple measurements in taxonomic problems. *Annals of Eugenics*, **7**, 179–88.

Flury, B. (1980) Construction of an asymmetrical face to represent multivariate data graphically. Technical Report no. 3, University of Berne, Department of Statistics.

Flury, B. (1984): Common principal components in *k* groups. *Journal of the American Statistical Association*, **79**, 892–98.

Flury, B. (1985) Analysis of linear combinations with extreme ratios of variance. *Journal of the American Statistical Association*, **80**, 915–922.

Flury, B. (1986) An asymptotic test for redundancy of variables in the comparison of two covariance matrices. *Statistics and Probability Letters*, **4**, 123–26.

Flury, B. and Constantine, G. (1985) The FG diagonalization algorithm. Algorithm AS 211, *Applied Statistics*, **34**, 177–83.

Flury, B. and Riedwyl, H. (1981) Graphical representation of multivariate data by means of asymmetrical faces. *Journal of the American Statistical Association*, **76**, 757–65.

Flury, B. and Riedwyl, H. (1983) Some applications of asymmetrical faces. *Proceedings of the Statistical Computing Section*, ASA Meeting Toronto 1983, pp. 226–31.

Flury, B. and Riedwyl, H. (1985): T^2-tests, the linear two-group discriminant function, and their computation by linear regression. *The American Statistician*, **39**, 20–25.

Freund, R.J. and Minton, P.D. (1979) *Regression Methods*. Dekker, New York.

Gnanadesikan, R. (1977) *Methods for Statistical Data Analysis of Multivariate Observations*. Wiley, New York.

Golub, G.H. and Van Loan, C.F. (1983) *Matrix Computations*. The Johns Hopkins University Press, Baltimore, MD.

Gunst, R.F. and Mason, R.L. (1980) *Regression Analysis and its Applications*. Dekker, New York.

Hald, A. (1952) *Statistical Theory and Engineering Applications*. Wiley, New York.

Hartung, J. and Elpelt, B. (1984) *Multivariate Statistik,* Oldenbourg, Munich.

Hawkins, D.M. (1980) *Identification of Outliers*. Chapman and Hall, London.

Healy, M.J.R. (1965) Computing a discriminant function from within-sample dispersion. *Biometrics*, **21**, 1011–12.

Hotelling, H. (1933) Analysis of a complex of statistical variables into principal components, *Journal of Educational Psychology*, **24**, 417–41.

Huber, P.J. (1985) Projection pursuit. *The Annals of Statistics*, **13**, 435–74.

Johnson, R.A. and Wichern, D.W. (1982) *Applied Multivariate Statistical Analysis*. Prentice-Hall, London.

Jolicoeur, P. (1963a) The degree of generality of robustness in *Martes americana*. *Growth*, **27**, 1–27.

Jolicoeur, P. (1963b) The multivariate generalization of the allometry equation. *Biometrics*, **19**, 497–99.

Jolicoeur, P. and Mosimann, J.E. (1960) Size and shape variation in the painted turtle: a principal component analysis. *Growth*, **24**, 339–354.

Kendall, M.G. (1957) *A Course in Multivariate Analysis*. Hafner Publishing Co. New York.

Kleiner, B. and Hartigan, J.A. (1981) Representing points in many dimensions as trees and castles. *Journal of the American Statistical Association*, **76**, 260–76.

Kreuter, U. (1975) Multivariate Kontrolle in der Qualitätssteuerung. Unpublished PhD-thesis, University of Berne, Department of Statistics.

Krzanowski, W.J. (1975) Discrimination and classification using both binary and continuous variables. *Journal of the American Statistical Association*, **70**, 782–790.

Krzanowski, W.J. (1979) Between-groups comparison of principal components.

290 References

Journal of the American Statistical Association, **74**, 703–707. (Correction note: 1981, **76**, 1022).

Krzanowski, W.J. (1988) *Principles of Multivariate Analysis: A User's Perspective.* Oxford University Press, Oxford.

Lachenbruch, P.A. (1975) *Discriminant Analysis.* Hafner, New York.

McCabe, G.P. (1975) Computations for variable selection in discriminant analysis. *Technometrics*, **17**, 103–109.

McCabe, G.P. (1984) Principal variables. *Technometrics*, **26**, 137–44.

Mardia, K.V., Kent, J.T. and Bibby, J.M. (1979) *Multivariate Analysis.* Academic Press, New York.

Montgomery, D.C. and Peck, E.A. (1982) *Linear Regression Analysis.* Wiley, New York.

Morrison, D.F. (1976, 2nd ed.) *Multivariate Statistical Methods.* McGraw-Hill, New York.

Moser, U. (1982) Wettkampfauswertung mit asymmetrischen Gesichtern. Unpublished manuscript, University of Berne, Department of Statistics.

Mosimann, J.E. (1979) Size and shape variables. In *Multivariate Methods in Ecological Work*, eds. L. Orloci, C.R. Rao and W.M. Stiteler, International Co-operative Publishing House, Fairland, Maryland, pp. 175–89.

Muirhead, R.J. (1982) *Aspects of Multivariate Statistical Theory.* Wiley, New York.

Neter, J., Wasserman, W. and Kutner, M.H. (1985) *Applied Linear Statistical Models.* Richard D. Irwin, Homewood, Illinois.

Parlett, B.N. (1980) *The Symmetric Eigenvalue Problem.* Prentice-Hall, Englewood Cliffs, NJ.

Pearson, K. (1901) On lines and planes of closest fit to systems of points in space. *Philosophical Magazine*, ser. 6, vol. 2, 559–72.

Pesaran, M.H. and Slater, L.S. (1980) *Dynamic Regression: Theory and Algorithms.* Halsted Press, Wiley, New York.

Peter, Prince of Greece and Denmark (1966) *Anthropological Researches from the 3rd Danish Expedition to Central Asia.* Munksgaard Publishers, Copenhagen.

Pillai, K.C.S. (1965) On the distribution of the largest characteristic root of a matrix in multivariate analysis. *Biometrika*, **52**, 405–14.

Pillai, K.C.S. and Flury, B.N. (1984) Percentage points of the largest characteristic root of the multivariate beta matrix. *Communications in Statistics (Theory and Methods)*, **13**, (18), pp. 2199–237.

Pillai, K.C.S. and Flury, B.N. (1985) Percentage points of the largest characteristic root of the multivariate *F*-matrix. Technical Report no. 17, University of Berne, Department of Statistics.

Rao, C.R. (1948) Tests of significance in multivariate analysis. *Biometrika*, **35**, 58–79.

Rao, C.R. (1970) Inference on discriminant function coefficients. In *Essays in Probability and Statistics*, eds. R.C. Bose, I.M. Chakravarti, P.C. Mahanalobis, C.R. Rao and K.J.C. Smith, University of North Carolina Press, Chapel Hill, pp. 587–602.

Reyment, R.A., Blackith, R.E. and Campbell, N.A. (1984) *Multivariate Morphometrics.* Academic Press, London.

Riedwyl, H. and Kreuter, U. (1976) Identification. In *Contributions to Applied Statistics*, ed. W.J. Ziegler, Birkhäuser, Basel, pp. 209–12.

Roy, S.N. (1957) *Some Aspects of Multivariate Analysis.* Wiley, New York.

Schuepbach, M. (1984) Asymface–Asymmetrical faces on IBM PC. Technical Report no. 16, University of Berne, Department of Statistics.

Searle, S.R. (1982) *Matrix Algebra Useful for Statistics.* Wiley, New York.

Seber, G.A.F. (1984) *Multivariate Observations*. Wiley, New York.

Silverman, B.W. (1986) *Density Estimation for Statistics and Data Analysis*. Chapman and Hall, London.

Srivastava, M.S. and Carter, E.M. (1983) *An Introduction to Applied Multivariate Statistics*. North Holland, New York.

Srivastava, M.S. and Khatri, C.G. (1979) *An Introduction to Multivariate Statistics*. North Holland, New York.

Tatsuoka, M.M. (1970) *Discriminant Analysis*. Selected Topics in Advanced Statistics, no. 6, Institute for Personality and Ability Testing, Champaign, Illinois.

Tufte, E. (1983). *The Visual Display of Quantitative Information*. Graphics Press, Cheshire.

Tyler, D.E. (1981) Asymptotic inference for eigenvectors. *The Annals of Statistics*, **9**, 725–36.

Wainer, H. (1983) On multivariate display. In *Recent Advances in Statistics*, eds. M.H. Rizvi, J. Rustagi and D. Siegmund, Academic Press, New York, pp. 469–508.

Wang, P.C.C. (ed., 1978) *Graphical Representation of Multivariate Data*. Academic Press, New York.

Weisberg, S. (1985, 2nd ed.) *Applied Linear Regression*. Wiley, New York.

Younger, M.S. (1979) *A Handbook for Linear Regression*. Duxbury Press, North Sciutate, Mass.

Index